1996

Soil reinforcement with geotextiles

R.A. Jewell MA PhD CEng

CONSTRUCTION INDUSTRY RESEARCH AND INFORMATION ASSOCIATION
6 Storey's Gate London SW1P 3AU
E-mail switchboard@ciria.org.uk
Tel: (0171) 222 8891   Fax: (0171) 222 1708

CIRIA and the author are grateful for the help given to this project by the funders, by the members of the Steering Group, and by the many individuals who were consulted. The author particularly acknowledges the encouragement he received from the late Professor Peter Wroth and the helpful criticism on the technical content of particular chapters from Dr M.D. Bolton, Mr D.I. Bush, Dr J-P. Giroud, Dr J.H. Greenwood, Professor C.J.F.P. Jones, Professor A. McGown, Dr G.W.E. Milligan and Dr R.T. Murray.

Soil reinforcement with geotextiles
Construction Industry Research and Information Association
CIRIA Special Publication 123, 1996

Keywords
Geotextiles, soil reinforcement.

Reader Interest
Geotechnical and structural engineers, local authorities, public utility engineers.

© CIRIA 1996

ISBN 0 86017 425 5
Thomas Telford ISBN
0 7277 2502 5

	CLASSIFICATION	
AVAILABILITY		Unrestricted
CONTENT		Subject area review
STATUS		Committee guided
USER		Structural and geotechnical engineers

Published by CIRIA, 6 Storey's Gate, Westminster, London SW1P 3AU and Thomas Telford

Contents

Contents

Contents

Contents

Contents

Special Publication 123 © CIRIA

List of Tables

List of Tables

List of Figures

List of Figures

List of Figures

List of Figures

Notation

$\bar{a}_b$	fraction of grid width available for bearing
$\bar{a}_s$	fraction of reinforcement plan area that is solid
A_b	bond allowance
A_{ls}	load-shedding (or sharing) allowance
B	width of a transverse member of a grid taking bearing
$\bar{B}$	effective width of loaded area
c'	effective cohesion
D	depth of footing below ground level
D_{50}	mean particle size
D_{max}	maximum particle size
e	load eccentricity on a footing
e	eccentricity of foundation reaction from centre of reinforced block
e	void ratio
e_{field}	field void ratio of compacted fill
e_{max}	void ratio at loosest condition
e_{min}	void ratio at densest condition
f_d	partial factor for mechanical damage
f_{env}	partial factor for chemical and biological environment
f_m	overall material factor
F_1	scale-effect factor for bearing stress ratio
F_2	shape-effect factor for bearing stress ratio
FS	factor of safety
Fs_a	factor of safety in a 'lumped-factor' design
G_s	specific gravity
h_c	depth where critical wedge intersects width face
h_w	height of phreatic surface above base of a slope
H	slope (or wall) height
H'	effective slope (or wall) height (allowing for vertical surcharge)
i	angle of backfill above a slope crest
i_q	reduction factor for bearing capacity under inclined loading
i_γ	reduction factor for bearing capacity under inclined loading
I_D	relative density
I_p	plasticity index
I_R	relative density index
J	secant stiffness of reinforcement for relevant time period

Notation

J_c	reference stiffness at end of construction
J_d	reference stiffness at end of design life
J_{50}	specific stiffness of a polymer
k	empirical constant in relation between relative density and angle of friction
K_o	coefficient of earth pressure at rest
K_{ar}	active earth pressure coefficient corresponding to design angle of friction for reinforced fill
K_{ab}	active earth pressure coefficient corresponding to design angle of friction for backfill
K_{ad}	design active earth pressure coefficient
K_d	design value of earth pressure coefficient
K_{Req}	required value of earth pressure coefficient
L	width of footing or block of reinforced soil
$\bar{L}$	effective width of footing for inclined loading
L_b, L_B	bond length
L_B	bond length for reinforcement layer at base of wall
L_{ds}	required reinforced length to prevent direct sliding
L_r, L_R	length of reinforcement
L_θ	length of inclined trial wedge
m	power to which OCR is raised in relating (s_u/σ'_v) for normally and overconsolidated states
n	slope definition in 1 vertical to n horizontal
N_c	bearing capacity factor
N_q	bearing capacity factor
N_γ	bearing capacity factor
OCR	overconsolidation ratio
p'_e	equivalent effective pressure with respect to normal consolidation line
P	tensile load in reinforcement
P_{Av}	available force allowing for bond
$P_{Available}$	available reinforcement force
P_b	gross reinforcement force
P_{base}	modified reinforcement force at base of wall
P_{bf}	thrust from backfill on reinforced block
P_d	design strength of reinforcement
P_{dam}	reinforcement strength allowing for mechanical damage
P_{env}	reinforcement strength allowing for chemical and biological environment
P_{EQ}	reinforcement force at equilibrium
P_{fill}	lateral thrust from the fill
P_{field}	strength of reinforcement in the field

Special Publication 123 © CIRIA

$(P_{field})_{t_d,T_d}$ strength of reinforcement in the field at design life, t_d, and design temperature, T_d

P_m mobilised force in reinforcement

P'_n effective normal force

P_r tensile force in reinforcement

P_R gross maximum force required for equilibrium

P_R gross available force

P_{ref} reference strength of reinforcement

$(P_{ref})_{t_d,T_d}$ reference strength of reinforcement at design time, t_d and temperature, T_d

P_{Req} required tensile reinforcement force

$P_{required}$ required reinforcement force

P_{RL} gross reinforcement force, likely lower value

P_{RU} gross reinforcement force, likely upper value

$P_{rupture}$ tensile force at which reinforcement ruptures

P_s shear force

P_s serviceability strength of reinforcement (i.e. at max. allowable elongation

P_v vertical load

P_{yield} tensile load at which reinforcement yields

$(P_R)_{1,2, etc.}$ horizontal resultant forces on wedges in stability analysis

q_b surcharge pressure above backfill

q_r surcharge pressure above reinforced zone

q_{sv} applied vertical surcharge

Q empirical constant for determining relative density index, I_R

Q maximum compaction force per unit width of roller

Q_h horizontal component of applied point load

Q_v vertical component of applied point load

r_o radius of slip circle

r_u pore pressure ratio

$(r_u)_d$ design value of pore pressure ratio

R reaction on a foundation

R resultant thrust

$R_{1,2,12,21\ etc.}$ reactions between wedges in stability analysis

R_h horizontal component of load on footing

R_v vertical component of load on footing

s' mean effective stress $(= (\sigma'_1 + \sigma'_3)/2)$

s_h horizontal spacing of reinforcement elements

s_u undrained shear strength

s_{ud} undrained shear strength of foundation

$(s_u)_d$ design undrained shear strength

$(s_u)_m$ mobilised undrained shear strength

Notation

s_v	vertical spacing of reinforcement layers
S	specific strength (of a polymer)
S	spacing between transverse members taking bearing
t	maximum shear stress $(= (\sigma'_1 - 6_3')/2)$
t'	time in creep test
t_d	design life
t_{env}	aged life
T	temperature
T_d	design temperature
u	porewater pressure
u_{max}	maximum pore pressure in a slope
$U_{1,2 \text{ etc.}}$	water upthrusts normal to sliding face of wedges
v_g	granular specific volume
v_i	specific volume at start of shearing
v_{cv}	specific volume at critical state (constant volume)
W	weight of reinforced soil block
$W_{1,2 \text{ etc.}}$	weight of wedge
W_r	width of reinforcement
X	distance of point load edge of crest.
$x \, (dx)$	shear displacement
$y \, (dy)$	vertical displacement
z	depth below ground surface
z'	effective depth in slope of effective height H'
$z_{1,2}$	depth below slope surface of clay embankment
z_z	depth below slope crest of change in reinforcement
z_{crit}	critical depth where bond length equals reinforcement length
z_w	depth to groundwater level
α	load inclination $(= \tau/s_u)$
$\alpha_b \, \alpha_B$	coefficient of bond
α_{ds}	coefficient of direct sliding
β	slope angle from horizontal
γ	unit weight of soil
γ_d	design value of unit weight of soil
γ_{eff}	effective unit weight of foundation soil allowing for buoyancy
γ_f	unit weight of foundation soil
γ'_f	submerged weight of foundation soil
γ_{max}	maximum dry density
γ_r	unit weight of reinforced soil
γ_{rd}	design unit weight of reinforced soil
γ_w	unit weight of water

δ	angle of skin friction, soil on planar reinforcement surface
δ_d	design angle of friction between soil and reinforcement
δ_f	inclination of inclined loading as footing ($= \tan^{-1} R_h/R_v$)
δ_{max}	maximum horizontal displacement
δ_p	peak friction angle between soil and reinforcement
δ_v	maximum settlement at crest of wall
δ_w	wall roughness
ΔP_s	improvement in shearing resistance
Δ_{qr}	increment of vertical surcharge
ε_3	maximum tensile strain in soil
ε'	elongation of polymer at time t' in creep test
ε_{EQ}	tensile elongation at force equilibrium
ε_{max}	maximum tensile strain
ε_r	tensile elongation of reinforcement
$\varepsilon_{rupture}$	elongation of reinforcement at rupture
ε_R	tensile elongation of reinforcement at force equilibrium
ε_{RL}	tensile elongation of reinforcement, likely lower value
ε_{RU}	tensile elongation of reinforcement, likely upper value
ε_s	tensile strain in soil at force equilibrium
ε_{SL}	tensile strain in soil, likely lower value
ε_{SU}	tensile strain in soil, likely upper value
ε_{yield}	elongation of reinforcement at yield
θ	inclination of reinforcement to vertical
θ_1	angle to horizontal of trial wedge
θ_b	optimum reinforcement orientation for bond
θ_{opt}	optimum orientation of reinforcement
θ_ε	optimum orientation of reinforcement in direction of maximum soil tensile strain
μ	vane strength correction factor
σ'	normal effective stress
σ_o	equivalent vertical stress acting at level of footing base
σ_o	maximum residual stress from compaction
σ_1'	major principal effective stress
σ_3'	minor principal effective stress
σ_{AV}	available stress
σ_b'	effective bearing stress on reinforcement
(σ_b'/σ_n')	bearing stress ratio
σ_{bc}	bearing capacity of foundation soil
σ_{bc}'	maximum effective bearing stress beneath rough footing of effective width $\bar{L}$

Notation

σ_{comp}	maximum horizontal stress caused by compaction
σ_d'	highest effective stress experienced by the soil
σ_d'	design normal effective stress
σ_f	applied vertical stress acting on effective footing width $\bar{L}$
σ_f	vertical stress applied across reinforced soil foundation
σ_f'	effective vertical stress below footing
σ_{max}'	maximum normal effective stress on reinforcement
σ_{min}	minimum direct stress
σ_{mob}	mobilised stress
σ_n'	normal effective stress
σ_p'	preconsolidation pressure
σ_{Req}	required stress
σ_v'	current vertical effective stress
σ_{yy}	direct stress on plane yy
τ	shear stress
τ_f	applied shear stress acting on effective footing width $\bar{L}$
τ_{yx}	shear stress
ϕ	angle of shearing resistance
ϕ'	angle of shearing resistance in terms of effective stress
ϕ_o'	mobilised angle of shearing resistance, at-rest conditions
ϕ_{bd}'	design angle of friction for backfill
ϕ_{cs}'	critical state angle of shearing resistance
ϕ_{cv}'	constant volume (large strain) angle of shearing resistance
ϕ_d'	design value of effective angle of shearing resistance
ϕ_e'	angle of friction in normalised plot
ϕ_f'	angle of shearing reistance of foundation soil
ϕ_f'	mobilised angle of shearing resistance at failuretb
ϕ_{fd}'	design angle of shearing resistance of foundation soil
ϕ_{fp}'	peak angle of shearing resistance of foundation soil
ϕ_m'	mobilised angle of friction
ϕ_{mob}'	mobilised effective angle of shearing resistance
ϕ_p'	peak effective angle of shearing resistance, i.e. secant value
ϕ_{peak}'	constant peak angle of friction, i.e. c, ϕ'linear envelope
ϕ_{ps}'	peak angle of friction in plane strain conditions
ϕ_{rd}'	peak angle of friction for reinforced fill
ϕ_{rm}'	angle of friction mobilised in reinforced soil
ϕ_{tc}'	peak angle of friction measured in triaxial compression
ψ	angle of dilation

1 Engineering with geotextiles

The term *geotextile*, as originally defined, refers to textiles (fabrics) used in geotechnical engineering. Two broad classes of geotextile have emerged namely *conventional geotextiles*, the typical products of the textile industry, including woven and non-woven fabrics, and the more recent *geotextile-related products*, such as geogrids and knitted fabrics, which are used in combination with, or in place of, conventional geotextiles (ISSMFE Technical Committee on Geotextiles, Giroud *et al.*, 1985).

The word *geotextile* is used in this book as a *generic term* to include both geotextiles and geotextile-related products. Individual categories of products are referred to by name only where strictly necessary.

The historical development of geotextiles is described in Giroud (1986) where several reasons are identified to explain why contractors, designers and owners so readily accept these materials. *Contractors* are interested in quicker, less weather-dependent construction, reduced volume of earthworks and the possibility of using poorer quality soils. *Designers* like the greater reliability and control which stems from the uniform properties of geotextiles, the ease of placement, and the ability of geotextiles to mitigate local soil defects. *Owners* favour cost savings in construction and maintenance budgets.

More fundamental reasons for growth in the use of geotextiles are identified by Giroud:

1. The properties of granular soils are complemented by those of membrane-like materials; granular soils may be disrupted by erosion or settlement, but a geotextile with tensile strength can remain continuous.
2. Geotechnical structures are usually formed by layered construction, and membrane-like materials easily form an interface between layers, or act as a liner or as protection at the ground surface.
3. Geotechnical structures are flexible and subjected to differential movements, and flexible membrane-like materials are compatible with this behaviour.

Another reason for the success of geotextiles is that an efficient use of materials can be achieved by *reinforcing* soil with optimally placed tensile elements. Once reinforced, the soil can often be loaded to levels which would otherwise approach (or exceed) failure, although still providing a safe reinforced structure, because of the presence of the reinforcement. Detailed observations of geotextile reinforced soil structures under *working conditions* often reveal equilibrium with the soil mobilising close to its peak shearing resistance, while the reinforcement carries proportionately less tensile force than allowed for in design. Thus the *compatibility* in soil reinforced by geotextiles often results in the soil strength being almost fully exploited so that the reserve of safety resides in the as yet under-used, but still available, reinforcement strength.

The systematic application of textiles did not immediately follow their first uses in civil engineering, such as cotton fabric (Beckham and Mills, 1935), but came with the availability of adequate products, in this case a synthetic fabric which could resist rot. Significant growth in applications only came once the fabrics were both *adequate* and *inexpensive*, with the introduction of spunbonded non-wovens in the early 1970s.

The large European and North American manufacturers of non-woven fabrics enjoyed great success in the 1970s because of their production capabilities. But smaller manufacturers also found success through innovation. New products such as strong woven fabrics, polymer grids and synthetic strips were developed in the late 1970s and early 1980s, leading to the wide range of geotextiles and geotextile-related products now used in geotechnical engineering.

1.1 What are geotextiles?

Geotextiles are made from polymer materials. The production of geotextiles may be considered as two steps. The first step consists in making linear elements such as filaments, fibres, tapes and yarns from polymer materials, the most commonly used being polyester, polypropylene, polyethylene and polyamide. The second step consists of combining these linear elements to make a permeable planar material.

There are two main types of conventional geotextile:

- **woven geotextiles** composed of two perpendicular sets of parallel linear elements systematically interlaced to form a planar structure
- **non-woven geotextiles** formed from filaments or fibres randomly arranged and bonded together to form a planar structure. Bonding is normally achieved by mechanical, thermal or chemical means.

Geotextile-related products have a coarser structure than conventional geotextiles and those used for soil reinforcement include:

- **geogrids** manufactured by heating and stretching a perforated polymer sheet in either one or two directions
- **alternative geogrid products** made from strips or yarns combined in two perpendicular directions to achieve a grid form, but with varying degrees of mechanical connection at the joints and protective sheathing
- **geomeshes** made by extrusion to form a relatively low strength and low stiffness material (only temporary reinforcement properties)
- **strips** comprising yarns laid parallel in a strip and held in position and protected by a polymer coating

- **webbings**, conceptually like a coarse woven fabric but made up from synthetic strips (above)
- **knitted geotextiles** made by knitting yarns together to form a planar structure
- **cellular products**, either manufactured by bonding strips of material into a cellular form, or formed on site by interconnecting grids to form a mattress.

The above categories are broadly in line with the draft European standard of terms and definitions for geotextiles and related products (CEN, 1990). Useful guides to available geotextile products and suppliers may be found in Ingold and Miller (1988) for Europe, and Koerner (1990) for North America.

1.2 Concepts for geotextile applications

This book considers the uses of geotextiles for *soil reinforcement*. Geotextiles are also widely used to *separate* dissimilar soils, such as in Figure 1.1, but these are largely empirical applications. The use of geotextiles as separators is discussed briefly below in order to distinguish between *reinforcement* and *separation*.

Separation is usually achieved with a non-woven or woven geotextile to prevent intermixing of poor *in-situ* soils with good quality granular materials subject to surface loading (Figure 1.1a.) The separator provides a barrier to migration of particles between the two dissimilar soils but allows the free transmission of water. One requirement for a separator is a sufficient tensile strength to maintain continuity and not rip, puncture or burst under the local stress concentrations caused by irregularities in the foundation or fill material.

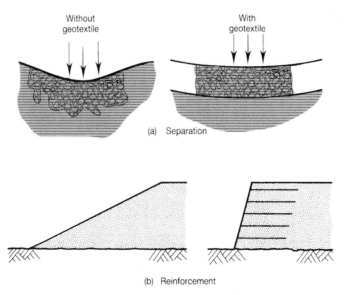

(a)   Separation

(b)   Reinforcement

Figure 1.1 *Geotextile functions (a) separation and (b) reinforcement*

The *separation* function of a geotextile is primarily to *maintain the integrity* of a good quality fill which would otherwise be reduced by the intermixing with poorer soil. A separator may also impart a degree of mechanical improvement as a tensile element. The important applications for geotextile separators in *temporary works* are on poor ground, e.g. access roads and working areas, or in the initial stages of embankment construction over soft foundation soils. The main application in *permanent works* is to resist intermixing and deterioration caused by repeated loading, such as in paved roads or railroads.

There are few general references about geotextile separation, although the application is described in Van Zanten (1986) and Koerner (1990). A set of technical notes on geotextile separation has been published in the Proceedings of the Institution of Civil Engineers, *Transport*, May 1992.

The *soil reinforcement* function of geotextiles is the *mechanical improvement* of soil. Reinforcement allows soil to carry greater shear loading than would otherwise be possible. When the disturbing forces are caused by the soil *self-weight loading*, such as in a soil slope or an embankment on a soft foundation soil, the inclusion of reinforcement can allow a steeper slope or embankment to be built (Figure 1.1b). Where the disturbing forces are caused by *external loads*, such as in an unpaved road or working platform, the inclusion of reinforcement can allow greater load to be applied.

Reinforcement achieves this *mechanical improvement* by supporting tensile force which acts (a) to reduce the shear force that has to be carried by the soil, and (b) to enhance the available shearing resistance in the soil, by increasing the normal stress acting on potential shear surfaces. These actions are illustrated in Figure 1.2 for an element of reinforced soil in a direct shear test.

Compressive and tensile strains develop when soil deforms in shear along a potential rupture surface (Figure 1.2a). Reinforcement acts efficiently when inclined in the

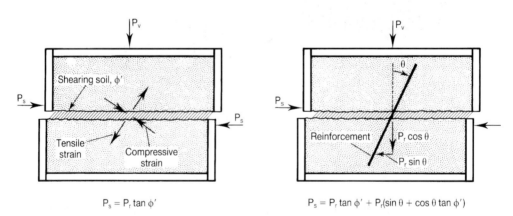

$$P_s = P_r \tan \phi' \qquad\qquad P_s = P_r \tan \phi' + P_r(\sin \theta + \cos \theta \tan \phi')$$

Figure 1.2 *Illustration of reinforcement action in direct shear: (a) tensile and compressive strains in soil, and (b) resultant reinforcement forces*

direction in which tensile strain develops in the deforming soil, so that shear deformation in the soil causes tensile force in the reinforcement (Figure 1.2b).

The benefit of reinforcement stems from the components of the tensile reinforcement force, P_r, acting on the shear surface in the soil. The tangential component, $P_r \sin \theta$, acts directly to resist the shear load applied to the soil (mechanism 1). The normal component, $P_r \cos \theta$, increases the normal force across the shear surface thereby enabling greater frictional shearing resistance to be mobilised in the soil (mechanism 2). In this case the shearing resistance is increased from:

$$P_s = P_v \tan \phi$$

in the *unreinforced* soil, to

$$P_s = P_v \tan \phi + P_r(\sin \theta + \cos \theta \tan \phi)$$

in the *reinforced* soil.

Geotextile reinforcement may also improve load carrying (or bearing) capacity by another, separate, mechanism which applies after the reinforcement has deformed sufficiently to act like a membrane in tension (Figure 1.3). Some of the normal stress from the applied loading on the concave side can be carried by the tensile force in the curved geotextile membrane, thereby reducing the stresses applied to the underlying soil on the convex side of the geotextile.

Membrane action requires locally applied loading and significant deformation. Examples where membrane action can be beneficial are (a) in a rutted unpaved road (Giroud and Noiray, 1981), (b) to prevent the collapse of fill into a sinkhole or cavity

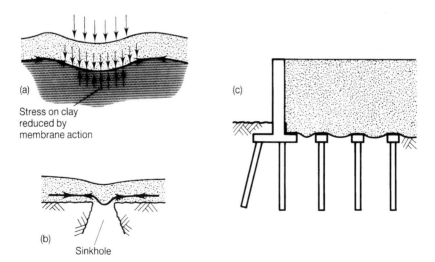

(a)

Stress on clay
reduced by
membrane action

(b)

Sinkhole

(c)

Figure 1.3 *Reinforcement supporting load by membrane action: (a) rutted un-paved road, (b) above a sinkhole and (c) in a piled embankment foundation*

(Giroud *et al.*, 1985), and (c) to assist load transfer between embankment fill and a piled foundation (Jones *et al.*, 1990).

1.3 Examples of the use of geotextiles

The range of applications for geotextile reinforcement in fill materials includes vertical walls, steep slopes and embankment slip repairs. Reinforcement can also be used in construction over soft foundation soils to improve the short-term stability of embankments and to allow increased live loading on thin granular layers such as unpaved roads and working platforms.

The applications are sometimes combined, such as the reinforcement of the foundation soil, using free-draining granular soil strengthened by layers of geotextile or a cellular mattress for example, beneath a reinforced soil wall (Figure 1.4).

Geotextiles may also be used in embankments on soft soil and in road foundations as a measure to limit differential settlement rather than to improve stability – although these two functions are closely related.

Reinforcement can also relieve stresses, for example where trench backfill is reinforced to help support subsequent surface loading. The horizontal soil stresses that will develop against the back of a conventional gravity retaining wall can also be reduced by reinforcing the backfill.

There are potential benefits in combining the *separation* and *reinforcement* functions of geotextiles in construction over poor ground. The separator can reduce intermixing between the fill and the foundation soils while the reinforcement enhances load-carrying capacity. It can be efficient when these distinct functions can be provided by a single product, such as a woven geotextile.

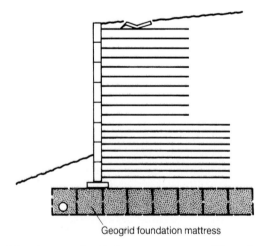

Geogrid foundation mattress

Figure 1.4 *Combined use of reinforcement to stiffen the foundation beneath a reinforced soil wall*

But there is a complex *interaction* between the *reinforcement* and *separation* functions of geotextiles which should be noted.

One mechanism of intermixing between fill and foundation soils is the opening and closing of tensile cracks at the base of a granular layer under repeated live loading, similar to the cracks on the underside of a concrete beam (Figure 1.5a). This mechanism allows the poorer foundation soil to be pumped up into the granular layer, causing the harmful intermixing of the two soil layers. Tensile reinforcement at the base of a granular layer can reduce localised cracking (although distributed micro-cracking will still occur) and thereby reduce or indeed eliminate this mechanism of intermixing (Figure 1.5b).

Thus a *reinforced* unpaved road over soft ground may be less susceptible to intermixing than the equivalent *unreinforced* road, and may even perform satisfactorily *without a separator*. However, the circumstances in which a separator may be omitted from a reinforced granular layer over soft ground have yet to be clearly defined.

1.4 Construction with geotextiles

Construction with geotextiles is usually compatible with conventional procedures and equipment: seldom is extra plant needed.

As discussed in more detail later, the effectiveness of reinforcement depends critically on its orientation and location in the ground. In almost all applications the horizontal direction is sufficiently close to optimum for practical purposes, so that generally only one extra step, the laying of the geotextile, is required in the sequence of placement and compaction of the fill.

There are additional requirements for construction with geotextiles which include:

1. Careful handling and storage of geotextiles to avoid degradation.
2. Adequate labelling of the geotextiles with clear indication of the correct direction of laying.

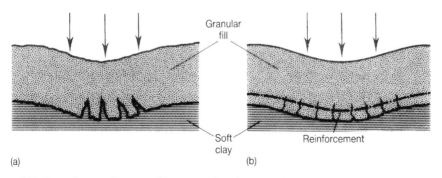

Figure 1.5 *Local tensile cracking at the base of a loaded granular layer: (a) unreinforced case, and (b) reinforced case*

3. Sufficient control of filling to ensure that geotextiles are placed at the correct elevations in the structure and are not unduly damaged by the placing and compaction of the fill.

It is also good practice, where possible, to tension the geotextile lightly before filling.

Placing reinforcement on a soft foundation soil is also straightforward as the geotextile is either laid directly on to the existing ground surface or on a thin initial fill layer. Preparation of the ground is generally needed only where irregularities would puncture or pierce the geotextile. Appropriate overlaps or seamed joints are required between adjacent sections of geotextile. For construction over extremely soft soils, it may be necessary to use low ground-pressure plant and to control initial filling to reduce the development of mud-waves.

In steep slopes and walls the placement of reinforcement layers must be linked with the construction of a face. Soft facings formed by wrapping the geotextile around the soil layers can require temporary external support and formers. Alternatively, the reinforcement can be connected to facing panel units.

In summary, construction with geotextiles is no less flexible than conventional earthworks, and often allows faster filling and reduced fill quantities. Special quality control procedures for geotextiles are easily combined with conventional site practice.

1.5 Geotextile capabilities

What can be achieved by a geotextile depends on its material properties and the form in which it is made. Both for *reinforcement* and for *separation* it is best first to determine and specify the required properties of the geotextile to achieve the desired function, and then to select a product that equals or exceeds the design requirements.

For example, soil reinforcement should be able to support the required design load without excessive elongation to ensure that the deformation of the structure is acceptable. Because geotextiles continue to deform (or creep) with time under load, it may be necessary to estimate the expected deformation at the end of construction and during the subsequent period to the end of the design life. This is particularly desirable for retaining walls and abutments where outward movement and settlement are important design considerations.

The strength requirements for a separator are much less onerous, and serve mostly to prevent perforation, tearing and ripping of the geotextile.

It should be noted that the magnitude of the force required from geotextile reinforcement can vary markedly between the different applications of reinforced soil. For example, individual reinforcement layers in a steep slope or wall might be required to support between 3 and 15 kN/m, whereas a single reinforcement layer beneath an embankment on soft soil might be required to support between 30 and 150 kN/m.

Similarly, the maximum tensile strain which can be tolerated in the reinforcement so that the structure does not become unduly deformed, also depends critically on the application. Typical limits to the acceptable maximum tensile strain in geotextile reinforcement are of the order: 1 to 2% for bridge abutments, 3 to 5% for steep slopes and 4 to 8% for embankments on soft soil.

Thus the factor influencing the selection of a geotextile reinforcement may be either (1) the *strength* or (2) the *load-elongation* properties of the material.

The *form* of the geotextile (woven, non-woven, geogrid or strip) can also be an important factor in design. The bond between the geotextile and the soil is more important for strips rather than planar reinforcement products (such as woven geotextiles and geogrids) which have a larger area of contact with the soil. In poorer quality soils, the extra bond capacity afforded by the surface area of geotextile sheets, or by geogrids which mobilise an additional bearing component of bond, can make these planar reinforcement materials preferable. These bond mechanisms are considered in Chapter 4.

1.6 Geotextiles as separators

Example applications for geotextile separators, most commonly non-woven fabrics, are indicated below:

1. A geotextile placed between the subgrade soil and an aggregate layer to form an unpaved road, a working platform or a storage area (Figure 1.6a).
2. A geotextile placed beneath railway ballast (Figure 1.6b), or beneath a paved road (Figure 1.6c). These are distinguished from the previous application by the higher quality of the foundation soil and the requirement to resist deterioration over very many load repetitions.

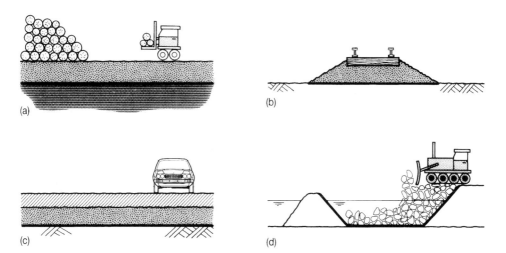

(a)

(b)

(c)

(d)

Figure 1.6 *Example applications of geotextile separators*

3. A geotextile placed underwater prior to reclamation filling (Figure 1.6d).

The important properties for the geotextile separator vary considerably between these applications. Greater resistance to repeated loading is required in railroads than in temporary access roads, while greater extensibility and resistance to puncture are needed for land reclamation.

In addition to having suitable filtration properties, the ability of the geotextile to prevent particle migration while allowing the free passage of water, a geotextile needs to have sufficient tensile strength to maintain the integrity of the separator layer.

1.7 Geotextiles as soil reinforcement

Four main applications for geotextile reinforcement are:

1. Vertical walls and abutments (Figure 1.7a).
2. Steep slopes (Figure 1.7b).
3. Slip prevention and remedial measures (Figure 1.7c).
4. Embankments on soft soil (Figure 1.7d).

In these applications, the reinforcement resists loading which comes mainly from the self-weight of the soil and the geometry of the structure.

An important distinction needs to be drawn between the slope applications in Figures 1.7a to c, and the use of reinforcement beneath an embankment on soft soil (Figure 1.7d). In the first three cases, the reinforcement has to maintain stability throughout the life of the structure. In an embankment on soft soil, the reinforcement is only required to boost stability during the critical period of construction and subsequent foundation consolidation; once the foundation soil has increased in strength the reinforcement is no longer required to ensure stability. This difference is illustrated in

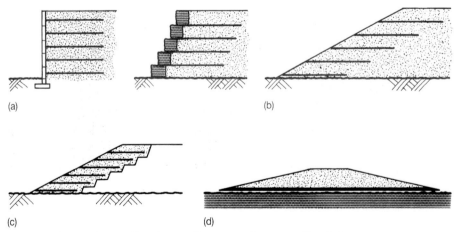

(a)   (b)

(c)   (d)

Figure 1.7 *Example applications of geotextiles as soil reinforcement*

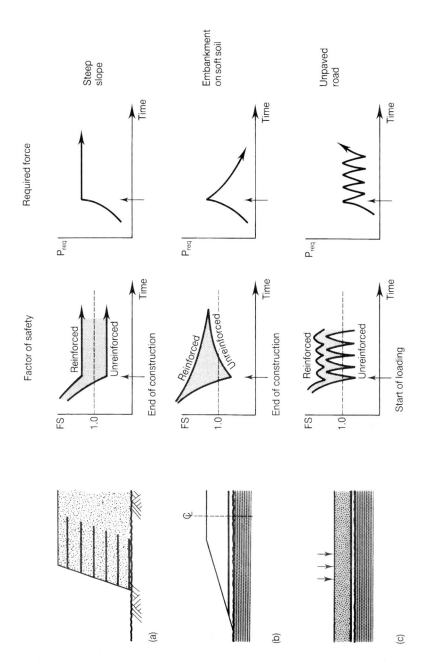

Figure 1.8 *Variation of required reinforcement force with time: (a) steep slopes and walls, (b) embankments on soft soil, and (c) unpaved roads*

Figure 1.8 by the variation with time of the factor of safety, with and without reinforcement, and the corresponding required reinforcement force.

Unpaved roads and working platforms are the main applications where geotextile reinforcement boosts the resistance to *externally applied load* (Figure 1.8c). In this case the required tensile force in the reinforcement responds to the repeated loads.

This variation over time of the required reinforcement force illustrated in Figure 1.8 is probably the most important factor governing the selection of a suitable geotextile product.

- Where sustained reinforcement force over long time periods is required, as in the slope applications, the *creep* characteristics of the reinforcement material usually govern the selection.
- For an embankment on soft soil, the reinforcement force is required over a relatively limited period (during construction and consolidation) so that the longer term mechanical properties of the geotextile may not be so important.
- The repeated loading in an unpaved road makes the response of the geotextile to rapid and cyclic loading a governing factor.

1.8 Geotextile compared with other solutions

Both economic and technical benefits can be achieved by using geotextiles. But it is largely the cost savings compared with conventional solutions that have encouraged applications, with savings up to 30% being reported for reinforced soil projects in both developed and developing countries.

Economies can stem from:
- reduced earth moving and landtake achieved by steepening soil slopes
- increased construction speed where reinforcement and facings are delivered ready for use
- unrestricted site access because reinforced soil is stable throughout construction
- the use of poorer fills strengthened by reinforcement.

Technical benefits include:
- a more efficient use of materials through combining the shearing resistance of soil with the tensile capacity of reinforcement
- the inherent flexibility and tolerance to deformation of a reinforced soil structure
- improved quality because critical components are produced and checked under factory conditions
- entirely new solutions made possible by geotextile materials.

But there can be *drawbacks* which include:

- some remaining uncertainty concerning the very long-term material properties and durability of geotextiles
- possible damage to geotextiles during storage, handling and installation
- awkward detailing at corners or in structures with irregular geometries
- incomplete codes and standardisation because of the novelty of geotextiles.

1.9 Synopsis of Chapter 1

(1) The term *geotextile* refers to textiles (fabrics) used in geotechnical engineering. Two broad classes are *conventional geotextiles*, the typical products of the textile industry, including woven and non-woven fabrics, and the more recent *geotextile-related products*, specially developed to be used in combination with, or in place of, conventional geotextiles. In this book, the term *geotextile* is used to include both geotextiles and geotextile-related products.

(2) The principal types of geotextile and geotextile-related products are
- woven, non-woven and knitted geotextiles
- geogrids, strips, webbings and geomeshes.

(3) Their principal uses are for separation, reinforcement and filtration, sometimes in combined systems.

(4) The purpose of separation is to maintain the integrity of an earth fill, preventing intermixing with poorer quality soils while permitting drainage.

(5) The purpose of reinforcement is the mechanical improvement of soil. The geotextile achieves this by reducing shear forces in the soil and increasing the available shearing resistance.

(6) Applications of geotextile reinforcement include:
- vertical walls, steep slopes and slip repairs
- embankments on soft soil
- unpaved roads and working areas.

Key references

Giroud, J.P. (1986). From geotextiles to geosynthetics: a revolution in geotechnical engineering. Proc. *3rd International Conference on Geotextiles*, Vienna, Vol. 1, 1–18.

Ingold, T.S. and Miller, K. (1988). *Geotextiles manual*. Thomas Telford, London.

Koerner, R.M. (1990). *Designing with geosynthetics*. 2nd edition, Prentice-Hall, New Jersey.

2   Polymer and geotextile properties

The polymer material properties relevant to reinforced soil design are described in this chapter, together with criteria for their selection and the methods of measurement.

The *strength* of polymer materials and their load-elongation properties (i.e. *stiffness*) vary with time under sustained load, and depend on the ambient temperature. Both *time* and *temperature* are important factors affecting the material properties of geotextiles.

The strength of reinforced soil depends jointly on the mobilised frictional shearing resistance in the soil and the mobilised axial tensile force in the reinforcement. These are linked through *strain compatibility*. Thus both the reinforcement *strength* and *stiffness* properties are important.

Geotextiles are used in the ground. Immediate changes to their material properties can be caused by *mechanical damage* and longer-term changes caused by the *chemical* and biological *environment* of the soil and groundwater.

Therefore, the measured properties of ex-works reinforcement materials only give a reference, and it is always necessary to assess the changes from these *reference properties* resulting from mechanical damage and the soil environment.

2.1 Polymer types

Suitable grades of high density polyethylene (HDPE), polypropylene and polyester are the polymer materials currently used most often to manufacture geotextiles for reinforced soil applications. The desirable properties include sufficient load-elongation behaviour at ambient temperatures, acceptably small creep deformation under sustained loads, only gradual strength reduction with time under load, and reasonable durability in the chemical and biological conditions found in typical soil environments.

Such desirable properties can only be achieved at some cost, and the relation between price and performance is significant in the choice of materials. For example, polypropylene is generally less costly than HDPE, but may creep more under sustained load. Polyaramid, a newer polymer type, has a higher stiffness and generally creeps less than the polymers named above, but it is more costly than either HDPE or polyester. Clearly the cost which is acceptable depends on the envisaged use, the design requirements for the reinforcement, and the economic benefits. Currently, HDPE and polyester are the most popular materials for soil reinforcement, with polypropylene being attractive where the loading is shorter term and the deformation less critical.

As new manufacturing processes and markets develop, the relative cost of different polymer materials and geotextile products will change.

2.2 Polymer properties

The material properties of a polymer are determined by many factors, and there is a *wide variation of properties for any polymer type*. Important factors are the physical form and structure of the polymer, the density, molecular weight, crystallinity and any additives, and the amount by which the material has been drawn during processing. Drawing, the stretching of a polymer material under load, can have a profound influence on the properties and is commonly measured as a *draw ratio*, the ratio of the length of the drawn material to the initial length of undrawn material.

Only some of the above characteristics of a polymer can be discovered from the direct appearance of the material and the manufacturer's data sheets. There is a need for classification of polymer reinforcement materials and types, such as already exists for steels and electrical laminates. But such classification is still at an early stage, and design engineers must usually rely on manufacturer's information.

The form of a geotextile product also influences the properties. For example the load-carrying elements in woven geotextiles are never perfectly aligned, and this leads to an extra component of extension as they straighten under load.

It is still useful, however, to group geotextiles by their basic polymer type (such as *polyester*) although quite significant variations in material properties should be expected within each type, depending on the precise grade, the additives, the amount of drawing and other aspects of processing.

Two general provisions in selecting design values for geotextile reinforcement are:

1. An adequate factor of safety between the *maximum allowable load* used in design and the *rupture strength* of the reinforcement.
2. A *maximum tensile elongation* in the geotextile, selected to ensure that the deformations in the reinforced soil structure will remain acceptable, even when the geotextile has been when subjected to load over the design life of the structure.

Either of these two requirements may govern the maximum force that a given geotextile reinforcement can be relied upon to provide in a serviceable structure. This focuses attention separately on the *strength properties* and on the *stiffness* (load-elongation) *properties* of geotextiles.

In common with metals, the dimensions of a polymer material under sustained load will change with time – the phenomenon known as *creep*. While for most metals creep is only important at temperatures above about 300°C, and so is of little importance for civil engineering purposes, creep at ambient temperatures is normal in polymers and is significant for reinforced soil design (Figure 2.1). Creep deformation depends on the chemical composition and the processing of the polymer material, as well as on the ambient temperature.

The progressive changes in the polymer during creep have the effect of gradually reducing the strength of the material with time. This is known as creep-rupture, stress-

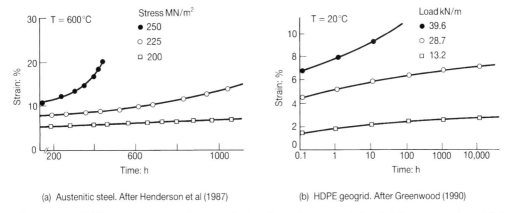

(a) Austenitic steel. After Henderson et al (1987)   (b) HDPE geogrid. After Greenwood (1990)

Figure 2.1 *Different types of creep behaviour in materials: (a) in a metal at high temperature, and (b) in a polymer at ambient temperature*

rupture or static fatigue. In general, a polymer material held under a sustained load would be expected to break, eventually. But under modest load this might only occur after a period of time considerably greater than the design life of the civil engineering works. There is a concept for a *critical stress* for some polymers where failure would never be expected when the material is subjected to a lesser stress; but it is difficult to obtain the very long-term data needed to fully substantiate the concept (Wilding and Ward, 1981).

In summary, the aim in design is to ensure that the reinforcement has adequate *strength* and *stiffness* properties bearing in mind the conditions in the ground and the period under load, represented by the design life and the design temperature (t_d, T_d).

2.2.1 Index properties

A baseline is needed against which to compare the influences of *time* and temperature on the properties of polymers. Standard *index tests* provide a measure of *index strength* and *stiffness* properties which help in the comparison of different materials and in quality control work. *Index tests* are carried out at relatively high rates of elongation and can be completed quickly.

The test described in (British Standard) BS 6906: Part 1 (BSI, 1987) is recommended for measuring the index tensile properties of geotextiles and geogrids. The sample size is 200mm wide by 100mm long, and a rate of elongation in the range 10 ± 3%/min is used. The test is carried out at a standard temperature 20 ± 2°C and relative humidity 65 ± 2%. The test reflects the predominantly uniaxial or plane-strain loading experienced by geotextile reinforcement in most reinforced soil applications.

It may be noted that the deformation of geotextiles is described generally in terms of load and elongation, rather than stress and strain. This is because the state of stress and strain in the filaments, yarns or sections of geogrid material vary from place to place, and are not precisely known.

2.2.2 Creep properties

Index tests load the polymer material to failure in a matter of seconds or minutes, and are of limited relevance to applications where the geotextile is subject to long-term sustained load for periods of months or years.

In such cases, *sustained-load creep tests* are required to determine the geotextile properties for design. Such tests should be carried out at ambient temperatures relevant to the conditions in the ground, and on wide samples to reflect the confinement in soil which resists any tendency for lateral contraction in the geotextile. The test outlined (British Standard) BS 6906: Part 5 (BSI, 1991) is recommended. The period under sustained load should ideally approach to within a factor of 10 the design life for the geotextile, to reduce the amount of extrapolation needed to estimate the properties at the design time and temperature (t_d, T_d). Extrapolation of the data over a greater period is often required in practice, but should not exceed a factor of 100.

Typical results from creep tests on a polyester geotextile are shown in Figure 2.2, plotted as elongation versus time, on a logarithmic scale. This shows the continuing, gradual increase in elongation with time under constant load, which is typical of polymer materials.

Failure in a creep test can occur after a period of time under load which depends on the load magnitude and the ambient temperature. The data in Figure 2.3 are for polyester yarn. In general, the *strength* of a geotextile can only be discussed usefully if the corresponding *time to failure* (or rate of elongation) and *temperature* are given.

2.3 Strength and stiffness of geotextiles

The *allowable load* for a geotextile that is used in design should be selected after considering both the *strength properties* and the *stiffness properties* of the geotextile appropriate to the loading period and temperature in the ground. The data on these

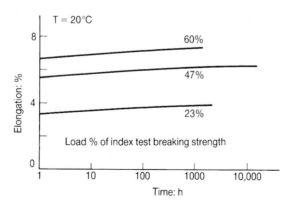

Terram WB 20/5. After Greenwood (1990)

Figure 2.2 *Sustained-load creep test on a polyester geotextile*

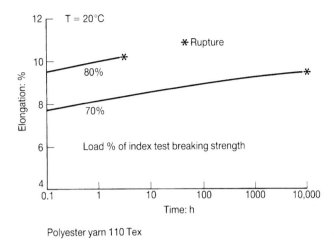

Polyester yarn 110 Tex

Figure 2.3 *Sustained-load creep tests causing failure in a polyester yarn*

properties are derived from sustained-load creep tests. This approach is consistent with limit state design where both *stability* (strength) and *serviceability* (stiffness) are investigated.

2.3.1 Strength properties

A polymer material, when highly loaded, may *yield* and then *rupture*, or it may simply *rupture* (with no perceptible prior yield). This is illustrated schematically in Figure 2.4 for a test (a) at a constant rate of elongation, and (b) under sustained load. When loaded with a constant rate of elongation, the yield load is defined as the highest one achieved in the test; *yield* is where the material supports a constant load at a constant rate of elongation (Figure 2.4a). Under sustained load the *yield point* is defined where the rate of elongation reaches a minimum, the point of inflection in Figure 2.4b. At this stage the material is once more supporting constant load at a constant rate of elongation. Thus the

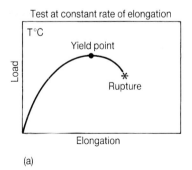

(a)

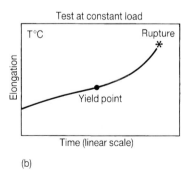

(b)

Figure 2.4 *Yield and rupture points: (a) at a constant rate of elongation and (b) under sustained load*

yield point is common to the two tests. However, *rupture* may intervene before yield occurs.

It is common to use the yield point to define the limit of material performance, because once it is exceeded rupture is imminent. The limiting load capacity, the *strength of the material* at a given *temperature*, can then be represented by plotting the yield or rupture load versus the corresponding time to 'failure'. The usual axes are *load* on a linear scale versus *time* on a logarithmic scale, as shown in Figure 2.5, although the load is sometimes plotted on a logarithmic scale.

For some geogrid materials, the limit of material performance has sometimes been defined in terms of a 'limit strain', rather than in terms of the measured yield or rupture point (McGown *et al.*, 1984). The data can be treated in the same way as before with the decreasing 'strength' with time plotted as described above to allow for extrapolation to greater time, beyond the test data.

2.3.2 Stiffness properties

The *allowable load* for design is typically only a small proportion of the short-term or *index strength* of the geotextile. But designers must still consider the relation between cumulative elongation and time under load for geotextiles in order to estimate the elongation that can be expected in the reinforcement. With current knowledge, prescriptive or empirical limits for the maximum acceptable elongation in the reinforcement are often introduced to ensure that the reinforced soil structure does not deform unduly.

Creep test data are again required. A plot of load versus elongation, on which a single curve represents the relation after a given time under load, indicates how the reinforcement stiffness reduces over time. The derivation of such *isochronous load-elongation curves* from creep test data is shown in Figure 2.6.

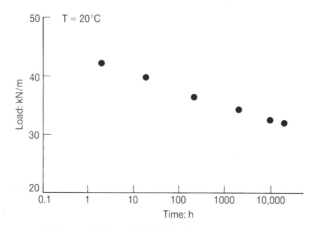

HDPE geogrid (Tensar SR80). (After Wrigley 1987)

Figure 2.5 *Strength properties for a uniaxial polyethylene geogrid*

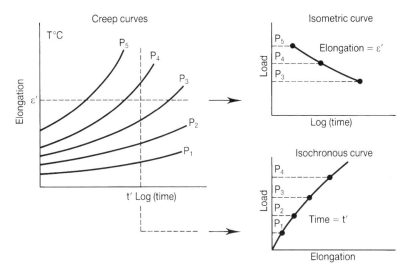

Figure 2.6 *Load-elongation relations found from creep test data*

The *isochronous curves* show directly how the load-elongation behaviour of a geotextile changes with loading periods, such as the time under load up to the end of construction, or between the end of construction and the end of the design life. The expected elongation in the reinforcement under a given load can be found directly from the isochronous curves. Similarly, when a maximum allowable elongation has been specified, the corresponding maximum load can be found directly from the isochronous curves.

2.3.3 Extrapolation for long-term properties

Many geotextiles and their constituent polymer materials were developed relatively recently, and so extrapolation of data is often required to find the properties relevant to practical design lives for engineering works.

Creep and creep-rupture curves can be extrapolated by eye using the most plausible extension of a line or a curve, the extrapolation appearing more credible if the information can be plotted to give a straight line, or fitted to an empirical mathematical formula. However, while empirical laws are useful and appear to add credibility, they must be treated with caution unless they can be shown to relate to actual physical mechanisms in the material. All extrapolation, whether by eye or by calculation, depends on the mechanisms of creep and rupture remaining the same during the period of extrapolation. If they do not, the extrapolation is invalid (RILEM, 1988).

Indeed it is the possibility that the mechanisms governing behaviour may change at times beyond the test period which is one of the greatest sources of uncertainty in extrapolation, since this can result in a discontinuous change in the measured variation of strength with time.

This phenomenon may occur due to a physical mechanism, as found in some unorientated polymer materials like polyethylene, for example. The result is that the actual period to rupture at lower stresses is shorter than found by extrapolating the rupture data from tests at higher stresses. To date, however, no evidence for such a physical transition has been found in the drawn polymers used to make most geotextiles (Greenwood, 1990).

In order to resist and minimise the risk of physical mechanisms causing behavioural changes, polymer technologists use additives and special processing in the manufacture of the raw materials of geotextiles. However, it is possible that chemical mechanisms may then cause similar discontinuous changes in behaviour, since if the additives included to inhibit a mechanism of degradation in the polymer become used up or exhausted in some way, then the inhibited mechanism may eventually take place (Sotton, 1986; Wisse, 1988).

As discussed earlier, the effect of temperature is to accelerate the mechanisms influencing polymer behaviour. Creep tests carried out over a range of temperatures provide the opportunity to support extrapolation by the superposition of results at higher temperature. That is, the same *pattern of behaviour* would be expected to be observed over a shorter test period at a higher temperature. Thus it is possible, in principle, to predict the long-term creep behaviour at ambient design temperatures from the response measured over a shorter period at higher temperatures.

Care is needed in the use of accelerated testing. Typically the elevated test temperature should not exceed the design temperature by more than about 30°C, and should not approach the temperatures where material transitions occur – such as the *glass transition temperature* for polyester at about 50 to 60°C.

There are accepted limits to the amount of extrapolation which is reasonable. It is sensible, and recognised as good practice, not to extrapolate the properties of a polymer material (at a given temperature) by more than one $\log_{10}$ cycle in time without other supporting evidence. Even allowing extrapolation by this factor, a 100-year design life would require results based on 10 years of testing. Since geotextiles are relatively new, and are being used in long-life applications, extrapolation of data by up to two $\log_{10}$ cycles of time is frequently required. It is recommended that this should be supported by data from accelerated testing (at higher temperature) wherever possible, and that increased safety margins should be adopted in view of the greater uncertainty.

Significant scatter is common in stress-rupture data and many repetitions of tests are needed if confidence limits are to be placed on the measured properties.

2.3.4 Aged life of geotextiles

The work of Sotton (1986), Verdu (1988) and Wisse *et al.*, (1990) suggests that the possible chemical breakdown of a geotextile in the very long term should be formally assessed. Such chemical breakdown sets an absolute limit to the design life of the geotextile irrespective of the magnitude of the applied load. A test for chemical breakdown exists in the electrical industry (CEI, 1990), but no similar test has been developed for geotextiles.

Chemical ageing tests are carried out at high temperatures with the material exposed to appropriate chemical environments. The time of failure at various temperatures is measured and plotted on a logarithmic scale against the inverse of temperature (for processes governed by the Arrhenius equation). This allows extrapolation of the data to the design temperature to find the aged life of the material, t_{env}, Figure 2.7.

In effect, chemical ageing tests aim to prove that a polymer reinforcement material can resist the active chemical processes that would otherwise lead to complete chemical breakdown in the long term. Given the high temperature of testing and the uncertainty in extrapolation, it is suggested that the aged life, t_{env}, should be required to exceed the design life of the structure by a factor of the order 3 (one half of one $\log_{10}$ cycle).

2.4 Measurement of reference properties

Reference properties are measured on ex-works geotextile products. The range of the data should include ambient temperatures equal to or greater than those which the reinforcement will experience in the ground. Separate allowance is made for the change in the properties caused by *installation damage* and the *chemical and biological environment* in the ground (Section 2.5.3). These changes depend on the soil and conditions at each site.

The test defined by BS 6906 Part 1 (BSI, 1987) is recommended to determine *index properties* (Section 2.2.1). At least five specimens should be tested to determine mean values. Properties for a geotextile are usually measured in both the longitudinal and the

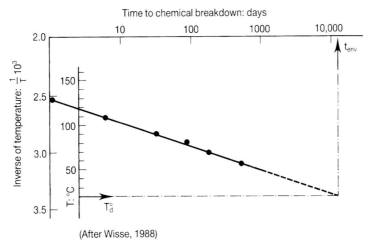

(After Wisse, 1988)

Figure 2.7 *Time to chemical breakdown as a function of temperature for a spunbonded polypropylene geotextile (after Wisse, 1988)*

transverse directions. The index load-elongation curve, maximum load and breaking load (if different) and the associated elongations for each should be reported (Figure 2.8).

Both the *reference-strength* and *reference-stiffness properties* for a geotextile should be determined under similar conditions to those above, but from creep tests where the load is applied rapidly and subsequently held constant at the desired level. The test in BS 6906 Part 5 (BSI, 1991) is recommended to determine the *creep properties* for a geotextile (Section 2.2.2). The test arrangement is similar to the index test, but the load is applied rapidly (between 2 to 60 seconds) and held constant thereafter.

Higher loads are chosen to observe rupture during creep tests to allow *creep-rupture properties* to be extrapolated (Figure 2.9). It is necessary to repeat the test several times

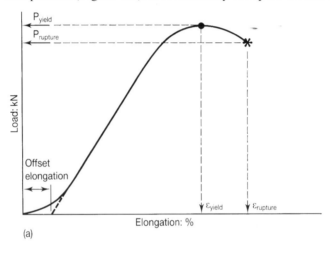

(a)

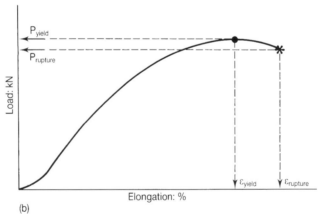

(b)

(After BS 6906: Part 1: 1987)

Figure 2.8 *Typical load-elongation response from index tests: (a) linear behaviour and (b) non-linear behaviour*

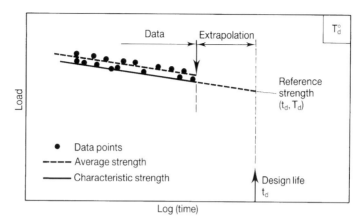

Figure 2.9 *Creep-rupture properties for a geotextile material*

at each load level because of the scatter found in creep-rupture data. Ideally, the aim should be to determine the variation of the safe *characteristic strength* of the material with time, commonly defined as the value only 5% of samples fail to achieve. The accuracy with which a characteristic value may be found depends on the number of test observations, and standard procedures are given in BS 2846 Part 2 (BSI, 1975).

Reference properties for a geotextile should be measured over a range of temperatures, including 10°C and 20°C the typical range for ground temperatures in temperate countries (Murray and Farrar, 1988). Data at higher temperatures are needed for applications in tropical climates, and at lower temperatures for colder regions.

2.5 Damage and durability of geotextiles

2.5.1 Mechanical damage

Polymer reinforcement can be damaged during construction. Physical damage of geotextiles can include punctures, tearing, pierced holes in which the yarns are separated but not torn, as well as abrasion of the yarns themselves. Such damage can reduce the life of the geotextile under load. In the case of geogrids, damage can result in cuts, splits and local crushing of members.

There have been many tests in which geotextiles have been buried in soil, extracted and tested, usually under *index test* conditions, as reviewed by Colin *et al.* (1986). The effects of construction on the properties of geogrid reinforcement buried in various soils is reviewed by Bush (1988), and recent tests on geotextiles by Watts and Brady (1990).

One effect of mechanical damage is to reduce locally the cross-section of material supporting load, thereby increasing the stress at these damaged places. This increased loading reduces the time to cause stress/rupture. Local stress concentrations caused by damage can also initiate failure by tearing in a geotextile, but a suitable test for this has not yet been devised. Because damage is local in nature, the overall load-elongation properties, which are dominated by the bulk of undamaged material, usually remain largely unchanged.

Thus mechanical damage reduces the *strength properties* of polymer reinforcement materials while leaving the overall *stiffness properties* substantially unchanged. The elongation to rupture, though, is reduced.

Until more extensive longer term testing of damaged materials has been carried out, it has to be assumed that the reduction in strength caused by mechanical damage to geotextiles which is measured in relatively short-term tests will apply in the same proportion over longer periods (Figure 2.10).

Thus the procedure is to subject samples of geotextile to damage caused by a range of installation procedures and fill materials, and to measure the loss of strength caused by the damage (Billing *et al.*, 1990; Paulson, 1990; Watts and Brady, 1990). This measured loss in strength is represented by a damage factor, f_d, which when applied to the reference strength allows for the anticipated damage to the geotextile in the ground.

Recommended damage factors determined in this way for some uniaxially drawn geogrid materials are summarised in Table 2.1 (Bush, 1988). Similar factors for woven polyester geotextiles and some polyester geogrids are given in Table 2.2 (Troost and Ploeg, 1990). Proper allowance for damage must be based on tests for each individual geotextile product, and this *product-specific* data should be supplied by manufacturers. The relevance of the data may be checked by independent testing on specific projects.

2.5.2 Chemical and biological durability

The ability of geotextiles to withstand the chemical and biological environment in the soil over a long period of time has attracted considerable study (RILEM, 1988). The

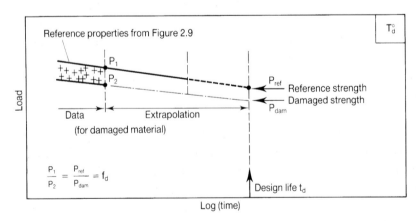

Figure 2.10 *Idealisation of mechanical damage reducing strength by a constant factor irrespective of time*

Table 2.1 Factors to allow for mechanical damage for some geogrid reinforcements made from drawn HDPE (Bush, 1988, Netlon, 1990)

Fill type	Well-graded fill maximum size D_{max} (mm)	Values of f_d for Tensar geogrids		
		SR55	SR80	SR 110
Coarse grained soils and crushed rocks	$D_{max} < 125$mm	1.70	1.40	1.40
Coarse grained soils, cobbles and gravel	$D_{max} < 75$mm	1.45	1.30	1.20
Sands	$D_{max} < 20$mm	1.25	1.20	1.10
Medium and fine sand, clay and PFA	$D_{max} < 2$mm	1.15	1.10	1.05

Table 2.2 Partial factors to allow for mechanical damage for some woven geotextiles and geogrids made from polyester (Troost and Ploeg, 1990)

Fill type	Well-graded fill maximum size D_{max} (mm)	Values of f_d for some polyester reinforcements			
		STABILENKA woven geotextiles		FORTRAC woven geogrids	
		≤ 300kN/m	> 300kN/m	≤ 55kN/m	≥ 55kN/m
Cobbles	$D_{max} < 200$mm	1.40	1.40	1.20	1.05†
Gravels	$D_{max} < 100$mm	1.35	1.14	1.15	1.03†
Sands	$D_{max} < 2$mm	1.17	1.10	1.10	1.02†
Clays	$D_{max} < 0.06$mm	1.10	1.10	1.05†	1.02†

† Although indicated in the table, values $f_d < 1.10$ are not recommended in this book, unless supported by specific evidence for the given site

principal areas of concern for polymer materials include oxidation, hydrolysis, alkaline attack, ultraviolet light and biological effects. All of these can reduce the strength of a polymer material.

On the other hand, additives and processing procedures are available and are extensively used to counteract these effects. Geotextiles usually contain carbon black to reduce the effects of ultraviolet light and to act as an anti-oxidant. However, the users of geotextiles seldom receive information about the nature or quantity of the additives in the polymer materials.

Results on materials recovered from sites indicate that geotextile products have a good resistance to typical soil environments, certainly up to a period of 10 years (Leflaive, 1988). The question now becomes whether the additives can remain effective throughout the design life, and whether they can stand up to more extreme environments, such as higher acidity or alkalinity. One concern is with any progressive physical loss of additives, such as by leaching, or by being rendered chemically neutral (Wisse et al., 1990).

Tests to establish the chemical durability of geotextiles are generally carried out by immersing the material in appropriate liquids for a period of time and determining any reduction in strength with a short-term tensile test (Billing *et al.*, 1990). It is possible to introduce a level of acceleration by increasing the temperature or the chemical concentration, but the accelerating factor introduced in this way has not yet been firmly established.

This approach is potentially inadequate in that it can not detect any interaction between sustained load and the chemical or biological environment, such as the stress-corrosion that promotes the growth of cracks in some metals and bulk polymers in the presence of certain solvents. Such interaction can only be determined by tests under sustained load in relevant chemical and biological environments, using damaged samples where appropriate. Wrigley (1987) completed such tests on *undamaged* samples of a geogrid, and Viezee *et al.* (1990) tested *damaged* polyester yarns and woven geotextiles.

Concern has been expressed about the effects of hydrolysis on polyester, but some of the data are from studies on quite different grades of polyester than used in modern geotextiles (Mitchell and Villet, 1987). Tests on the grades of polyester currently used for geotextiles have shown only small strength reduction due to hydrolysis within the normal pH range for soils (Montalvo, 1989); Risseeuw and Schmidt, 1990). However, more extensive and systematic testing is still required to investigate in more detail the long-term effect of humid and alkaline environments on commercially available polyester reinforcement materials.

The longer that a geotextile is in the ground and subject to environmental influences, the greater will be the loss in strength (Figure 2.11). The reduction factor to allow for the soil environment should be for the worst conditions at the end of the design life. The increasing influence of the soil environment with time makes the precise determination of this factor, f_{env}, rather difficult.

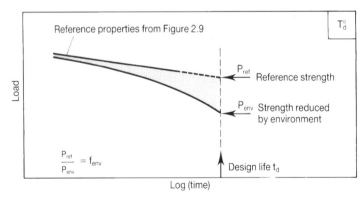

Figure 2.11 *Progressive influence with time of the soil environment on strength*

2.5.3 Material properties in the ground

At present, designers have to rely on manufacturer's information on the factors for *mechanical damage*, f_d, and the effects of the *chemical and biological environment*, f_{env}, for geotextile products. The soil, groundwater and other environmental aspects of the site need to be checked to ensure that they fall within the quoted range for which the data apply.

It is relatively simple to conduct site trials to assess *mechanical damage* by recovering freshly installed geotextile material under project conditions. Representative samples of damaged material can then be subjected to *index tests* to check the damage factor assumed in design.

Unfortunately, degradation caused by the *chemical and biological environment* can only be measured in long-term tests, which are generally impractical for individual project studies. Thus the onus rests firmly with manufacturers to determine the suitable factors, f_{env}, to allow for the environmental degradation of their products over the range of soil and groundwater conditions for which they are recommended.

Much more testing in independent research laboratories on mechanical, chemical and biological degradation of geotextiles is urgently required.

2.6 Synopsis of Chapter 2

(1) The material properties of polymer materials depend on *time* and *temperature* and an appropriate combination of these must be chosen when selecting properties for design.

(2) The behaviour of polymer materials under sustained load may be considered in terms of *strength properties* and *stiffness* properties.

(3) The use of polymer materials in the ground (in the form of geotextiles) causes changes in the material behaviour away from the *reference properties* measured on the ex-works product, because of *mechanical damage* and the soil *chemical and biological environment*.

(4) There are two distinct types of test carried out on geotextile materials. Relatively rapid, constant rate of elongation *index tests* provide broad comparisons between materials, and are useful for quality control purposes. *Sustained-load creep tests* determine the material properties which are required for most reinforced soil design purposes.

(5) There is a need for *extrapolation* of material properties because of the long design life in many reinforced soil structures. Appropriate safety margins have to be introduced to allow for the uncertainties in extrapolation.

Key references

British Standards Institution (1987). *British Standard Methods of Test for Geotextiles*, BS 6906: Part 1, Determination of the tensile properties using a wide-width strip. British Standards Institution, London.

Jewell, R.A. and Greenwood, J.H. (1988). Long term safety in steep soil slopes reinforced by polymer materials, *Geotextiles and Geomembranes*, Special issue on Durability, Vol. 7, Nos. 1 & 2, 81–118.

RILEM (1988). *Durability of Geotextiles*. Chapman and Hall, London.

Van Zanten, R.V. (ed.) (1986). *Geotextiles and Geomembranes in Civil Engineering.* Balkema, Rotterdam.

3   Geotextile products

The current range of geotextile products are described in this chapter, and some basic data on polymer material properties are given as a reference to allow for broad comparisons between alternative materials.

Two main features distinguish the different polymer reinforcement products:

1. *The material which supports the main axial (longitudinal) loading*, usually either yarns or drawn polymer elements (Figure 3.1a).
2. *Whether or not there are transverse members* which can bond with the soil in bearing (Figure 3.1b).

In most reinforced soil applications, such as retaining walls, steep slopes and embankments on soft soil, the reinforcement is required to support substantial axial tensile force in the longitudinal direction only. This can be achieved most efficiently by aligning the load-carrying members, the yarns or drawn elements, as straight as possible to minimise any deformation caused by straightening.

The requirements for *bond*, or the requirement for the geotextile to act additionally as a *separator*, influence whether it is preferable to bundle the load-carrying elements to form individual members, or whether to distribute them more uniformly as in a woven geotextile.

Where substantial reinforcement forces are required in two perpendicular directions it is usually best to place two reinforcement layers perpendicular to one another. An

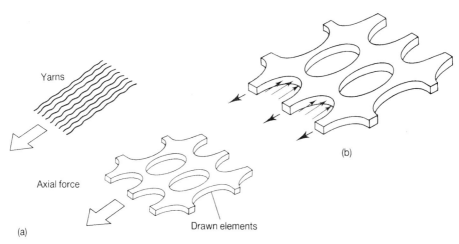

Figure 3.1 *Requirements for reinforcement: (a) axial load-carrying capacity and, for geogrids, (b) adequate transverse member arrangement*

example would be at the end of a reinforced embankment adjacent to a bridge abutment (Figure 3.2). The main reason for this recommendation is that a single material with significant strength in two directions would require joints to be made in one of the main load-carrying directions, between adjacent widths of material. Whenever possible, it is preferable to use continuous lengths of reinforcement (free of joints) in the main load-carrying direction.

Embankments on soft soil are a special case. The main reinforcement force acts across the width of the embankment, but, during construction, a lesser force is often required to maintain stability along the length of the embankment beneath the temporary slope

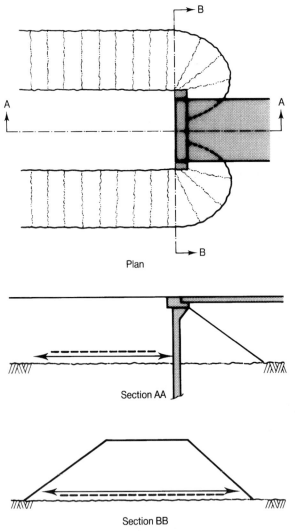

Plan

Section AA

Section BB

Figure 3.2 *Significant reinforcement in two perpendicular directions is best achieved by two separate layers*

formed by filling (Figure 3.3a). Because the magnitude of this second reinforcement force can be limited by controlling the slope formed by filling, and because the force acts only during filling, it is acceptable to use a single reinforcement material that has strength in two perpendicular directions. Widths of geotextile are then placed *across* the embankment, to avoid joints in the main load-carrying direction, but sewn overlapped joints between adjacent widths provide the continuity and the lesser strength in the direction of filling (Figure 3.3b).

The additional benefit of a separator between the embankment and the soft foundation soils may be desirable, and woven geotextile sheets sewn together have been found attractive in these cases. Composites combining reinforcement and separation materials may also be used. Another alternative is to provide a continuous base layer to the embankment formed with a cellular reinforcement mattress made by jointing geogrid material and filled with free-draining soil (Figure 3.3c).

3.1 Woven geotextiles

The load-carrying filaments, fibres and yarns in woven geotextiles are aligned in specific directions. This is usually along the geotextile (the longitudinal or *warp direction*), and across the geotextile (the transverse or *weft direction*).

The number of load-carrying elements in each direction may be varied to give a wide range of strengths. For reinforced soil applications, the strength along the geotextile is often significantly higher than across it. Further, the additional extension in a geotextile caused by straightening of the main load-carrying elements (e.g. the yarns) under load

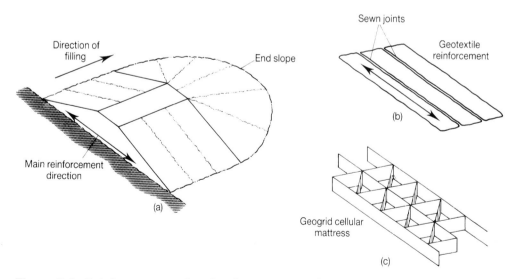

Figure 3.3 *Reinforcement of embankments on soft soil: (a) temporary force in the direction of filling, (b) jointed layers of reinforcement and (c) a cellular mattress*

can be minimised by using a weave that keeps them as straight as possible, such as a straight-warp weave (Figure 3.4).

A woven geotextile can act as a filter in soil allowing a flow of water through the material while holding back the soil particles, thus providing *separation* as well as reinforcement, and this can be an additional benefit in reinforced soil construction over poor foundation soils.

The form of the load-carrying elements in woven geotextiles depends on the *polymer material* and the *manufacturing process*. Polyester is widely used in stronger wovens, often in the form of multifilament yarns, while polypropylene is typically used in the form of fibrillated or split tapes.

The advantage of spreading the load-carrying elements to form a sheet reinforcement material are:

1. to maximise the contact area between the reinforcement and the soil which increases frictional bond,
2. to enable the reinforcement to act as a *separator* at the interface between the fill and the soft soil,
3. to allow the reinforcement to be wrapped at the face of a steep slope or wall to retain the soil fill.

Woven geotextiles can be used in all of the main reinforced soil applications, but are particularly suited to steep slopes, slip repairs and embankments on soft soil. They are generally used in wall construction only where a wrapped face is acceptable, as connection details with a permanent facing makes them less convenient, although this can be accommodated by new construction techniques (Jones *et al.*, 1988).

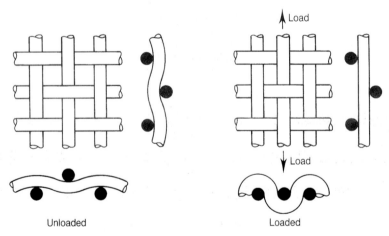

Unloaded   Loaded

Figure 3.4 *Geometric components of deformation caused by straightening of load-carrying elements in a woven geotextile (after Van Harten, 1980)*

3.2 Geogrids

Reducing the area of contact between the reinforcement and the soil by gathering the load-carrying elements into strips reduces the available frictional bond. But this can be overcome if the reinforcement has surfaces on which the soil can bear directly, as in a grid (Figure 3.1b). To be effective, these bearing members (the transverse elements of a grid) and the junctions with the longitudinal load-carrying members have to be able to support and transmit the bearing stresses which develop.

Geogrid reinforcement is formed by a patented process of punching holes in a sheet of undrawn polyethylene or polypropylene material which is then drawn (extended at an elevated temperature), in what will become the main load-carrying direction, to form a *uniaxial geogrid* (Mercer, 1987). Drawing the polymer material in this way improves the strength and stiffness properties (Ward, 1984). Geogrids can be proportioned so that the transverse members are able to support the soil bearing stresses, and transmit the loading to the longitudinal members through the continuous joints (Figure 3.5).

For applications in which load-carrying capacity is required in two perpendicular directions, the drawing process may be repeated in the transverse direction to form a *biaxial geogrid* reinforcement. Biaxial geogrids are generally less strong than uniaxial geogrids.

Geogrid reinforcement can be used in all the main reinforced soil applications, although generally it is not as strong as the heavier woven geotextile products. A particular feature of geogrid reinforcement is the excellent bond that can be developed through the interaction between the geogrid and the soil to mobilise bearing stresses.

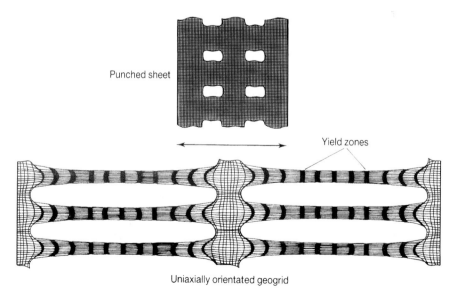

Figure 3.5 *Uniaxial geogrid reinforcement formed by a patented process of punching holes in a sheet followed by drawing (after Mercer, 1987)*

3.2.1 Geogrid-like products

The manufacturers of sheathed strip materials have produced geogrid-like reinforcement by connecting the strips in two perpendicular directions (Figure 3.6a). A drawback with this arrangement is that the load generated by bearing on the transverse members has to be transferred at the junctions through the sheathing material, which is not generally designed for such load-carrying purposes. However, some load transfer at these junctions by frictional shear may occur due to the compressive stresses caused by confinement in the soil.

The junction detail is greatly improved when there is more direct connection made by interweaving the yarns before coating them with the protective sheathing (Figure 3.6b). Although these geogrid products are relatively recent, a wide range is available and they have been widely used.

It is interesting to note that the polyester grid products allow a more robust reinforcement to be manufactured from polyester yarns when lower strengths are required than offered by the normal range of woven geotextiles. Manufacturers found it preferable to bundle together the fewer yarns required, and to coat them with a protective layer, and form a grid product rather than a woven geotextile.

A major consideration for geogrid-like products is the action of the transverse bearing members. If these have a relatively low bending stiffness, then the bearing stresses from the soil might need to be transmitted to the longitudinal members of the geogrid in tension, with the transverse members acting like cables rather than beams. The strength of the junctions must be adequate to transmit the envisaged loadings.

The range of applications for geogrid-like products is the same as given in the previous section.

3.2.2 Geomeshes

Geomeshes are usually formed by extrusion with counter-rotating die (Figure 3.7). The resulting tube of diamond-shaped mesh is cut to form a sheet. Because the polymer

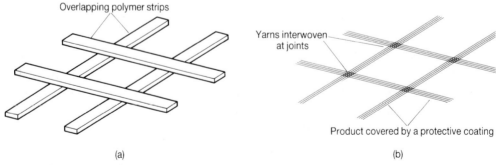

(a)   (b)

Figure 3.6 *Geogrid-like products: (a) connected sheathed strips and (b) interwoven bundled yarns with a protective coating*

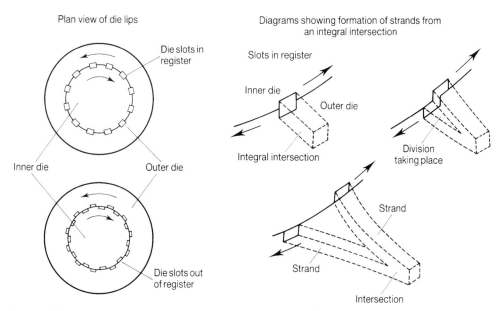

Plan view of die lips

Diagrams showing formation of strands from
an integral intersection

Figure 3.7 *Counter-rotating die for manufacturing geomesh materials (after Mercer, 1987)*

material is not drawn during the manufacture of geomeshes, the resulting products have strength and stiffness properties which are generally inadequate for soil reinforcement purposes, other than for light, short-term loading.

3.3 Other geotextile products

3.3.1 Non-woven geotextiles

A wide range of non-woven geotextiles is available, distinguished mainly by how the filaments are entangled and bonded together. Non-woven geotextiles can support tensile force, but because the filaments are not aligned in any particular direction the loading causes much more elongation than in an equivalent material with aligned load-carrying elements. Confinement of a non-woven geotextile in soil restricts the ability of the filaments to straighten under tensile load, and hence reduces the extensibility. Even so, non-woven geotextiles are generally much more extensible than woven geotextiles.

An important feature of non-woven geotextile materials is the wide range of pore size openings and thicknesses which can be achieved, which makes these products ideally suited to act as filters in soil. The ability to transmit water flows while retaining soil particles is also central to the use of non-wovens as *separators*.

There is undoubtedly some element of *reinforcement* present when non-woven geotextiles are included in unpaved road construction. But the greater deformation required to mobilise the reinforcement force in a non-woven material implies that ruts must usually develop. Research has shown that to reinforce an unpaved road without significant rutting requires the use of reinforcement materials with much greater stiffness than can be found in current non-woven geotextiles, as described in Chapter 12 (Love *et al.*, 1987).

Thus, *non-woven geotextiles* are most commonly used as *separators*, but they can also provide some reinforcement for soil in relatively short-term applications, such as unpaved roads, if significant deformation is acceptable.

3.3.2 Knitted geotextiles

Traditional knitted geotextiles are similar to non-wovens in that the load-carrying filaments are not aligned. However, warp knitting enables bundles of load-carrying filaments to be aligned in given directions, and this type of product is called a directionally structured fabric or *DSF* (Rankilor, 1988). Thus *DSF* products can provide an alternative to woven geotextile reinforcement.

3.3.3 Sheathed materials

Sheathed materials are made by gathering together the load-carrying filaments or yarns into a strip or a rod, and then sheathing the yarn bundle with a protective layer. The sheath holds the filaments in place as well as reducing the damage caused by contact with the soil.

Reinforcement strips made from polyester yarns and a polyethylene sheath are used as an alternative to metal reinforcement strips in reinforced soil walls, and as the load-carrying elements in loop-anchor walls. Sheathed strips have also been used at the base of embankments where two layers are laid to provide reinforcement in two perpendicular directions (Figure 3.2).

3.4 Comparing reinforcement materials

Some basic data on properties are summarised below to allow broad comparisons to be made between different reinforcement materials made from fibres and yarns, such as woven geotextiles and sheathed strips, and for some geogrids. Only the *reference properties* are discussed.

The aim of this section is to provide a general reference against which quoted properties for individual products can be assessed. This should help users to differentiate more easily between the different polymer materials and products. A detailed description of polymer material behaviour is given in Chapter 2, and manufacturer's data for their products should always be sought.

Only the processed grades of the stronger polymers currently used for soil reinforcement are considered. The range of properties for any particular polymer type would otherwise vary too widely to be of practical value, as explained in Section 2.2.

The unit measure of strength in textile engineering is called the *specific strength*, and is defined in terms of the load-carrying capacity of a unit quantity of polymer (Van

Zanten, 1986). The standard units are load in Newtons and quantity of material (yarn) in Tex, where one Tex is the weight in grams of one kilometre of a single yarn. The *specific strength* is measured in units of Newtons/Tex.

The same property is useful for geotextiles as it can equally be expressed in units more familiar to engineers. The *specific strength, S,* can be expressed in kiloNewton metres per gram (kNm/g), i.e.

$$\frac{N}{Tex} \equiv \frac{N}{g/1000m} \equiv \frac{1000Nm}{g} \equiv \frac{kNm}{g} \equiv \left(\frac{kN}{m}\right)\left(\frac{m^2}{g}\right) = S$$

The *specific strength* can be used to determine approximately how much polymer material, (g/m^2), would be needed to provide a geotextile of a required strength, (kN/m), as illustrated by the examples below.

3.4.1 Example cases
Woven geotextile
For a *woven geotextile,* the amount of polymer required per square metre in the load-carrying direction, g/m^2, to provide a desired strength per metre width, kN/m, is found from the equation

Required strength = Specific strength × Required weight of polymer

$$\frac{kN}{m} = \frac{kNm}{g} \times \frac{g}{m^2} \qquad\qquad ...(3.1)$$

The amount of polymer needed to provide strength across the width of the geotextile can similarly be determined, so that the total weight of the geotextile may be found, g/m^2. If different polymers are used in the longitudinal and transverse directions, the weights of each constituent polymer can be calculated and reported.

Reinforcement strip
For a *reinforcement strip* the desired strength is usually expressed in terms of load capacity, kN, so that the required amount of polymer is given as a weight per metre length of strip, g/m. In this case

Required strength = Specific strength × Required weight of polymer

$$kN = \frac{kNm}{g} \times \frac{g}{m} \qquad\qquad ...(3.2)$$

3.4.2 Data on specific strength and stiffness
Typical data on the *strength* and *stiffness* properties of different polymers at 20°C, and for loading periods corresponding to the *index test* and for load applied continuously over *one-year* and *10-year* periods are given below.

The *strength* is deduced from the creep-rupture data for the loading period, t_d. The *stiffness* properties are for an applied load equal of *half the current strength* for the loading period, and quoted as a secant stiffness, J_{50}.

The typical range of *specific strength*, S, and *specific stiffness*, J_{50} per gram, for the most common polymer materials used for soil reinforcement are recorded in Table 3.1.

The *specific stiffness* in Table 3.1 indicates the extensibility for the polymer constituent of a geotextile, and does not allow for any geometric component of extension caused by straightening of the filaments and yarns, as occurs in woven geotextiles (Figure 3.4). This effect needs to be added for woven geotextiles, because the total extension results from the elongation of the polymer plus any geometric component of extension. The magnitude of the geometric extension depends more upon the geotextile weave than on the polymer type, and typical values are indicated in Table 3.2.

3.4.3 Properties for woven geotextiles

To illustrate the data in Table 3.1, typical *index strength* properties for woven geotextiles with total weight 120 g/m^2, distributed as 100 g/m^2 aligned in the longitudinal direction and 20 g/m^2 aligned in the transverse direction, are summarised in Table 3.3.

Table 3.1 Typical reference properties for yarn at 20°C and 65% relative humidity

| Material | Draw | Specific strength S | | | Specific stiffness J_{50}/g | | |
| | | $\dfrac{kN\ m^2}{m\ g}$ | | | $\dfrac{kN\ m^2}{m\ g}$ | | |
Loading period	ratio	Index	1 year	10 year	Index	1 year	10 year
Polypropylene	5–10	0.2–0.4	0.05–0.3	0–0.2	1.3–5	0.1–1.8	0–1.2
Polyester	8–10	0.5–0.7	0.35–0.5	0.3–0.45	5–7	5–7	4–6
Polyamide	8–10	0.5–0.6	0.35–0.4	0.3–0.45	3–4	3–4	2.5–3.5

Table 3.2 Geometric component of extension caused by the weave in woven geotextiles (after den Hoedt, 1986)

Weave type	Extension due to weave
Straight warp woven	1 to 2%
Woven with crimp†	2 to 5%

† Larger values are possible, but the quoted values apply to the strong wovens.

Table 3.3 Comparison of index strength of three woven geotextiles of weight 100 g/m² in the longitudinal direction and 20 g/m² in the transverse direction (from data in Table 3.1)

Material	Index strength (longitudinal direction) kN/m	Index strength (transverse direction) kN/m
Polypropylene	30–40	6–8
Polyester	70–80	14–16
Polyamide	70	14

Note: data for 20°C and 65% relative humidity.

The corresponding *elongation* in the longitudinal direction caused when the woven geotextiles are loaded to half their respective breaking loads are given in Table 3.4 (using the average load when a range is indicated in Table 3.3). Finally, a figure for the total elongation is given, assuming 1.5% of geometric extension caused by the weave of the geotextile (Table 3.2).

3.4.4 Properties for geogrid reinforcement

The properties for drawn geogrid reinforcement also may be represented, but only in a more product-specific fashion. The difference is that a uniaxial geogrid, for example, is manufactured with a specific geometry so that the properties of the material can only be expressed in terms of the overall weight of the geogrid.

Specific strength and *specific stiffness* data for *uniaxial geogrids* made from high density polyethylene (HDPE) are given in Table 3.5. Similar data for biaxial geogrids made from polypropylene are also included.

Table 3.4 Comparison of index elongation of three woven geotextiles of weight 100 g/m² in the longitudinal direction and 20 g/m² in the transverse direction (from data in Tables 3.1 and 3.3).

Material	Load (longitudinal direction) kN/m	Stiffness (longitudinal direction) kN/m	Extension (polymer) %	Total Extension (polymer and crimp) %
Polypropylene	17.5	200–300	5.5–9	7–9.5
Polyester	37.5	700–800	4.5–5.5	6–8
Polyamide	35	200–300	12–18	13.5–19.5

Note: data for 20°C and 65% relative humidity.

Table 3.5 Typical geogrid reference properties at 20°C and 65% relative humidity

Material Loading period	Draw ratio	Specific strength S			Specific stiffness J_{50}/g			Unit cost
		$\dfrac{\text{kN m}^2}{\text{m} \quad \text{g}}$			$\dfrac{\text{kN m}^2}{\text{m}\epsilon \quad \text{g}}$			$\dfrac{\pounds}{\text{kg}}$
		Index	1 year	10 year	Index	1 year	10 year	
Polyethylene†	5–9	0.09–0.11	0.05–0.06	0.04–0.05	1.0–1.2	0.6–0.8	0.4–0.6	2–4
Polypropylene‡	5–9	0.08–0.11	—	—	1.0–1.6	—	—	2–4

† Uniaxial SR series geogrids; strength indicated for stronger, longitudinal direction
‡ Biaxial SS series geogrids; strength indicated for stronger, transverse direction

3.5 Synopsis of Chapter 3

(1) Two features distinguish the form of the different geotextile products:
 • the material supporting the main axial load, typically yarns or more substantial drawn polymer elements;
 • whether, or not, there are transverse members which bond with the soil in bearing.

(2) There are two components of elongation in a geotextile:
 • elongation of the polymer material itself, and
 • a geometric component of extension caused by straightening of the load-carrying elements (which can be minimised by initially aligning them).

(3) *Specific strength* and *specific stiffness* data for the typical grades of processed polymer material used to make strong geotextile reinforcement may be used to make broad comparisons of *reference properties*.

Key references

Van Harten, K. (1986). The relation between specifications of geotextiles and their essential properties. *Geotextiles and Geomembranes,* Vol. 3, 53–76.

Van Zanten, R.V. (ed.) (1986). *Geotextiles and Geomembranes in Civil Engineering.* Balkema, Rotterdam.

4 Reinforced soil behaviour

Tensile axial force in reinforcement improves the shearing resistance of soil, and reinforcement acts most effectively when placed in a direction in which *tensile strain* develops in the soil.

The load-elongation properties of the reinforcement influence the rate at which force can be mobilised as the soil deforms. The mobilised reinforcement force must remain in equilibrium with the surrounding soil, otherwise the reinforcement pulls out when the *bond* stress is exceeded.

The shear strength of reinforced soil is determined jointly by the mobilised shearing resistance in the soil and the mobilised tensile force in the reinforcement. The relative magnitude of these mobilised resistances depends on the deformation properties of the constituent soil and reinforcement materials. The question of strain *compatibility* between the soil and reinforcement materials must be considered so that appropriate combinations of *resistances* can be chosen for use in design analysis.

The inclusion of reinforcement in soil introduces the possibility of new failure mechanisms involving *direct sliding* across the surface of a reinforcement layer.

4.1 How reinforcement strengthens soil

The concept of how reinforcement strengthens soil, introduced in Section 1.2, is described below.

Soil shearing resistance stems from frictional contact between soil particles subject to effective compressive stress. The effective stress is the portion of the total stress transmitted through the particle contacts rather than through the porewater pressure.

Soil deforms when it is loaded in shear. In addition to any elastic distortion of the soil particles themselves, shear deformation occurs as soil particle contacts realign to mobilise shearing resistance. The deformation is observed as an overall strain in the soil, and both compressive and tensile strains usually develop when soil shears.

When reinforcement is placed in soil it can develop bond through frictional contact between the soil particles and the planar surface areas of the reinforcement, and from bearing stresses on transverse surfaces which exist in grids or ribbed strips. Deformation in the soil causes tensile or compressive force to develop in the reinforcement, depending on whether the reinforcement is inclined in a direction of tensile or compressive strain in the soil. The mobilised reinforcement force, ultimately limited by the available bond, acts to alter the force equilibrium in the soil.

Fundamental studies have shown that reinforcement is most effective when aligned in a direction of tensile strain in soil, so that tensile reinforcement force develops (McGown *et al.*, 1978). This tensile force, acting across a potential rupture surface, (a) directly supports some of the applied shear loading, and (b) increases the normal stresses in the soil on the rupture surface, thereby allowing greater frictional shearing resistance to be mobilised. This was illustrated for a direct shear test on reinforced soil in Figure 1.3.

The case of reinforcement in a steep slope is illustrated in Figure 4.1. An unreinforced slope of soil with an effective frictional shearing resistance, ϕ', no cohesion, $c' = 0$, and zero porewater pressure, is shown in Figure 4.1a. The self-weight loading of the soil causes a disturbing shear force, P_s, to act on the section of the shear surface shown. In the unreinforced slope, this is resisted by the available soil frictional resistance, $P'_n \tan \phi'$.

A horizontal layer of reinforcement in a steep slope will be inclined to typical critical shear surfaces at about $\theta \approx 20$ to $30°$. Shear deformation in the soil will cause tensile force to be mobilised in the reinforcement, P_r, and provide two additional components of resistance in the slope (Figure 4.1b). The tangential component of the reinforcement force, $P_r \sin \theta$, directly resists the disturbing shear force in the soil, while the normal component of the force, $P_r \cos \theta$, mobilises additional frictional shearing resistance, $P_r \cos \theta \tan \phi'$. The same two components of reinforcement action were identified previously in the direct shear test (Figure 1.3).

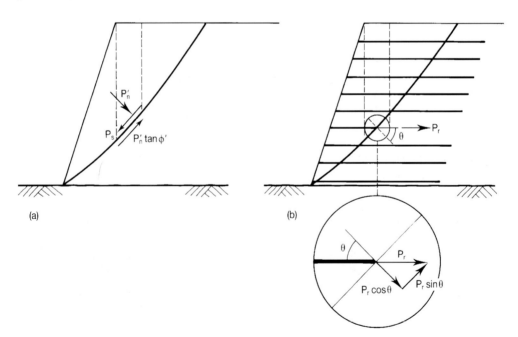

(a)   (b)

Figure 4.1 *Effects of reinforcement on equilibrium: (a) unreinforced slope and (b) allowing for the reinforcement force*

4.2 Reinforcement orientation and stiffness

The improvement in shearing resistance, ΔP_s, resulting from a reinforcement force, P_r, can be expressed by the equilibrium equation of forces

$$\Delta P_s = P_r \, (\sin \theta + \cos \theta \tan \phi') \qquad \qquad ...(4.1)$$

where the angle of the reinforcement, θ, is defined in Figures 1.3 and 4.1.

A plot of the function (Equation (4.1)) then indicates that a fixed tensile force, P_r, acts most effectively at an optimum orientation $\theta_{opt} = 90° - \phi'$, as shown in Figure 4.2.

In practice, the degree of improvement depends critically on the magnitude of the mobilised reinforcement force, P_r, and this too influences the optimum orientation. There are two physical mechanisms which should be considered.

First, the force that a strong reinforcement layer can carry is limited ultimately by the *bond* between the reinforcement and the soil, developed through frictional shear mechanisms (Section 4.4). The bond stress is greatest when the maximum *compressive stress* in the soil acts perpendicular to the plane of the reinforcement. The optimum orientation of reinforcement for bond, θ_b, is indicated in Figure 4.3a.

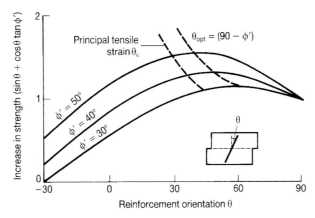

Figure 4.2 *Improvement in shearing resistance as a function of the reinforcement orientation*

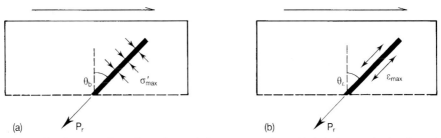

Figure 4.3 *Optimum directions for reinforcement in soil: (a) to maximise bond, and (b) to maximise tensile strain*

Second, the reinforcement *stiffness* properties influence the soil shear deformation required to mobilise the reinforcement force. The maximum possible tensile strain in the reinforcement is equal to the tensile strain in the adjacent soil in the direction of the reinforcement. Thus reinforcement orientated in the direction of maximum *tensile strain* will experience the greatest elongation for any given shear deformation in the soil. This optimum reinforcement orientation, θ_ε, is illustrated in Figure 4.3b.

Fortunately, the principal axes of *stress* and *incremental strain* are closely aligned in shearing soil so that the two optimum orientations described above are approximately equal, i.e. $\theta_b \cong \theta_\varepsilon$. Furthermore, the orientation that maximises the reinforcement force in compact soils, about $45° \geq \theta \geq 25°$, is very similar to the orientation in which the reinforcement force acts most efficiently (Figure 4.2).

This leads to the rule of thumb that geotextile reinforcement should be placed in soil at an orientation within the range $45° \geq \theta \geq 0°$ with respect to critical slip surfaces (Figures 4.1 and 4.3). This is roughly the horizontal direction in the main reinforced soil applications.

More detailed discussion of the above behaviour and supporting data may be found in Jewell and Wroth (1987).

4.3 Strain compatibility

It is useful to consider the amount of *tensile strain* which develops in the soil and the reinforcement in order to assess the equilibrium in reinforced soil. This helps ensure that (1) the design values selected for the reinforcement force and the soil shearing resistance can realistically be mobilised together, and that (2) the equilibrium can be achieved with acceptable deformation in the structure.

The relevant behaviour for soil is the relation between *mobilised shearing resistance*, ϕ'_{mob}, and maximum *tensile strain*, ε_3, under the loading conditions found in reinforced soil structures (Figure 4.4a).

The *isochronous load-elongation curves* for geotextile reinforcement define the relation between mobilised reinforcement force, P_r, and tensile elongation, ε_r, corresponding to the loading period and the temperature (t_d, T_d), in a reinforced soil structure (Figure 4.4b).

The equilibrium in the reinforced soil may be investigated using a *compatibility curve* constructed by assuming that there is equal tensile strain in the reinforcement and in the soil in the direction of the reinforcement. In the simplest form, a *compatibility curve* is a plot of (a) the maximum *required force* for equilibrium in the soil, which depends on the mobilised shearing resistance, and (b) the corresponding maximum *available force* from the reinforcement (Figure 4.5).

A simple compatibility curve may be found by assuming that the reinforced soil structure is built and initially held in equilibrium by imaginary external forces. Such an equilibrium with zero tensile strain would correspond with an earth pressure *at rest* in the soil and zero reinforcement force. Deformation and tensile strain will develop as the external support is removed. The net *required force* for equilibrium in the structure will progressively reduce to a minimum when the peak shearing resistance of the soil is mobilised, ϕ'_p (Figures 4.4a and 4.5). Continued deformation beyond this point will result in the *required force* for equilibrium increasing once more as the soil shearing resistance falls toward the large-strain or constant-volume angle of friction, ϕ'_{cv}.

On the other side, the *available force* mobilised in the reinforcement simply increases as tensile strain develops in the soil. The rate of increase in available force depends on the reinforcement stiffness properties (Figure 4.4b) and the number of layers of reinforcement intersecting the potential rupture surface. Equilibrium is reached, and the

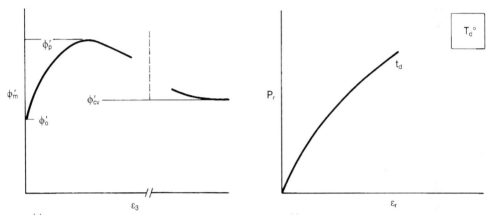

Figure 4.4 *Relations for strain compatibility: (a) mobilised soil shearing resistance, and (b) mobilised reinforcement force*

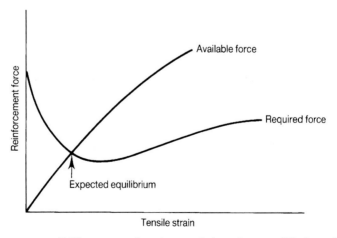

Figure 4.5 *The compatibility curve for determining the equilibrium in reinforced soil (after Jewell, 1985)*

need for any external support completely removed, once the *required* and *available forces* balance (Figure 4.5).

4.4 Interaction between soil and reinforcement

As well as the properties of the soil and the reinforcement materials themselves, the properties of their interaction are also important for reinforced soil. There are two limiting modes of interaction (Figure 4.6):

1. *Direct sliding*, in which a block of soil slides over a layer of reinforcement.
2. *Pullout*, in which a layer of reinforcement pulls out from the soil after it has mobilised the maximum available *bond* stresses.

Modified direct shear tests and pullout tests can be used to measure these interaction properties, but it is necessary to be clear about the relevance of each (Figure 4.6).

Modified direct shear tests are suitable for measuring the *coefficient of direct sliding* between soil and any type of reinforcement material (Figures 4.6c and d). For a woven or non-woven geotextile, *direct sliding* occurs between the soil and the geotextile material over the full plan area of contact. For practical purposes, these geotextiles may be supported either on a solid block or on soil in the lower half of the direct shear apparatus (Figure 4.6c). In contrast, the *direct sliding* resistance for geogrids is generated both by soil sliding over soil through the apertures of the grid, as well as by soil sliding over the material of the geogrid itself. This means that geogrids have to be tested with soil in the lower half of the direct shear apparatus (Figure 4.6d).

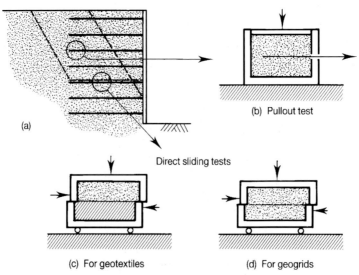

(a)

(b) Pullout test

Direct sliding tests

(c) For geotextiles

(d) For geogrids

Figure 4.6 *Interactions between soil and reinforcement*

Modified direct shear tests are relatively simple to perform with either arrangement. The larger 300×300mm direct shear apparatus and the procedures described in BS 6906: Part 8 are recommended (BSI, 1991).

Pullout tests model the second mode of interaction, the development of bond stress, but are difficult to interpret (Figure 4.6b). Special apparatus is required, but even then the results can be greatly influenced by the conditions in the test (Palmeira and Milligan, 1989).

For *woven* and *non-woven geotextiles*, the bond mechanism on either side of the reinforcement is very similar, if not identical, to that in direct sliding. The *bond coefficient* obtained from pullout tests on these materials has been found to agree closely with the *direct sliding coefficient* measured in modified direct shear tests. Thus for practical purposes there is no reason to perform pullout tests on woven and non-woven geotextiles; sufficient data on interaction may be obtained from the much simpler modified direct shear test.

For *geogrid reinforcement*, however, the mode of interaction during pullout is quite different from that in direct shear, as clearly established by tests using a photoelastic technique (Dyer, 1985; Milligan *et al.*, 1990). The data indicate that geogrids develop bond partly through concentrations of bearing stress against the transverse members of the grid, whereas they develop direct sliding resistance partly by shear of soil over soil through the apertures, and partly by shear of soil over the planar geogrid surface areas.

Thus the bond coefficient for a geogrid can only be measured by pullout tests. These require considerable skill and care both in execution and interpretation, particularly in relation to measurements affected by boundary conditions and when testing more extensible materials. Pullout test results can be – and often have been – misleading.

However, it is usually sufficient for design purposes simply to calculate the bond coefficient for geogrid reinforcement based on the grid dimensions and the soil properties (Jewell, 1990). The analysis is for a general case (Figure 4.7). When the

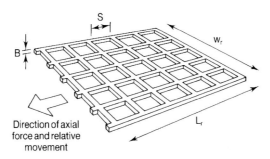

$\bar{a}_s$ Fraction of grid surface area that is solid
$\bar{a}_b$ Fraction of grid width w_r available for bearing

Figure 4.7 *Definition of dimensions for reinforcement*

fraction of the reinforcement plan area is set to unity, $\bar{\alpha}_s = 1$, the relations reduce to those relevant to woven and non-woven geotextiles.

4.5 Coefficient of direct sliding

The resistance to direct sliding of a block of soil across a layer of reinforcement (Figure 4.6a) depends on (a) shear between the soil and the planar surfaces of the reinforcement, and (b) the soil-to-soil shear through the apertures of the reinforcement. The overall direct sliding resistance is defined by a coefficient, α_{ds}.

The theoretical expression for direct sliding resistance recommended for design is

$$\alpha_{ds} \tan \phi' = \bar{a}_s \tan \delta + (1 - \bar{a}_s) \tan \phi' \qquad \qquad ...(4.2)$$

where $\tan \delta$ is the skin friction for soil shearing over the planar surfaces of the reinforcement, and the other terms are defined in Figure 4.7 (Jewell *et al.*, 1984). The *coefficient of direct sliding* is

$$\alpha_{ds} = \bar{a}_s \frac{\tan \delta}{\tan \phi'} + (1 - \bar{a}_s) \qquad \qquad ...(4.3)$$

For a woven or non-woven geotextile, for which $\bar{a}_s = 1$, the *coefficient of direct sliding* is analogous to the skin friction between a construction material and soil,

$$\alpha_{ds} = \frac{\tan \delta}{\tan \phi'} \qquad \qquad ...(4.4)$$

The coefficient of direct sliding is in the range $1.00 \geq \alpha_{ds} \geq 0.60$ for a wide variety of woven and non-woven geotextiles and soils (Williams and Houlihan, 1987). The lower values apply to geotextiles with smooth, even surfaces. The minimum possible direct sliding resistance would be of the order $\alpha_{ds} = 0.4$ which applies for soil shearing over smooth metal (Potyondy, 1961; Kishida and Uesugi, 1987). Woven geotextiles with significant surface roughness mobilise greater direct sliding resistance in the range $\alpha_{ds} \approx 0.8$ to 1.0.

The skin friction between granular soil and a solid sheet of polymer (such as HDPE) is of the order $\tan \delta \approx 0.6 \tan \phi'$. Many available geogrids have an area ratio of the order $\bar{a}_s = 0.5$. When substituted into Equation (4.3), this gives a typical *coefficient of direct sliding* resistance for geogrids $\alpha_{ds} \approx 0.8$.

Modified direct shear tests are simple and inexpensive to carry out, and theoretical values for the *coefficient of direct sliding* can be checked easily for specific combinations of soil and geotextile.

4.6 Coefficient of bond

The two main mechanisms of load transfer which provide bond between soil and reinforcement are skin friction and bearing stress (Figure 4.8). Bond can be defined in terms of a *bond coefficient*, α_b.

The contribution to bond from skin friction depends on the planar surface area of the reinforcement, $\bar{a}_s$, and the skin friction, $\tan \delta$.

The contribution to bond from the bearing stress acting on transverse members depends on the ratio of the bearing surface area to the plan area, $\bar{a}_b B/2S$, and on the ratio of the bearing stress to the stress acting normal to the plane of the reinforcement, σ'_b/σ'_n (Figures 4.7 and 4.8).

The theoretical expression for bond (Jewell *et al.*, 1984) is

$$\alpha_b \tan \phi' = \bar{a}_s \tan \delta + \left(\frac{\sigma'_b}{\sigma'_n}\right)\left(\frac{\bar{a}_b B}{2S}\right) \qquad \qquad ...(4.5)$$

and the *bond coefficient* is then

$$\alpha_b = \bar{a}_s \frac{\tan \delta}{\tan \phi'} + \left(\frac{\sigma'_b}{\sigma'_n}\right)\left(\frac{\bar{a}_b B}{2S}\right)\frac{1}{\tan \phi'} \qquad ...(4.6)$$

As before, the result for woven and non-woven geotextiles may be found by setting the terms $\bar{a}_s = 1.00$ and $\bar{a}_b = 0.00$

$$\alpha_b = \frac{\tan \delta}{\tan \phi'} = \alpha_{ds} \qquad \qquad ...(4.7)$$

which confirms that the *bond* and *direct sliding coefficients* are indeed equivalent for these materials (Section 4.5).

The parameters for the general case in Equation (4.6) are well defined except for the bearing stress ration, σ'_b/σ'_n (Figure 4.8). Relations giving theoretical upper and lower

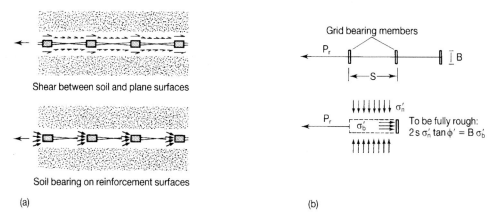

Figure 4.8 *Bond between reinforcement and soil: (a) mechanisms and (b) defini-tions for analysis*

limits to this bearing stress ratio have been found to bound the data on bearing stress recorded in pullout testing (Figure 4.9). The lower curve is recommended for design,

$$\left(\frac{\sigma'_b}{\sigma'_n}\right)_\infty = \tan(\pi/4 + \phi'/2)e^{(\pi/2 + \phi')\tan\phi'} \qquad \qquad ...(4.8)$$

and some values are given in Table 4.1

When typical parameters for geogrid reinforcement are substituted into Equation (4.6) it shows that the maximum possible bond in compact granular soil, $\alpha_b \approx 1.00$ (equivalent to a rough sheet), can be achieved by geogrids with a geometry of the order $S/\bar{a}_b B < 20$.

The two separate components which contribute to the bond of grid reinforcement are summarised in Table 4.2 for a range of grid geometries and soil angles of friction, assuming a typical skin friction $\tan \delta = 0.6 \tan \phi'$ between the soil and the polymer material. The *bond coefficient* for any desired combination of these can be found by adding the two components, subject to the limit $\alpha_b \leq 1.00$.

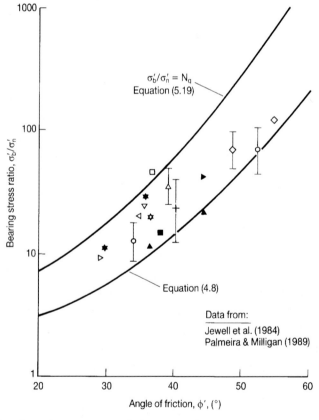

Figure 4.9 *Bearing stresses on reinforcement*

Table 4.1 Bearing stress ratio for soil reinforcement

ϕ'	σ_b'/σ_n'†	ϕ'	σ_b'/σ_n'†
16	2.26	31	6.29
17	2.39	32	6.82
18	2.54	33	7.42
19	2.70	34	8.10
20	2.87	35	8.85
21	3.06	36	9.70
22	3.27	37	10.66
23	3.49	38	11.74
24	3.73	39	12.98
25	4.00	40	14.39
26	4.30	41	16.01
27	4.62	42	17.08
28	4.98	43	20.03
29	5.37	44	22.54
30	5.80	45	25.47

† Equation (4.8)

Palmeira and Milligan (1989) have shown that there is an important *scale effect* due to the mean particle size, D_{50}, which increases the bearing load transfer once $B/D_{50} < 10$ (Figure 4.10). This finding is consistent with the scale effects observed in other bearing capacity problems (Kerisel, 1972). The empirical relation shown in Figure 4.10 is recommended to allow these scale effects to be taken into account

$$\left(\frac{\sigma_b'}{\sigma_n'}\right)_s = \left(\frac{20 - B/D_{50}}{10}\right)\left(\frac{\sigma_b'}{\sigma_n'}\right)_\infty = F_1\left(\frac{\sigma_b'}{\sigma_n'}\right)_\infty \qquad \text{...(4.9)}$$

and applies when $B/D_{50} < 10$. The bearing stress ratio $(\sigma_b'/\sigma_n')_\infty$ is for a continuum (no particle size effects) and is defined by Equation (4.8) for bearing on transverse members of circular cross-section. The test data indicate that this may be increased by a factor 1.2 for bearing on transverse members of rectangular cross-section.

Thus both *scale effects* (Equation 4.9) and the *shape factor* (described above) can increase the load transfer in bearing by up to a factor two or more, which explains the scatter in the data (Figure 4.9). The previous expression for the *bond coefficient* of geogrid reinforcement (Equation 4.6) may now be rewritten as

$$\alpha_b = \bar{a}_s\frac{\tan\delta}{\tan\phi'} + F_1 F_2\left(\frac{\sigma_b'}{\sigma_n'}\right)_\infty\left(\frac{\bar{a}_b B}{2S}\right)\frac{1}{\tan\phi'} \qquad \text{...(4.10)}$$

The factor F_1 allows for scale effects and is defined in Equation (4.9) when $B/D_{50} < 10$; otherwise $F_1 = 1.00$. The shape factor $F_2 = 1.0$ for circular bar, and $F_2 = 1.2$ for rectangular bar. The bearing stress ratio for a continuum $(\sigma_b'/\sigma_n')_\infty$ is given by Equation (4.8).

4.7 Example interaction coefficients

4.7.1 Woven geotextile

A woven geotextile product is to be used in a compacted granular fill. Direct shear testing over the range of normal effective stress that will apply in the structure gave a measured peak direct sliding resistance between the fill and the geotextile in the range $0.85 \geq \alpha_{ds} \geq 0.75$. Note that $\alpha_{ds} = \tan \delta_p/\tan \phi_p'$, where the peak angles of friction are ϕ_p' for the fill alone, and δ_p between the soil and the geotextile surface.

In the case of a woven geotextile the coefficient of direct sliding is equal to the coefficient of bond (Equation 4.7). The lower value in the measured range is selected for design so that in this case $\alpha_{ds} = \alpha_b = 0.75$.

The selection and application of factors of safety for reinforced soil design are described in Chapters 6. It may be noted here that the factor of safety applied to the soil

Table 4.2 Bond coefficients for grid reinforcement (Equation 4.6)

(1) Component of α_b from surface shear†
(First term in Equation 4.6)

$\bar{a}_s$	ϕ' 25°	ϕ' 30°	ϕ' 35°	ϕ' 40°	ϕ' 45°
0.10	0.06	0.06	0.06	0.06	0.06
0.25	0.15	0.15	0.15	0.15	0.15
0.50	0.30	0.30	0.30	0.30	0.30
0.75	0.45	0.45	0.45	0.45	0.45

(2) Component of α_b from bearing stress‡
(Second term in Equation 4.6)

$S/\bar{a}_b B$	ϕ' 25°	ϕ' 30°	ϕ' 35°	ϕ' 40°	ϕ' 45°
10	0.43	0.50	0.63	0.86	1.00
25	0.17	0.20	0.25	0.34	0.51
50	0.09	0.10	0.13	0.17	0.25
100	0.04	0.05	0.06	0.09	0.13

† $\tan \delta/\tan \phi' = 0.6$.
‡ Subject to a maximum doubling from particle size effects, Equation (4.9)

shearing resistance also applies to the interaction resistances. For example, if a factor of safety $FS_s = 1.3$ were applied to the peak soil strength $\phi'_p = 40°$ to derive a design frictional resistance $\phi'_d = 33°$, then the corresponding design angle of friction between the soil and the reinforcement would be $\delta_d = 26°$, from Equation (4.7), with interaction coefficients $\alpha_{ds} = \alpha_b = 0.75$.

In other words, while the peak angle of friction between the soil and the reinforcement could be as high as $\tan \delta'_p = 0.75 \tan \phi'_p$, or $\delta_p = 32°$, the lesser value $\delta_d = 26°$ would be used in design.

4.7.2 Geogrid

A range of geogrids with different strengths but made from the same polymer material and with the same geometry are to be used to reinforce a granular fill. The basic skin friction between the parent polymer material and the granular soil is measured to be not less than $\tan \delta = 0.60 \tan \phi'$. The geogrid members cover 40% of the plan area so that $\bar{a}_s = 0.40$, the remaining 60% of the plan area comprising the grid apertures. The ratio of the spacing between the transverse grid members and the area against which bearing stresses may develop is $S/\bar{a}_b B = 20$ (Figure 4.7).

The coefficient of direct sliding may be calculated from Equation (4.3) to give $\alpha_{ds} = 0.24 + 0.60 = 0.84$. The first component is due to the shear between the soil and the solid grid surfaces while the second component is due to shear in the soil through the grid apertures.

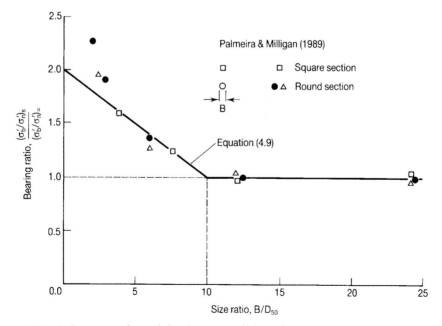

Figure 4.10 *Influence of particle size on soil bearing stress*

The coefficient of bond for the grid depends on the frictional properties of the soil and on any particle size effects. If the design angle of friction for the soil is $\phi'_d = 33°$, the basic bearing stress between the soil and the transverse members of the geogrid would be $\sigma'_b/\sigma'_n = 7.42$ from Table 4.1.

Assuming that there is no benefit from either the shape of the transverse members or from particle scale effects, i.e. $F_1 = F_2 = 1.00$, the basic coefficient of bond for the geogrids would be $\alpha_b = 0.24 + 0.28 = 0.52$ from Equation (4.10). Again, the first component is due to shear between the soil and the solid grid surfaces, and the second component is due to soil bearing stresses.

In the case of geogrids with rectangular transverse members that present a plane perpendicular surface for soil bearing it is permissible to allow for a *shape factor* $F_2 = 1.2$ (Section 4.6). Also, if the mean particle size is large relative to the transverse members of the grid it is also permissible to allow for increased load transfer due to *scale effects*. In the case where $B/D_{50} = 5$ (i.e. where on average the transverse members are 5 particle diameters deep) the factor to allow for scale effects would be $F_1 = 1.5$ (Equation 4.9). The influence of these two factors would increase the bond coefficient by almost 50% to $\alpha_b = 0.24 + 0.51 = 0.75$ (Equation 4.10).

As mentioned earlier, the interaction properties for design are calculated using the design value for the soil shearing resistance, and thus carry the same margin of safety as the soil.

4.8 Synopsis of Chapter 4

    (1) Tensile reinforcement strengthens soil by
- directly supporting some of the applied shear loading, and
- increasing the normal stress in the soil thereby mobilising greater frictional shearing resistance.

    (2) The optimum orientation for reinforcement is in the direction of principal tensile strain, which is close to the horizontal direction in the main reinforced soil applications.

    (3) Equilibrium in reinforced soil depends on the stress-strain properties of both the soil and the reinforcement, and can be investigated using a *compatibility curve* (Figure 4.5).

    (4) *Direct sliding* and *pullout* are the two limiting modes of interaction between reinforcement and soil (Figure 4.6). The two properties of interaction, the *coefficient of direct sliding*, α_{ds}, and the *bond coefficient*, α_b, are needed for design.

    (5) Pullout testing is often unreliable. It is usually sufficient for design to calculate the *bond coefficient* from the theoretical analysis.

Key references

British Standards Institution (1991). *British standard methods of test for geotextiles, BS 6906: Part 8*, Determination of sand-geotextile frictional behaviour by direct shear. British Standards Institution, London.

Jewell, R.A. (1990). Reinforcement bond capacity, *Géotechnique*, Vol. 40, No. 3, 513–518.

Palmeira, E.M. and Milligan, G.W.E. (1989) Scale and other factors affecting the results of pullout tests of grids buried in sand, *Géotechnique*, Vol. 39, No. 3, 511–524.

Williams, N.D. and Houlihan, M.F. (1987). Evaluation of interface friction properties between geosynthetics and soils, *Geosynthetic '87 Conference*, New Orleans, pp. 616–627.

5   Soil strength and bearing capacity

The strength and deformation behaviour of granular and clay soils are discussed to provide a background to the choice of strength parameters for reinforced soil design. The discussion refers to *compact soils*, which includes dense granular soils, compacted clay fills and (*in situ*) overconsolidated clays, and to *soft clay*, as found in naturally deposited, lightly overconsolidated clay foundations.

The main themes are (a) the sharing resistance of *compact soils* expressed in terms of effective stresses, and (b) the undrained strength of *soft clay* soils, relevant to soft foundation problems.

Bearing capacity theory is reviewed with reference to the influence of combined vertical and horizontal loading which is important for reinforced soil. The two cases are (a) *drained* bearing capacity, relevant to granular soils and the long-term equilibrium in clay foundations, and (b) *undrained* bearing capacity, relevant to the rapid loading of soft foundations beneath embankments and unpaved roads.

5.1 Angles of friction

Soil is a frictional material with a shearing resistance governed by effective stresses. An element of soil can remain in equilibrium if the mobilised shearing resistance does not exceed the currently available peak strength. The equilibrium in an element of soil with a *mobilised* angle of friction, ϕ'_m, less than the *peak* angle of friction, ϕ'_p, is shown on Mohr's circle of stress in Figure 5.1.

The mobilised angle of friction can be expressed in terms of the maximum ratio of shear stress to normal effective stress in the soil, $(\tau/\sigma')_{max} = \tan \phi'_m$, or in terms of the principal stresses

$$\frac{t}{s'} = \frac{(\sigma'_1 - \sigma'_3)}{(\sigma'_1 + \sigma'_3)} = \sin \phi'_m \qquad \text{...(5.1)}$$

where $t = (\sigma'_1 - \sigma'_3)/2$ is the maximum shear stress and $s' = (\sigma'_1 + \sigma'_3)/2$ is the mean effective stress in the soil, for the *plane strain* conditions which apply in most reinforced soil applications.

Two other angles of friction are important.

The *constant volume* (or critical state) angle of friction, ϕ'_{cv}, is the reliable strength which can be mobilised in soil even at large strain (Schofield and Wroth, 1968). A well defined range $35° \geq \phi'_{cv} \geq 30°$ applies for many granular soils (predominantly quartz or silica), although higher values are possible (Bolton, 1986). Clay soils have a lower

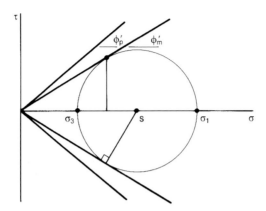

Figure 5.1 *Equilibrium stresses in frictional soil*

constant volume angle of friction and in many cases $\phi'_{cv} \leq 25°$. An example is $\phi'_{cv} \approx 23°$ for London clay (Parry, 1960).

Tensile strain in soil is the mechanism which causes tensile force to be mobilised in the reinforcement (Section 4.1). When the mobilised shearing resistance in soil is less than the value corresponding to *at rest* conditions, $\phi'_m < \phi'_o$, the strains in the soil are wholly compressive. In other words, the *at rest* angle of friction has to be mobilised before reinforcement acts beneficially. It may be anticipated for reinforced soil that $\phi'_m \geq \phi'_o$, although inextensible reinforcement can constrain the mobilised shearing resistance to remain close to *at rest* conditions.

The data for soils under *at rest* conditions have been collated by Ladd *et al.* (1977), and are found to be in reasonable agreement with Jaky's simplified equation (Wroth, 1972),

$$K_o = 1 - \sin \phi'_{tc} \qquad\qquad ...(5.2)$$

where ϕ'_{tc} is the peak angle of friction measured in a *triaxial compression* test (Figure 5.2). The mobilised angle of friction under *at rest* conditions, ϕ'_o, can be found from Mohr's circle of stress,

$$\sin \phi'_o = \left(\frac{1 - K_o}{1 + K_o}\right) \qquad\qquad ...(5.3)$$

For compact granular soils, the above relations indicate that the mobilised angle of friction under *at rest* conditions, ϕ'_o, is often only slightly less than the constant volume angle of friction for the soil, ϕ'_{cv}.

5.1.1 Peak shearing resistance

Progress in the theoretical understanding of soil behaviour, built on the knowledge of a critical state for soil, and on the accumulation of high quality test data on soils, has allowed a theoretical understanding to be developed to link what were previously

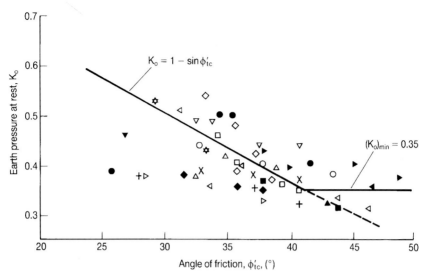

Figure 5.2 *Relation between* K_o *and peak angle of friction for normally consolidated granular soils (after Ladd et al., 1977)*

considered to be diverse aspects of soil behaviour (Atkinson and Bransby, 1978; Bolton, 1979; Wroth and Houlsby, 1985; and Wood, 1990). This has revealed:

- soil is a frictional material with a shearing resistance that depends on the soil density and effective stresses
- on shearing, soil deforms until it reaches a critical state where it can continue to deform with no further change in soil density or shearing resistance
- whether the soil's response to loading is *drained* or *undrained* depends upon the relative rates of shearing and porewater pressure dissipation. Nevertheless, the effective frictional characteristics of the soil still apply.

Two classes of soil behaviour are relevant to reinforced soil design: (a) the properties of compact granular and compact clay soils used for reinforced fills and those found *in situ* beneath reinforced structures, and (b) the properties of soft, saturated clay foundation soils over which embankments and unpaved roads are to be built.

5.2 Strength of compact soils

5.2.1 Basic concepts

As indicated earlier, (a) the critical state angle of friction, and (b) the relation between the density and mean effective stress for the soil at the critical state, are important properties of soil. Compact soils mobilise a peak angle of friction greater than the critical state angle of friction, and the magnitude of this extra component of strength increases as a function of the 'distance' of the soil from the critical state line. Thus the peak strength of soil depends on both the soil *density* and the *mean effective stress*.

5 Soil strength and bearing capacity

A distinction between 'granular' and 'clay' soil stems from the approach used to assess the state of the soil with respect to the critical state line. While soil density or specific volume is a convenient measure for granular soils, the use of an over-consolidation ratio or an equivalent pressure for the soil relative to the normal consolidation line has been the measure most often used for clay soils. Wood (1990) has shown that these two approaches are broadly equivalent. The pattern of increasing peak angle of friction with distance from the critical state line for sands and clays is illustrated in Figure 5.3.

Thus the *drained* peak angle of friction for a compact soil depends on the mean effective stress and the soil density and this generally leads to a curved envelope of measured peak strength.

The simplest engineering approximation to the variable strength data found for compact soil is to attribute a cohesion and an angle of friction to the soil (Figure 5.4). While this approximation is satisfactory over the range of data for which it was derived,

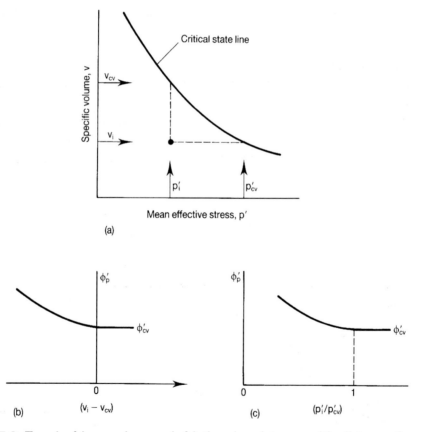

Figure 5.3 *Trend of increasing peak frictional resistance with distance from the critical state line: (a) critical state line, and peak strength versus (b) initial specific volume, and (c) initial overcompression*

it is less satisfactory outside this range, particularly at low effective stress.

The alternative is to allow for a variable (secant) peak angle of friction that varies depending on the soil density and the applied mean stresses (Figure 5.4). The advantage of this approach is that the strength is not overestimated at low stress level, while the critical state angle of friction is correctly identified as the limiting (minimum) strength at high stress level. As can be seen in Figure 5.4, the use of a secant peak angle of friction selected for the highest stress that will be experienced by the soil, σ'_d, will provide a safe shearing resistance for the soil at all lesser stresses.

The use of the second approach above is supported by practical equations for granular soils which are described later (Bolton, 1986). An equivalent set of practical relations for compact clay soils is not yet available, although the basic pattern of behaviour is similar (Wood, 1990; Scarpelli, 1991). However, it is shown later how the choice of a constant peak angle of friction for clay, ϕ'_{peak}, gives rise to a varying apparent cohesion, c', as a function of the water content of the clay (see Wroth and Houlsby, 1985). As discussed further below, it is considered preferable to select drained strength parameters for clay in terms of a variable peak angle of friction, ϕ'_p.

5.2.2 Granular soils

Two separate components contribute to the drained *frictional shearing resistance* of compact granular soil.

The first component of frictional resistance is constant and depends largely on the soil mineralogy (ϕ'_{cv}, discussed above) and provides a *reliable lower limit* to the available strength of the soil irrespective of the density or the mean stresses (over the practical range for engineering).

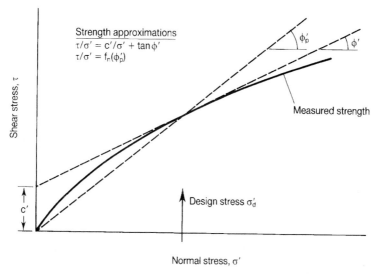

Figure 5.4 *Approximations to a curved strength envelope*

The second component of frictional resistance is caused by interlocking between closely packed particles which have to move apart to shear relative to one another, causing an increase in volume. The relation between volumetric strain and shear strain is called *dilation*. The rate of dilation depends on the *relative density* and *mean effective stress* in the soil, which also govern the peak shearing resistance of the soil.

The variation in peak angle of friction with soil density and mean effective stress is simplified on a plot of peak angle of friction versus mean effective stress on a logarithmic scale (Figure 5.5). A reliable peak angle of friction for a compacted fill would be that corresponding with the lowest expected density and the highest expected mean effective stress in the fill, as in Figure 5.5.

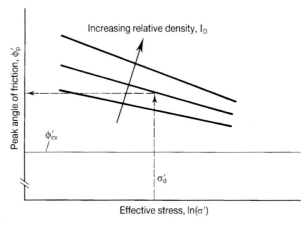

Figure 5.5 *Variation of peak angle of friction with mean stress in granular soil*

The equations suggested by Bolton (1986) to describe the strength of granular soil are expressed in terms of an empirical relative density index I_R,

$$I_R = I_D(Q - \ln s') - 1 \qquad \qquad ...(5.4)$$

where $I_D = (e_{max} - e)/(e_{max} - e_{min})$ is the standard definition of relative density, and the mean effective stress in this case, s', applies for *plane strain* loading. A constant $Q = 10$ fits the data for typical quartz and silica sands, while lower values are found for more crushable soils, such as $Q = 8$ for chalk and limestone (Bolton, 1986).

The empirical limits to the relative density index are $4 \geq I_R \geq 0$. At low effective stress, the value of I_R corresponding to a mean effective stress $s' = 150$ kN/m² is recommended as a cut-off where $s' \leq 150$ kN/m² (Bolton, 1987). This limit applies for many routine soil structures up to about 10m high, for which Equation (5.4) may be simplified. For the case $Q = 10$,

$$I_R \approx 5I_D - 1 \qquad \qquad ...(5.5)$$

The relative density index, I_R, combines the effects of soil density and mean effective stress so that the peak angle of friction is given by a simple linear function,

$$\phi'_p = \phi'_{cv} + kI_R \qquad \qquad ...(5.6)$$

where Bolton (1986) proposed the values $k = 3$ for *triaxial* conditions and $k = 5$ for *plane strain* conditions. More recent evidence (Pedley, 1990) suggests that a multiplier $k = 4$ might be more appropriate for shear box data (Section 5.2.3).

The data from triaxial compression tests on a wide variety of sands shown in Figure 5.6 illustrate the above relations (Bolton, 1986).

Strength and compaction

A link between degree of *compaction*, in terms of a maximum dry density achieved in a vibrating hammer compaction test, and *relative density* can be established if it is assumed that the measured maximum dry density, γ_{max}, corresponds with the minimum void ratio e_{min}, so that

$$e_{min} = \frac{G_s \gamma_w}{\gamma_{max}} - 1 \qquad \qquad ...(5.7)$$

where G_s (≈ 2.65) is the specific gravity of solids and γ_w the unit weight of water. Compaction to 95% of the test maximum density in the field would give a void ratio e_{field}

$$e_{field} = \frac{G_s \gamma_w}{0.95 \gamma_{max}} - 1 \qquad \qquad ...(5.8)$$

from which the relative density can be found from the measured range between the maximum and minimum void ratios for the soil ($e_{max} - e_{min}$). This might typically be of the order 0.3 to 0.6 for granular soils (Lambe and Whitman, 1969; Bolton, 1986).

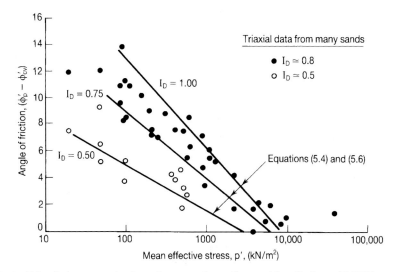

Figure 5.6 *Triaxial strength data for sands collected by Bolton (1986)*

Methods to measure the maximum void ratio are not well established, but those based on rapidly inverting a sample of soil in a cylinder (either the soil dry or under water) are most common.

To illustrate the relations, consider a granular fill with a maximum dry density $\gamma_{max} = 17.5$ kg/m^3, a specific gravity $G_s = 2.65$ and for which it is measured that $(e_{max} - e_{min}) = 0.3$, hence $e_{min} = 0.51$ from Equation (5.7). The compaction in the field should be at least, say, 95% of the maximum dry density, so that $e_{field} = 0.59$ from Equation (5.8), a relative density (73%), $I_D = 0.73$.

For a typical granular fill with $\phi'_{cv} = 32°$, in a routine application where $s' < 150$ kN/m^2, the relative density index and the peak *plane strain* angle of friction would be $I_R = 2.7$ from Equation (5.5), and $\phi'_{ps} = 45°$ from Equation (5.6).

The reduction in strength if the fill were compacted to 90% of maximum dry density, rather than the 95% specified, may also be calculated. The void ratio in the fill would be $e_{field} = 0.68$, equivalent to a relative density $I_D = 0.43$ which would deliver a peak angle of friction of only $\phi'_{ps} = 38°$, compared with $\phi'_{ps} = 45°$ for the properly compacted fill.

The possible range of friction angles for granular fill in routine applications is indicated in Table 5.1.

For comparison with the above, the triaxial strength data for sands summarised by Been and Jefferies (1986) are shown in Figure 5.7. These are plotted in the form of Figure 5.3b with peak angle of friction versus the difference (at the same mean effective stress) between the specific volume of the sand at the start of shearing and at the critical state, $(v_i - v_{cv})$ (see Wood, 1990, for a discussion of these data). Although not strictly equivalent, Bolton's relative density index (Equation 5.6) may be equated approximately as

$$I_R \approx - 15(v_i - v_{cv}) \qquad\qquad ...(5.9)$$

for these triaxial conditions, i.e. $k = 3$.

Table 5.1 Typical peak angles of friction for compacted granular fills in routine applications ($s'_{max} < 150$kN/m^2)

Relative density†	I_D		70%	40%
Relative density index	I_R	eqn. (5.5)	2.5	1
Peak angle of friction‡ $\phi'_{cv} = 35°$	ϕ'_{ps} ϕ'_{tc}	$k = 5$ $k = 3$	47.5° 42.5°	40° 38°
Peak angle of friction‡ $\phi'_{cv} = 30°$	ϕ'_{ps} ϕ'_{tc}	$k = 5$ $k = 3$	42.5° 37.5°	35° 33°

† Compaction to 95% of maximum dry density should give $I_D \geq 70\%$
‡ Equation (5.6). Note that $k = 4$ may apply for shear box data

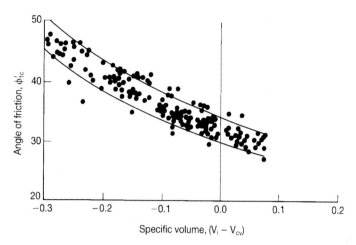

Figure 5.7 *Peak angle of friction for sand in triaxial compression (after Been and Jefferies, 1986)*

Design angle of friction

The peak angle of friction in a granular soil depends on both density and mean effective stress, as described above, and the possible combinations of these in a structure should be considered when selecting a representative peak strength for design.

Strain compatibility is another important factor for design. Shear strain is required to mobilise the peak shearing resistance, and the soil strength reduces thereafter as the soil shears toward the critical state. This loss of strength can occur with relatively little *displacement* if the shearing is concentrated within a narrow zone or rupture surface in the soil (i.e. small displacements across a thin zone can cause high shear strains). This interdependence between mobilised shearing resistance and shear strain means that it may be unduly optimistic to assume that the peak shearing resistance in the soil will be mobilised equally along an incipient rupture surface.

Another factor is the possibility of preferential rupture along bedding planes in the soil, such as may be formed by filling. This can lead to a reduced peak shearing resistance compared with other orientations for rupture through soil (Arthur and Menzies, 1972).

The way to allow for these and other uncertainties in a 'lumped factor' design is to make a conservative estimate of the representative peak shearing resistance for the fill and then to apply a factor of safety of the order $FS_s = 1.3$ to 1.5 to derive a reliable angle of friction for design, $\tan \phi'_d = (\tan \phi'_p)/FS_s$. Slightly pessimistic values are usually selected for the other variables in design, such as the loadings and porewater pressures (Simpson *et al.*, 1981).

The ideas of limit state design are being introduced increasingly into geotechnical engineering, and have given rise to the idea simply of selecting the reliable constant-volume angle of friction for design, $\phi'_d = \phi'_{cv}$ (Bolton, 1981). This idea is appealing for reinforced soil where polymeric materials might permit significant deformations to occur in the soil (McGown *et al.*, 1984).

Both approaches lead to similar angles of friction for design involving compact granular fill, as can be illustrated by the relations introduced earlier. The results in Table 5.2 are for two granular soils with a constant-volume angle of friction $\phi'_{cv} = 30°$ and 35°, respectively. These angles of friction would be chosen directly for design following the second approach above.

To arrive at the same design values after applying a lumped factor of safety $FS_s = 1.3$ to a representative peak strength would require peak angles of friction for the two soils $\phi'_p = 37°$ and 42°, repectively (Table 5.2). Assuming the most conservative relation between relative density and peak angle of friction, $k = 3$ for triaxial loading, indicates that both soils would need to have a relative density index in the field not less than $I_R = 2.3$ (Equation 5.6) or a relative density $I_D \approx 70\%$ (Equation 5.5) in a routine application. It was shown earlier that standard compaction of 95% of the maximum dry density should normally result in a denser fill than this.

5.2.3 Testing granular soils

The direct shear test is convenient for granular soils and reproduces the plane strain conditions of most reinforced soil applications. Because of recent developments, a commentary on the test and its interpretation is included below.

Triaxial compression testing is also widely used for granular soils. Well-established procedures can be followed and these are described in standard texts (Bishop and Henkel, 1957).

Comment on the use of *in situ* tests such as the pressuremeter, cone or SPT, to determine the properties of granular foundation soils is beyond the scope of this book.

Direct shear test

The direct shear test is the only routinely used *plane strain* test for compacted granular fills. The test is improved by larger 300×300mm apparatus (DTp, 1978; SETRA, 1979; GCO, 1989) rather than the standard 60×60mm Casagrande shear box. Further

Table 5.2 Peak strength and relative density index corresponding with $FS_s = 1.3$

Design strength $\phi'_d = \phi'_{cv}$	Peak strength $\tan \phi'_p/\tan \phi'_d = 1.3$	Relative density index† I_R for $(\phi'_p - \phi'_{cv})$	Relative density I_D
30°	37°	2.3	67%
35°	42°	2.3	67%

† From Equation (5.6) using $\phi'_p \approx \phi'_{bc}$ and $k = 3$

improvement can be made by reducing any rotation of the sample during the test so as to reproduce more closely simple shear deformation (Wernick, 1977; Jewell, 1989).

The central plane in the direct shear test is one along which no net horizontal strain can occur, because of the rigid end-walls. As a result, the shearing resistance on the central plane is expected to be less than the full plane strain angle of friction of the soil, as found in the simple shear apparatus. On the other hand, the direct shear test arrangement is relatively crude and the shearing resistance measured in usually higher than would be found in a corresponding simple shear test, typically by about 10% (Potts *et al.*, 1987).

In direct shear tests the shearing resistance is usually measured along the bedding planes in the soil, on samples prepared conventionally through the top of the apparatus. As mentioned earlier, this is a critical orientation for rupture in soil that has a lower peak shearing resistance than at other orientations (Arthur and Menzies, 1972). Because of these factors, the peak angle of friction measured in direct shear tests on compact granular soil may often be comparable to that measured in triaxial compression tests (Tatsuoka, 1987). The following interpretation is recommended.

(1) Test arrangement

The direct shear test illustrated in Figure 5.8 shows increments of shear displacement, dx, and vertical displacement, dy, which define the angle of dilation in the soil, ψ,

$$dy/dx = \tan \psi \qquad ...(5.10)$$

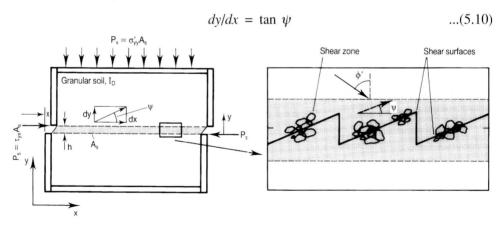

Figure 5.8 *Definitions for the direct shear test*

(2) Peak angle of friction

The measured shearing resistance and dilation (vertical displacement, y) are convention-ally plotted against the shear displacement (Figure 5.9). A soil should be tested at least at one relative density, I_D, and three vertical stresses.

The measured peak shearing resistance can be used to define the peak angle of friction, $\tan \phi_p' = (\tau_{yx}/\sigma_{yy})_{max}$, and the measured values of peak friction plotted against

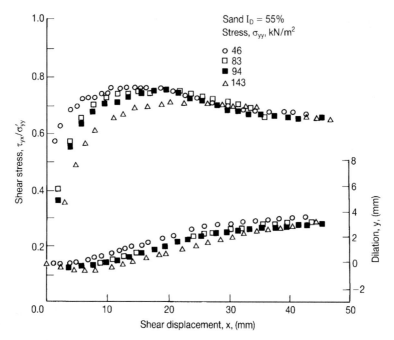

Figure 5.9 *Typical results from a direct shear test on compact granular soil*

the logarithm of the applied vertical stress to reveal the trend of decreasing strength with increasing applied stress (see Figure 5.5).

(3) Constant-volume angle of friction

The shear displacement required for granular soil to reach the critical state is often too great to allow the accurate measurement of the constant-volume angle of friction directly. But where a constant shearing resistance is reached, with no futher dilation, then the constant-volume angle of friction may be calculated from the measured shearing resistance, $\tan \phi'_{cv} = (\tau_{yx}/\sigma_{yy})_{cv}$.

An alternative is to prepare loose samples and test these under relatively high vertical stress so that the measured shearing resistance climbs gradually toward the critical state angle of friction. There may be practical drawbacks to this approach caused by the large vertical compression in the sample that can occur during such a test. A crude but effective supplementary test for the constant-volume angle of friction is to measure the limiting angle in the laboratory of a slope formed from the loose, dry granular soil subject to excavation at the toe.

Perhaps the best method is to determine the constant-volume angle of friction by subtracting the component of strength due to dilation from the total measured angle of friction. The analysis of a direct shear test is best carried out when dilation is greatest.

The equation due to Bolton (1986) linking the soil strength and dilation is simple and fits the available data,

$$\phi'_{cv} = \phi' - 0.8\psi \qquad \qquad ...(5.11)$$

where for the analysis of direct shear tests, $\phi' = \tan^{-1}(\tau_{xy}/\sigma_{yy})$ and $\psi = \tan^{-1}(dy/dx)$, measured in degrees. It is often sufficient to use the measured peak values of friction and dilation in Equation (5.10).

(4) Use of Bolton's relations

A benefit of the theoretical relations introduced earlier is to provide a framework against which to assess the results of direct shear tests.

There are two constants which must be determined to fit the equations to the data; the constant Q in Equation (5.4), and the constant k in Equation (5.6). It is sufficient to use the applied vertical stress as the measure of the mean effective stress, $\sigma'_{yy} = s'$.

For predominantly quartz and silica soils it can be assumed that $Q = 10$ and a best fit to the data sought by adjusting the value of the constant k (in the range 3 to 5) for possible values of ϕ'_{cv}. Recall that $k \approx 4$ should apply to the data from direct shear tests.

In seeking a fit to the data recall that values $Q < 10$ can apply for crushable soils, while $Q > 10$ can apply for soils with grains of harder minerals and finer particle sizes.

5.2.4 Compact clay soils

A simple and practical method (similar to that for granular soils) to relate the state of a compact clay soil with a peak angle of friction and dilation has not yet been developed.

Nevertheless the same basic concepts apply (Section 5.2.1) as illustrated by the data for London clay (Figure 5.10). The plot of this triaxial test data by Henkel (1956), for London clay at failure, is in terms of an equivalent pressure, p'_e, with repect to the normal consolidation line, as described by Wroth and Houlsby (1985) and Wood (1990).

In this normalised plot, the data suggest that a conventional linear envelope defined in terms of a normalised cohesion, $c' = 0.022p'_e$, and friction angle, ϕ'_e, would fit the data as well as a curved envelope passing through the origin. However, the corresponding range for the cohesive component of strength for individual samples of clay depends critically on the water content as shown in Figure 5.10b.

The above data are replotted in Figure 5.11 in terms of a variable peak angle of friction versus the mean effective stress at failure (recall Figure 5.3c). Allowing for the scatter, the critical state angle of friction, $\phi'_{cv} = 22.3°$, provides a reasonable lower limit to the data. The trend of increasing peak angle of friction with overconsolidation is indicated by the dotted line in Figure 5.11. The linear envelope from Figure 5.10 overestimates the strength of the clay greatly at high values of overconsolidation (i.e. low mean effective stress).

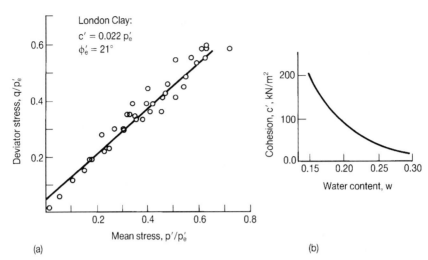

Figure 5.10 *Normalised peak strength data from triaxial compression tests on London clay (data from Henkel, 1956, replotted by Wroth and Houlsby, 1985)*

The effective stress calculations in this book, and the discussion on selecting strength parameters for design, are expressed in terms of a frictional shearing strength only (Section 5.2.1).

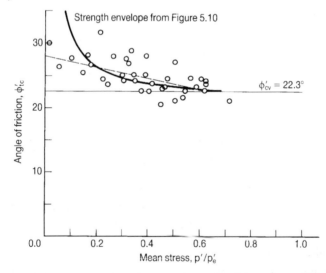

Figure 5.11 *Peak angle of friction for London clay (data from Figure 5.10)*

In cases where the peak strength properties for a clay have been interpreted already in terms of cohesion and friction they may be converted into an equivalent peak angle of friction ($c' = 0$), as for the London clay data above. In the general case, a Mohr-Coulomb strength envelope

$$\tau = c' + \sigma' \tan \phi' \qquad \qquad ...(5.12)$$

has a corresponding peak angle of friction, ϕ'_p, at a given design stress, σ'_d,

$$\tan \phi'_p = \frac{c'}{\sigma'_d} + \tan \phi' \qquad \qquad ...(5.13)$$

However, please recall that any errors in the linear approximation of Equation (5.12) must lead to similar errors in the peak angles of friction calculated from Equation (5.13). This is particularly for cases beyond the range of the data from which the linear envelope was derived (typically at both low or high effective stresses). It is always preferable to reinterpret the original test data.

Design shearing resistance

The comments on the selection of representative peak strength parameters for compact granular soil apply equally to compact clay soil (Section 5.2.2). The design angle of friction is selected after considering both (a) a factored representative peak strength and (b) the constant-volume angle of friction.

Porewater in compact clay soil can allow swelling and softening to occur which progressively reduces the peak shearing resistance with time. In cases where softening is possible, typically where there is stress relief – as in many clay fills and slopes – it may be prudent to rely solely on the constant-volume angle of friction for the clay in the long-term, and to select this value as the representative peak shearing resistance.

For stiff clays in foundations beneath reinforced soil structures, care must be taken that there are no pre-existing shear surfaces which may have become slickensided or polished, so that the angle of friction may have reduced toward a *residual* value lower than the critical state angle of friction (Skempton, 1970). The susceptibility of a clay to develop slickensided surfaces may be judged by the granular specific volume,

$$v_g = 1 + \frac{(volume\ of\ water\ +\ volume\ of\ platey\ particles)}{(volume\ of\ rotund\ particles)}$$

The data on residual angle of friction for a number of soils plotted in Figure 5.12 suggest that low residual angles of friction may be expected for granular specific volumes greater than about 3 (Lupini *et al.*, 1981; Wood, 1990).

5.2.5 Testing clay soils

No special comment is made here on the range of *in situ* and laboratory tests for stiff clay foundation soils.

Shear box tests may be carried out on clay fills compacted into the apparatus and allowed to come into equilibrium with the applied vertical stress before being sheared slowly to ensure *drained* conditions. The comments on shear box testing in Section 5.2.3 apply equally to compact clay fills, including, for example, the testing of less well

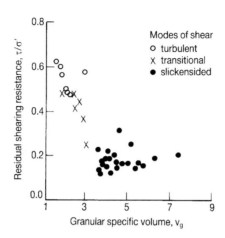

Figure 5.12 *Residual angle of friction versus granular specific volume (after Lupini et al., 1981)*

compacted samples under high vertical stress as a means to measure the constant-volume angle of friction.

5.3 Soft clay foundations

Soft clay foundations are often formed from fine soil particles transported and deposited by water. Such soils are often layered, each layer representing a different phase of deposition, and saturated because of the high groundwater levels at these sites. Such soft clays are *normally consolidated* when there has been an increasing effective stress due to deposition. But if the effective stress has reduced, so that the current stress is not the largest experienced, then the clay is *overconsolidated*.

Because of the fine size of particles and the low permeability of soft soils, the loading from construction is often too rapid to permit any significant drainage in the foundation, and the soft clay responds in an *undrained* manner. Drainage and consolidation only occur more gradually with time. In response to undrained shear, the soil shears toward a critical state with no change in volume (no drainage) but with porewater pressure changes caused by the loading. The *undrained shear strength*, s_u, applies once the clay has reached the critical state, and depends on the constant-volume angle of friction for the soil and the current effective stresses. Thus the undrained shear strength depends on the mode of the shearing (Wroth, 1984). The values and parameters discussed in this book are for simple shear deformation which has been found to be most applicable to the stability analysis of embankments on soft soil (Section 5.3.4).

5.3.1 Consolidation history

The effective stresses which govern the *undrained shear strength* in a soft clay foundation are the current vertical effective stress (at the start of loading), σ'_v, and the previous maximum stress experienced by the soil, σ'_p.

Two common causes of overconsolidation are (a) erosion at the ground surface, and (b) a drop in the groundwater table followed by a subsequent rise (Figure 5.13).

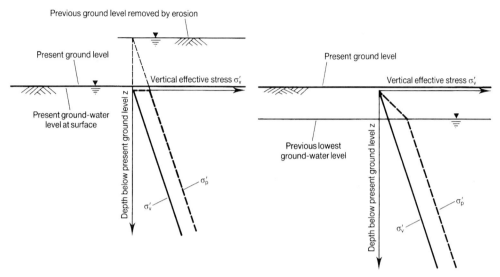

Figure 5.13 *Two causes of overconsolidation in a soft clay foundation (a) reduction in ground level and (b) previous lowering of groundwater (after Parry, 1972)*

The undrained shear strength for a *normally consolidated* clay, $\sigma'_v = \sigma'_p$, is found to depend on the current vertical effective stress (Ladd *et al.*, 1977),

$$\frac{s_u}{\sigma'_v} = \text{constant} \qquad \qquad ...(5.14)$$

where the constant is typically in the range 0.20 to 0.30 (Ladd, 1981; Leroueil *et al.*, 1985). The spread of values deduced from back-analysis of embankment failures and from laboratory simple shear tests are summarised in Figure 5.14, and indicate a gradual increase with plasticity index.

Overconsolidation is measured by the ratio of the past maximum and the current vertical effective stress

$$\frac{\sigma'_p}{\sigma'_v} = OCR \qquad \qquad ...(5.15)$$

where *OCR* is the overconsolidation ratio.

The data for soft clay follow a well-drained pattern of an increasing ratio of undrained shear strength to current vertical effective stress with *OCR* (Ladd *et al.*, 1977),

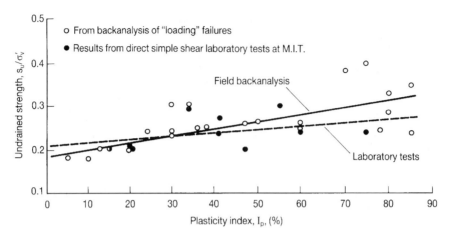

Figure 5.14 *Values of the shear strength ratio* s_u/σ'_v *for normally consolidated clays (Ladd, 1981)*

$$\left(\frac{s_u}{\sigma'_v}\right)_{oc} = \left(\frac{s_u}{\sigma'_v}\right)_{nc} (OCR)^m \qquad\qquad ...(5.16)$$

where the subscripts, *nc* and *oc*, represent the clay in the normally consolidated and the overconsolidated states respectively, and the constant $m \approx 0.8$. Although this finding was based on empiricism, Equation (5.16) may be derived theoretically from the critical state models of soil behaviour (Wroth and Houlsby, 1985; Wood, 1990).

5.3.2 Lower limit to undrained shear strength

Only in special circumstances, such as a very recently deposited soil, will a soft clay foundation be less than normally consolidated (i.e. $OCR_{min} \geq 1$). A rough first estimate for the lowest possible shearing resistance in the clay at depth may then be determined as $s_u = 0.22\sigma'_v$ (Equation 5.14).

For groundwater at or above the ground surface, $\sigma'_v = (\gamma - \gamma_w)z$, where γ is the unit weight of the foundation soil, γ_w the unit weight of water and z the depth below the ground surface. The results illustrated in Figure 5.15 are for $\gamma = 16kN/m^3$ and $\gamma_w = 10kN/m^3$.

5.3.3 Expected undrained shear strength

Soft clay foundations are usually slightly overconsolidated, and the degree of overconsolidation at depth may be determined by oedometer tests. A typical pattern of overconsolidation with depth in a soft clay foundation subjected to a fluctuating groundwater level is shown in Figure 5.15. The groundwater is currently at the ground surface but previously was drawn down 3m below the ground surface.

Knowing the OCR at each depth, the undrained shear strength may be calculated from Equation (5.16). The results in Figure 5.15c are based conservatively on the values $(s_u/\sigma'_v)_{nc} = 0.22$ and $m = 0.8$.

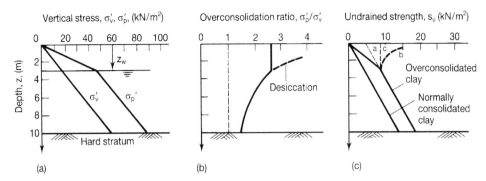

Figure 5.15 *Example of a foundation overconsolidated by previously lowered groundwater (a) effective vertical stresses, (b) overconsolidation ratio and (c) undrained shear strength*

In practice, the weakest soil in a *lightly overconsolidated* soft clay foundation often occurs at the previous deepest level of the groundwater (Parry, 1972). The soil above the groundwater often experiences increased effective stresses caused by desiccation, which causes greater overconsolidation (Figure 5.15b). The undrained shear strength found by allowing for pore suction only is indicated by the line *oa* in Figure 5.15c. But Parry's observation suggests it should be safe to assume a uniform strength in the near-surface soil, the line *oc* in Figure 5.15c, with a magnitude equal to the strength of the clay at the level of the deepest drawdown of the groundwater.

5.3.4 Testing soft clay foundations

A programme of soil index tests and *in situ* vane tests is a minimum where a stability analysis for an embankment over a soft clay stratum is required (Chandler, 1988). Normally the data would be supplemented by oedometer tests in Rowe cells to investigate the consolidation history at the site. Shear strength data measured by consolidated undrained triaxial compression tests are also frequently required.

In the interpretation of the test data to select design parameters, attention has to be given to the difference in *undrained shear* strength measured by *vane* tests and *triaxial compression* tests. Indeed, it is the *simple shear* tests values of undrained shear strength which have been found most appropriate for embankment foundation design and which coincide most closely with the strength measured by vane tests (Wroth, 1984).

Field vane test

There is wide support for Bjerrum's (1972) assertion that the shearing resistance measured by the field vane test 'may be the best possible solution for computing the stability of embankments on soft clay for practical purposes' (Chandler, 1988). The *corrected strength* from *field vane* tests is linked strongly with the relations for soft clay reviewed above.

Mesri (1975) was the first to combine Bjerrum's (1972) vane correction factor, μ, with the anticipated strength ratio for *young clay* (normally consolidated, s_u/σ_v', to find an almost constant value almost independent of plasticity index (Figure 5.16),

$$\left(\frac{s_u}{\sigma_v'}\right)_{nc} \approx 0.22 \qquad \qquad ...(5.17)$$

A similar manipulation for *aged clays* (overconsolidated) showed that the design shearing resistance suggested by Bjerrum could be expressed approximately as,

$$\left(\frac{s_u}{\sigma_v'}\right)_{oc} \approx 0.22 \; OCR \qquad \qquad ...(5.18)$$

Larsson (1980) investigated relations of this form using data from the back-analysis of embankment failures to conclude (Figure 5.17):

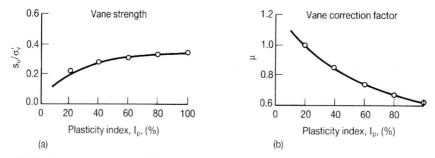

Figure 5.16 *Interpretation of the relation between shearing resistance and vane correction factor μ for normally consolidated clays (after Mesri, 1975)*

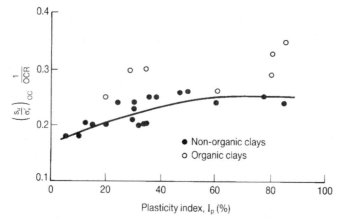

Figure 5.17 *Relation between undrained shearing resistance and plasticity index from the back-analysis of embankment failures (after Larsson, 1980)*

1. Undrained shearing resistance is not completely independent of plasticity index.
2. The relations for undrained strength apply mostly for non-organic clays, and may under-predict the shearing resistance of organic clays.

Chandler (1988) has argued that the drop in the undrained strength ratio for low plasticity clays may be partly due to the greater disturbance caused by vane insertion in more sensitive clays (which often have a low plasticity index I_p).

The strong similarity between corrected vane strengths, the undrained strength measured in laboratory simple shear tests, and the strength deduced from the back-analysis of collapsed embankments (i.e. 'field' strengths), has been supported further by the recent data (Leroueil *et al.*, 1985; Jamiolkowski *et al.*, 1985; Chandler, 1988). The data confirm that on average $(s_u/\sigma'_v)_{nc} \approx 0.22$ to 0.25, and suggest that over-consolidation may bring a slightly greater benefit with an exponent $m \approx 0.95$, Equation (5.16), compared with $m = 0.8$ in Ladd *et al.* (1977).

Chandler (1988) has also drawn attention to the significant influence of strain-rate, or time effects, on undrained shear strength. He has suggested correction factors for more rapid loading which will be referred to for unpaved road design (Chapter 12).

The conclusion is that there is a very strong theoretical and practical basis for the selection of appropriate design undrained shearing resistance for soft clay foundations. The corrected undrained shear strength from vane tests and the data on consolidation (OCR) should all lead to a consistent picture for soft foundation soils.

5.4 Drained bearing capacity

The analysis for the long-term bearing capacity beneath a steep reinforced slope or wall is usually idealised to an equivalent problem of a shallow footing subject to applied vertical and lateral loading. This idealisation of a footing at a depth below the ground surface, D, and extending infinitely into the page, is shown in Figure 5.18.

Consider vertical and horizontal forces, (R_v, R_h), acting at a distance, e, from the centreline of a footing of width, L (Figure 5.18). This combined loading is at an

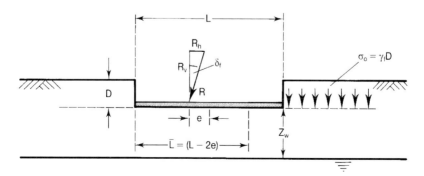

Figure 5.18 *Definitions for the drained analysis of bearing capacity*

inclination, tan δ_f = R_h/R_v. Embedment of the footing, D, is taken into account by assuming an equivalent vertical stress σ_o = $\gamma_f D$ acts at the level of the footing base, where γ_f is the unit weight of the foundation soil.

The analysis for a strip footing under combined loading is well established in soil mechanics. The equations presented by Vesic (1975), which may be found in Winterkorn and Fang (1975), reflect the current practice and are summarised below.

The standard equations may be modified to allow for eccentric loading. It has been shown to be sufficient to adjust the width of the footing, $\bar{L}$ = $L - 2e$, and thus to design for increased applied stresses, σ_f = $R_v/\bar{L}$ and τ_f = $R_h/\bar{L}$ which act over the smaller effective width, $\bar{L}$ (Figure 5.18). The subscript ( )$_f$ represents the stresses applied to the foundation soil.

The maximum bearing stress, σ'_{bc}, beneath a rough strip footing of effective width $\bar{L}$ is given by the equation,

$$\sigma'_{bc} = i_q N_q \sigma'_o + 0.5 i_\gamma N_\gamma \bar{L}\, \gamma_{eff} \qquad ...(5.19)$$

where i_q and i_γ are reduction factors to allow for load inclination, σ_o is the vertical stress in the surrounding soil (Figure 5.18) and γ_{eff} the *effective* unit weight of the foundation soil beneath the footing to allow for buoyancy. If the highest likely groundwater level reaches to a depth below the footing $z_w < \bar{L}$, then

$$\gamma_{eff} = \gamma'_f + (z_w/\bar{L})\,(\gamma_f - \gamma'_f) \qquad ...(5.20)$$

where γ_f is the bulk unit weight and γ'_f the submerged unit weight of the foundation soil.

The values for the bearing capacity factors N_q and N_γ are given by the following equations which are evaluated in Table 5.3:

$$N_q = \tan^2(45 + \phi'/2)\,\exp(\pi \tan \phi') \qquad ...(5.21)$$

and

$$N_\gamma = 2(N_q + 1)\tan \phi \qquad ...(5.22)$$

The reduction factors for load inclination can be found from:

$$i_q = (1 - \tan \delta_f)^2 \qquad ...(5.23)$$

and

$$i_\gamma = (1 - \tan \delta_f)^3 \qquad ...(5.24)$$

Other semi-empirical correlations, such as for the effects of sloping ground, may be found in Vesic (1975).

5.4.1 Influence of inclined loading
The very significant reduction in foundation bearing capacity due to inclined loading is often not appreciated. The influence of inclined loading is illustrated below for a

Table 5.3 Bearing capacity factors (Vesic, 1975)

ϕ'	N_q	N_γ	ϕ'	N_q	N_γ
16	4.3	3.1	31	20.6	26.0
17	4.8	3.5	32	23.2	30.2
18	5.3	4.1	33	26.1	35.2
19	5.8	4.7	34	29.4	41.1
20	6.4	5.4	35	33.3	48.0
21	7.1	6.2	36	37.8	56.3
22	7.8	7.1	37	42.9	66.2
23	8.7	8.2	38	48.9	78.0
24	9.6	9.4	39	55.7	92.3
25	10.7	10.9	40	64.2	109.4
26	11.9	12.5	41	73.9	130.2
27	13.2	14.5	42	85.4	155.6
28	14.8	16.7	43	99.0	186.5
29	16.4	19.3	44	115.3	224.6
30	18.4	22.4	45	134.9	271.8

centrally loaded footing, $e = 0$ and $\bar{L} = L$, bearing on the surface of a foundation soil, $D = 0$ well above the groundwater table, $\gamma_{eff} = \gamma_f$.

The influence of inclined loading, $R_h/R_v = \tan \delta_f$, is shown first on a plot of bearing capacity versus load inclination (Figure 5.19). This diagram applies for all angles of

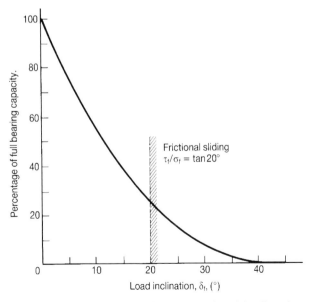

Figure 5.19 *Reduction in bearing capacity due to load inclination*

friction for the foundation soil. The bearing capacity is expressed as a percentage of the value for vertical loading only, and a cut-off is indicated to represent the lateral sliding of the footing across the surface of the foundation. This latter sliding failure depends on the angle of friction of the foundation soil and the roughness of the footing.

The important point in Figure 5.19 is that a load inclination of only about 10° is sufficient to halve the capacity of a foundation to support vertical loading.

Another view of the limiting combined loading is shown in Figure 5.20 for the case of a foundation soil with $\phi'_f = 30°$, and a footing that slips laterally when $\delta_f = 20°$. The dotted lines of constant load inclination marked on the figure again show how dramatically the inclined loading reduces the bearing capacity.

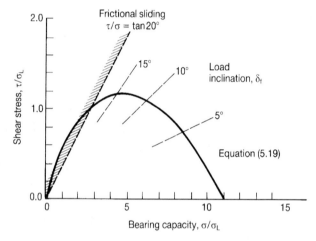

Figure 5.20 *Drained bearing capacity under combined loading*

5.4.2 Allowable bearing pressure

The traditional approach in foundation design has been to estimate an ultimate bearing capacity using the peak angle of friction for the foundation soil, ϕ'_{fp}, and then to apply a reduction factor of the order 2 to 3 to find an *allowable bearing pressure* for design.

The alternative is to determine the allowable bearing pressure by using a *design angle of friction* for the foundation soil, ϕ'_{fd}, directly in the bearing capacity analysis. This latter approach is preferred and used in this book.

5.5 Undrained bearing capacity

The bearing capacity of a footing on the surface of a deep deposit of soft clay with uniform shear strength, s_u, may be found by applying either the upper or lower bound theorems of plasticity to give the exact solution

$$\sigma_{bc} - \sigma_o = s_u \left(1 + \frac{\pi}{2} + \cos^{-1} \alpha + \sqrt{1 - \alpha^2} \right) \qquad \qquad ...(5.25)$$

where the shear stress applied to the clay surface τ_f defines the load inclination $\alpha = \tau_f/s_u$ (Figure 5.21). (A description of the analysis may be found in Bolton, 1979.)

The traditional bearing capacity factor is defined as $N_c = (\sigma_{bc} - \sigma_o)/s_u$, and Equation (5.25) shows that it varies anywhere between the well-known value $N_c = (2 + \pi)$ in the absence of surface shear stress, $\alpha = 0$, to half that value $N_c = (1 + \pi/2)$ when the maximum shear stress is applied, $\alpha = +1$.

5.5.1 Influence of inclined loading

The envelope defining the limiting combinations of applied vertical and shear stress is plotted in Figure 5.22a. This indicates how shear stress in the range $0 \leq \tau_f/s_u \leq 1$ reduces the bearing capacity by a factor of 2 before the footing slides laterally, at the limit $\tau_f/s_u = 1$.

There are two other factors which may restrict the bearing capacity further. First, if the contact between the footing and clay surface is not perfectly rough then lateral direct sliding may occur under a lesser shear stress, $(\tau_f/s_u)_{ds}$. Second, if any drainage can occur at the surface of the soft clay in contact with the footing, then direct sliding might be governed by the *effective stress* conditions at this contact, represented by a limiting frictional criterion, $\tau_f/\sigma_f' = \tan \delta$ (Figure 5.22b).

Note the striking resemblance between the envelope of limiting load combinations for *undrained* bearing capacity shown in Figure 5.22b and for the *drained* case in Figure 5.19.

5.6 Synopsis of Chapter 5

(1) Soil is a frictional material with a shearing resistance that depends on the soil density and effective stresses.

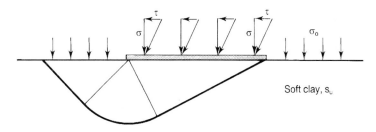

Figure 5.21 *Definitions for the analysis of undrained bearing capacity*

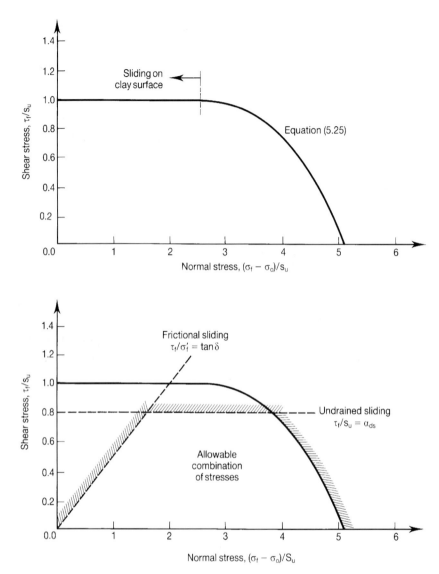

Figure 5.22 *Undrained bearing capacity under combined loading*

(2) The relation between the rate of shearing and the rate at which porewater pressure can dissipate in soil significantly influences the response of loading and determines whether the soil is *drained* or *undrained*.

(3) The critical state or *constant-volume* angle of friction for a granular soil is a reliable strength, even at large strain, and may be used with confidence for design.

(4) The *constant-volume* angle of friction for a clay may be reached in the long-term by softening (stress release) and progressive shearing. The use of

ϕ'_{cv} in design may need to be accompanied by an additional factor of safety.

(5) The *undrained* behaviour of soft clay is well understood and significant guidance is available for the use of *vane testing* to measure strength properties *in situ*.

(6) Inclined loading, which often occurs in reinforced soil applications, reduces dramatically the bearing capacity of foundation soils for both *drained* and *undrained* loading conditions.

Key references

Bolton, M.D. (1986). The strength and dilatancy of sands, *Géotechnique*, Vol. 36, No. 1, 65–78.

Chandler, R.J. (1988). The *in situ* measurement of the undrained shear strength of clays using the field vane. In A.F. Richards (ed.) ASTM Special Publication 1014, ASTM, Philadelphia, pp. 13–44.

Wood, D.M. (1990). *Soil Behaviour and Critical State Soil Mechanics*. Cambridge, Cambridge University Press.

Vesic, A.S. (1975). Bearing capacity of shallow foundations. In H.F. Winterkorn and H.Y. Fang (eds) *Foundation Engineering Handbook*. Van Nostrand Reinhold, ch. 3.

6 Design values and safety margins

The soil and the reinforcement both influence the behaviour of reinforced soil structures, and the equilibrium is too complex to be reflected adequately by a single 'lumped' factor of safety. Rather, the procedure is to select representative *design values* for the parameters influencing stability, or the working equilibrium, and then to perform calculations to show that possible undesirable *design situations* will not occur.

The *limit state* method of design is set out in International and European Standards (ISO 2394 and CEB Bulletin III) and is being widely introduced in geotechnical engineering. The draft European code on foundation engineering (EC7, 1989) and the draft British Standard on reinforced soil (BSI, 1991) are both based on the *limit state* methodology.

There are two main areas of concern for design. First, the risk of collapse must be shown to be acceptably small by *means of ultimate limit state* calculations. Second, the risk that deformation may interfere with the function of the structure must be shown to be acceptably small by *means of serviceability limit state* calculations.

Because of the range of geotextile materials, and their properties, used for soil reinforcement, it is helpful in design to identify separately the role of the soil and of the reinforcement on the equilibrium.

The limit state method of design for reinforced soil is outlined below. The selection of design values for the main parameters is then discussed for *ultimate* and *serviceability limit state* calculations. The *design situations* which should be considered for reinforced soil and the form of the calculations are considered in Chapter 7. The design calculations for each of the five main applications for reinforced soil are then described in Chapters 8 to 12.

6.1 Basis of calculations

6.1.1 Design situations

Design situations are those sets of physical conditions for which it should be demonstrated that limit states will not occur. The selected design situations should be sufficiently severe and sufficiently varied so as to encompass all resonable conditions which can be foreseen to occur during the construction and the use of the proposed structure.

The detailed description of design situations should include, as appropriate:

- the disposition and classification of the various zones of soil, rock and elements of construction which could be involved in the limit state event

- the loads and their combinations
- effects due to the environment within which the design is set, including the following:
  - groundwater levels, including their variations due to possible flooding, failure of drainage systems, etc.
  - excavation, erosion and scour, leading to changes in the geometry of the ground surface
  - weathering and freezing
  - the effects of time and the environment on the strength and other properties of materials, including chemical or microbiological sources of degradation, or holes created by animal activities
- earthquakes
- subsidence due to mining or other causes
- the tolerance of the structure to deformations
- the effect of new construction on existing structures and services.

6.1.2 Design values of parameters

The values of the applied loads, the properties of soils, reinforcement and other materials, the geometrical data, and the constraints entered into the calculations are called *design values*.

The selection of design values should take into account:

- the consequences of the occurrence of the limit state, including the risk to life and economic repercussions
- the nature of the structure and its behaviour, e.g. structures in which partial or complete collapse can occur without warning
- the possibility of unfavourable variations, and the independence or interdependence of the parameters in the calculation
- the quality of the workmanship and the level of construction control.

6.1.3 Required and available forces

In equilibrium calculations involving the reinforcement, it is helpful to separate the *required forces* needed from the reinforcement to achieve the desired equilibrium in the soil, and the *available forces* due to the inclusion of reinforcement layers.

The *required forces* depend on the soil properties, the porewater pressures, the soil geometry and the loadings. These required forces can usually be satisfied by a variety of reinforcement materials and layouts. The alternatives are best compared in terms of the *available forces* provided by the reinforcement in each case, which depend on the reinforcement material properties, the reinforcement layout and the bond with the soil.

6.2 Loadings

6.2.1 Self-weight loading

The self-weight loading of the soil is usually an important factor governing the required reinforcement forces in a reinforced soil wall or slope. The maximum and minimum values of the unit weight of the soil may be measured to define the bounds to the possible field value. Specifications often require that the soil unit weight in the field is monitored during construction.

Typically the *maximum expected unit weight* for the soil would be selected for *ultimate* limit state calculations.

The *expected unit weight* for the soil would normally be used in *the serviceability* limit state calculations.

Normally the base of the reinforced zone in a steep slope will be embedded below the final level of the adjacent ground. The benefit to stability should be ignored (i.e. the structure designed for the full height) to allow for the risk of unplanned excavation close to the toe of the slope.

6.2.2 Surcharge loading

Sometimes the applied loadings that should be assumed for design are prescribed in related codes. In such cases the prescribed loads should be used. Otherwise the *worst expected live loading* should be used for *ultimate* limit state calculations.

In all cases a *minimum uniform vertical surcharge* of 10 kN/m^2 acting on the crest of retaining walls, slopes and embankments should be considered in *ultimate* limit state calculations.

The *expected surcharge loading* should be used in *serviceability* limit state calculations.

6.2.3 Water pressures

It is usual to include drainage measures to control the water pressures that may arise from groundwater or infiltration. Where such measures are not provided, the most adverse water pressures that are considered to be reasonably possible should be allowed in the *ultimate* limit state calculations. Where the structure is subject to tidal action, the most adverse drawdown conditions should be assumed.

The risk of a rising groundwater table which might reduce the bearing capacity beneath a reinforced soil wall or steep slope should be considered.

The consequences of a blockage or failure in any drainage arrangements in the structure should be considered for *ultimate* limit state calculations, as should the consequences of possible leakage from other pipelines adjacent to the structure.

The *expected* water pressures in and around the structure should be used in the *serviceability* limit state calculations.

6.3 Soil properties

6.3.1 Representative values of soil strength

Representative values are cautious estimates of the mass properties of the soil as it exists in the field. The selected values should be based on a careful assessment of the range of factors that might govern the performance of the structure during construction and in service. This assessment should take account of geological information, relevant data from previous projects, the results of laboratory and field measurements and the standard of interpretation of these.

The selection of representative values does not depend on the severity of the limit state under consideration but should take account of the mechanism or mode of deformation being considered. For example, different representative strengths would be required for shear in a fissured material depending on whether the shear surface was free to follow the fissures or constrained to intersect intact material.

6.3.2 Design values of soil strength

The design value of soil strength represents the strength which is assumed to be mobilised as a limit state occurs.

6.3.3 Drained analysis

Representative values for the peak strength and the critical state (constant volume) strength of the soil should be assessed.

The representative peak strength should be appropriate for the anticipated stresses and soil density in the ground. Preferably the strength should be described by a secant angle of friction, ϕ'_p, although values of cohesion, c', and friction, ϕ'_{peak}, may be used.

The representative critical state strength should correspond to the constant volume angle of friction, ϕ'_{cv}.

It should be demonstrated by calculation that stability can be obtained in the structure mobilising a soil strength which does not exceed the greater of:

$$\tan \phi'_m \leq \tan \phi'_d = \text{greater of} \left\{ \frac{\tan \phi'_p}{1.25}, \tan \phi'_{cv} \right\} \qquad ...(6.1)$$

The partial factor 1.25 is relatively modest but is considered adequate because in *ultimate limit state* calculations it is used in conjunction with the most adverse loadings and soil geometry considered reasonably possible. While Equation (6.1) allows the option to select the design value of soil shearing resistance based on the peak strength, direct use of the critical state shearing resistance is recommended for most *ultimate limit state* calculations. The partial factor 1.25 applied to a cautious estimate of the peak shearing resistance would normally be used in the *serviceability limit state* calculations.

In compact clays subject to stress relief or seasonal variations of porewater pressure, the long-term peak strength could deteriorate to the critical state strength. The requirements set by Equation (6.1) are considered to be sufficiently cautious to accommodate this possibility in most cases.

6.3.4 Undrained analysis

The representative undrained shear strength in a foundation should be appropriate to the known properties and stress history (overconsolidation) of the soil. It is likely that the undrained strength will gradually increase with depth in the ground.

Stability should be demonstrated with the condition that the mobilised undrained strength in the foundation does not exceed the following limit:

$$(s_u)_m \leq (s_u)_d = \left\{ \frac{s_u}{1.5} \right\} \qquad \qquad ...(6.2)$$

The partial factor of safety 1.5 is greater than in the case of drained analysis to reflect the increased uncertainty of the effect of construction on soft ground. In cases where significant deformations in the construction are acceptable, such as in some low embankments built over soft soils, the partial factor of safety may be reduced, but not to less than 1.2.

Where some drainage can occur while the loading is applied, the beneficial influence of the increased vertical effective stress on the undrained shear strength of the soft clay should be taken into account and the higher strength used for calculation. This is analogous to the enhanced strength (compared with the initial strength) measured in a consolidated undrained compression test on soft clay.

In these cases it is recommended that the increased undrained shear strength of the clay be assessed and used in a total stress analysis, as discussed by Ladd (1991). The design situation envisaged when loading soft clay is a rapid *undrained* failure and collapse. The local increase in porewater pressure in soft clay as it is sheared, undrained, close to failure, is usually not properly taken into account in an effective stress analysis, which consequently overestimates the stability.

6.4 Reinforcement properties

The *available force* in a reinforcement layer depends on the reinforcement properties and the bond between the reinforcement and the soil.

The following concepts apply for polymer reinforcement:

1. Polymer material properties depend on *time* and *temperature, and* an appropriate combination of *design time* and *design temperature* (td, T_d) must be selected. The design temperature is normally the maximum one at which the reinforcement will be required to support sustained load. Usually the most critical design time

corresponds with the end of the design life, although for embankments on soft clay the design time is usually limited to the period required for consolidation in the foundation.

2. It is convenient to describe polymer materials in terms of *strength* and *stiffness* properties. The datum is the properties of the ex-works material, at the relevant temperature T_d, and these are called the *reference properties*.

3. The *material properties for design* are those which apply to the reinforcement in the ground, corresponding to the relevant combination of design time and temperature (t_d, T_d). Application in the ground affects the *reference properties* because of *mechanical damage* from handling and installation, and degradation from prolonged exposure to the *soil environment*. The influence of these factors varies significantly depending on the soil, the site conditions and the reinforcement material.

A practical way to estimate the *field strength*, $(P_{Field})_{t_d,T_d}$, *of the* reinforcement in the ground at (t_d, T_d), is to use the *reference properties* reduced by two factors, determined from test data relevant to the particular soil conditions and method of construction (Figure 6.1):

1. a *damage factor*, f_d, to allow for the mechanical damage in the ground
2. an *environmental factor*, f_{env}, to allow for the chemical environment and microbiological exposure in the ground.

$$(P_{Field})_{t_d,T_d} = \frac{(P_{Ref})_{t_d,T_d}}{f_d f_{env}} \qquad \qquad ...(6.3)$$

Mechanical damage and the soil chemical environment normally reduce the reinforcement strength properties much more than the stiffness properties.

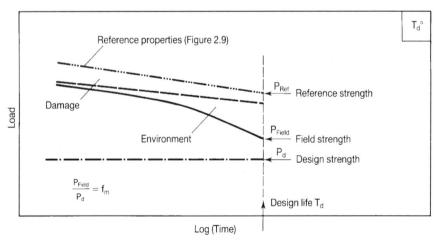

Figure 6.1 *Reinforcement strength properties*

An overall *material factor*, f_m, is applied to the *field strength* in order to derive the *design strength*, P_d, for the reinforcement.

$$P_d = \frac{(P_{Field})_{t_d, T_d}}{f_m} \qquad \qquad ...(6.4)$$

The material factor is needed to provide a margin between the *design strength* and the *expected strength* of the reinforcement in service at the end of the design life. This partial factor is intended to cover:

- the uncertainty inherent in the extrapolation of test data
- possibly greater reduction of strength in the field than that deduced from control specimens
- possible synergism between mechanical damage and the soil chemical environment which reduces strength further than anticipated
- higher than expected temperature in the ground, particularly close to face connections
- materials strengths occasionally falling below the specified characteristic value.

A discussion of values for the *damage* and *environmental factors* may be found in Section 2.5. As yet there are no generally agreed magnitudes for the *material factor* and whether is should vary for different reinforcement materials. The values in Table 6.1 reflect the current knowledge.

6.4.1 Reinforcement properties for serviceability

Two different approaches may be used to check the serviceability of reinforced soil structures. Both depend on the *stiffness*, or load-elongation properties of the reinforcement appropriate to the conditions in the ground.

The first approach is to adopt a prescriptive value of *maximum allowable elongation* (strain) in the geotextile reinforcement. Such a value is normally based on experience, and supported by data from physical modelling and numerical analysis. The *serviceability strength*, P_s, is the force which would cause the *maximum allowable elongation* to develop in the reinforcement at the end of the design life. This may be

Table 6.1 Material factor (f_m) as a function of the required extrapolation of data at the design temperature (T_d)

	No extrapolation	1 $\log_{10}$ cycle extrapolation (factor of 10)	1.5 $\log_{10}$ cycles extrapolation (factor of 30)	2 $\log_{10}$ cycles extrapolation (factor of 100)
Supported by accelerated testing	1.3	1.5	1.8	2.2

found directly from the load-elongation properties of the material at the appropriate design time and temperature.

Serviceability is then checked by repeating the equilibrium calculations discussed earlier, but using more realistic values for the design parameters (Chapter 7), to demonstrate that equilibrium may be maintained without mobilising reinforcement force in excess of the serviceability strength:

$$P_m \le \{P_s\} \qquad ...(6.5)$$

If the reinforcement *design strength* (Equation 6.4) is found to be less than the *serviceability strength* (Equation 6.5), then the ultimate limit state calculation is likely to govern the design. The serviceability condition is normally important where only small structural deformations are acceptable, or if the reinforcement material is particularly extensible or prone to significant creep deformation.

The second approach to examine serviceability is to complete a full equilibrium analysis, assuming that the design shearing resistance of the soil is mobilised, in order to determine the magnitude and distribution of force in the reinforcement layers required to provide equilibrium. The net elongation in each layer of reinforcement may then be found from these calculated forces and the known load-elongation properties. The reinforcement elongation is a significant component of the deflection of reinforced soil structures.

6.5 Interaction properties

The two main interactions between the reinforcement and the soil are described by the *bond* coefficient and the *direct sliding* coefficient. These are expressed as factors which are applied to the shear strength of the soil to give the interaction shearing resistance (Section 4.4).

In general, it is sufficient in design to apply these interaction coefficients directly to the *design value* of the soil shearing resistance, with no additional margin of safety.

6.6 Summary of design values

The partial factors described above, and the selection of design values for the material strengths and loadings for ultimate limit state calculations, are summarised in Table 6.2.

6.7 Synopsis of Chapter 6

(1) It is helpful in design to distinguish between the *required reinforcement forces* for equilibrium which depend on the soil properties, the soil geometry and the applied loadings, and the *available reinforcement forces* which depend on the reinforcement material properties, the reinforcement layout and the bond with the soil.

Table 6.2 Summary of design values and partial factors for the main parameters in ultimate limit state calculations (drained analysis)

Loadings	Factor	Comment	Section
Soil self weight: choose the **maximum expected unit weight**			(6.2.1)
Applied surcharge load: choose the **worst expected surcharge load**		Design surcharge loading may be specified in related codes	(6.2.2)
Choose the **most adverse groundwater regime reasonably possible**			(6.2.3)
Soil			
Choose the **critical state shearing resistance**	1.00	A safe design value of soil shearing resistance	(6.3.3) Eqn 6.1
Choose a **representative peak shearing resistance**	1.25	Provides a margin of safety on the representative peak strength	(6.3.3) Eqn 6.1
Reinforcement			
Start with the **reference strength** at (t_d, T_d)		Properties based on long-term test data	(6.4) (2.4)
Allow for use in the ground	f_d	Factor based on test data to allow for **mechanical damage**	(6.4) (2.5.1)
	f_{env}	Factor based on test data to allow for the **chemical and biological environment**	(6.4) (2.5.2)
Based on **the field strength from above**, at (t_d, T_d), calculate the **design strength**	f_m	Specified **material factor** allowing for poorer performance and extrapolation of data	(6.4) Eqn. 6.3

(2) The equilibrium in reinforced soil is too complex to be reflected adequately by a 'lumped' factor of safety. Rather, the procedure is to select representative *design values* for the parameters influencing the stability and the working equilibrium, and then to perform calculations to show that possible undesirable *design situations* will not arise.

(3) There are two main areas of concern for design. The possibility of collapse must be shown to be an acceptably small risk by means of *ultimate limit state* calculations, and the possibility that deformation might interfere with the function of the structure must be shown to be sufficiently unlikely by means of *serviceability limit state* calculations.

(4) The selection of *design values* should take into account the consequences of the limit state, whether collapse can occur without warning, the possible variability of parameters and workmanship.

(5) Where *a drained analysis* is appropriate, *the design strength* for the soil is selected from either the *critical state angle of friction* or a factored value of the *representative peak angle of friction* (Equation 6.1). Generally the former shearing resistance is chosen, and substantially removes the need to consider the influence of the reinforcement stiffness on the mobilised strength in the soil.

(6) Where *undrained analysis* is appropriate the *design strength* for the soil is based on a factored value of the *undrained shear strength* for the soil (Equation 6.2).

(7) The relevant properties for the reinforcement are those which apply *in the ground, at the end of the design life, t_d, and at the appropriate design temperature, T_d.* The influence of *mechanical damage* during installation, and the influence of exposure to the soil *chemical and microbiological environment* during the design life, are allowed for by factors f_d, and f_{env} respectively. These factors are applied to reduce the appropriate *reference strength*, to give the *field strength*.

(8) Because of the long life of many reinforced soil structures, there is a need for extrapolation of data. The *material factor, f_m,* provides the margin of safety between the *design strength* used for analysis and the *field strength* of the reinforcement.

Key references

British Standards Institution (1991). *Code of practice for strengthened/reinforced soil and other fills.* Draft BS 8006, for public comment.

Commission of the European Communities (1989). *Eurocode No. 7: geotechnics.* First, incomplete draft, November 1989.

Comité Européen du Beton (1975). *Common unified rules for different types of construction material.* CEB Bulletin 111.

International Standards Organisation (1973). *General principles for the verification of the safety of structures.* ISO 2394.

7   Limit states

The design calculations for all the applications of reinforced soil are presented following a similar format.

7.1 Design equilibrium

In a stability analysis for reinforced soil, the *required forces* or *stresses* for equilibrium in the soil are calculated so that a reinforcement layout may be found, by trial and error, to provide *available forces* or *stresses* which exceed the required values.

It is usually convenient to express the analysis for *steep slopes and walls* in terms of the required *stresses* for equilibrium in the soil, and the available *stresses* provided by the multiple layers of reinforcement spaced apart (Figure 7.1).

For *applications on soft soil* it is often preferable to consider the gross required *force* for equilibrium in the soil, and the gross available *force* provided by the one or more reinforcement layers spaced closely together near to the surface of the soft foundation soil (Figure 7.2).

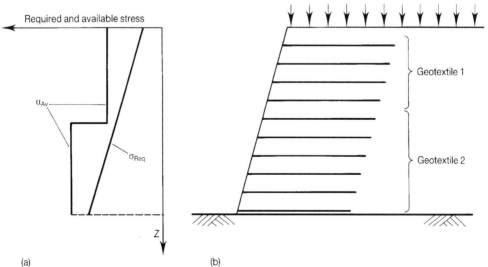

(a)   (b)

Figure 7.1 *Equilibrium in a steep reinforced slope expressed in terms of required and available stresses*

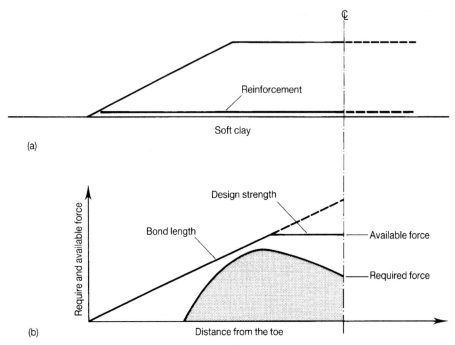

Figure 7.2 *Equilibrium (foundation stability) for an embankment on soft soil expressed in terms of required and available forces*

The design requirement is that on all possible failure mechanisms:

$$Available\ stress \geq Required\ stress \qquad ...(7.1a)$$

or

$$Available\ force \geq Required\ force \qquad ...(7.1b)$$

Design values of the input parameters are used on both sides of the equilibrium equation and these incorporate the safety margins. A safe soil shearing resistance and pessimistic porewater pressures and applied loadings are assumed to calculate the *required stresses* for equilibrium. Similarly, a safe design strength and interaction properties for the reinforcement are assumed to calculate the *available stresses.*

Finally, for steep reinforced slopes and walls it is necessary to check that there is acceptable external and foundation stability. The checking must include possible critical failure mechanisms involving preferential direct sliding of the soil across the surface of one or more reinforcement layers.

7.2 Ultimate limit states: design situations

All potential failure mechanisms must be considered in design.

7.2.1 Internal and overall equilibrium

In *steep slopes and walls*, there are two separate design checks for potential failure mechanisms intersecting the reinforcement layers, namely *internal* and *overall equilibrium*:

1. *Internal equilibrium.* This is checked to ensure that blocks of reinforced soil will not fall out of the face of the structure at any elevation (Figure 7.3).
2. *Overall equilibrium.* This is checked to ensure that the *unreinforced soil* behind the reinforced zone is adequately held in equilibrium, to avoid potential failure mechanisms passing through both the unreinforced and the reinforced zones (Figure 7.4).

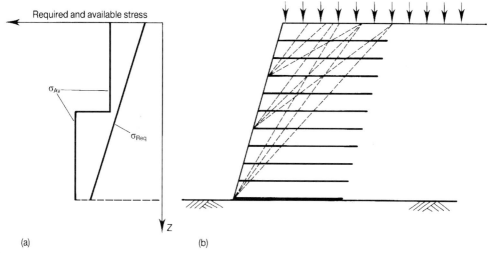

Figure 7.3 *Internal equilibrium for a steep reinforced slope*

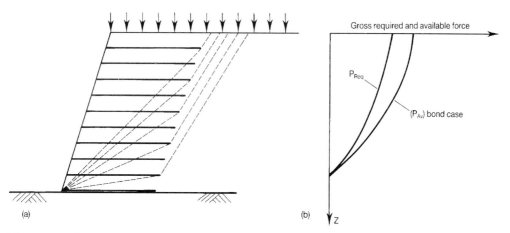

Figure 7.4 *Overall equilibrium for a steep slope and wall*

7.2.2 External equilibrium

Another requirement for steep slopes and walls is to ensure that there is adequate *external* stability considering the *reinforced zone* as a rigid block.

First, the bearing conditions between the *reinforced zone* and the underlying foundation must be checked to ensure that it will not (a) slide outward over, (b) exceed the bearing capacity of, or (c) apply an excessively eccentric loading to the underlying foundation soil. These three limit states are unacceptable and the *reinforced zone* must be proportioned to avoid them (Figure 7.5).

Second, the *external equilibrium* must be checked to ensure that the overall layout of the structure, or site, which can be achieved through reinforcing the soil, does not activate potential deep-seated failure mechanisms passing around the reinforced zone (Figure 7.6).

7.2.3 Construction over soft soil

Embankments and unpaved roads over soft foundation soils may be strengthened by one or more reinforcement layers placed close to the foundation surface. The design steps for

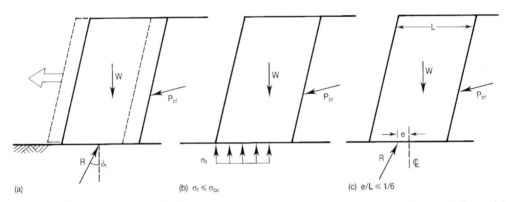

Figure 7.5 *External equilibrium check on foundation capacity: (a) direct sliding, (b) bearing capacity, and (c) eccentricity*

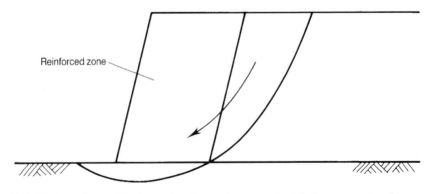

Figure 7.6 *External equilibrium check on deep-seated failure mechanisms*

these cases are similar to those outlined above for steep slopes and walls, with the following differences.

First, it is preferable to express the analysis in terms of the required and available *forces* in the reinforcement (Figure 7.2).

Second, the focus for design on soft soil is the reistance of the foundation to the applied embankment or live loading. Potential *foundation failure mechanisms* involving the foundation soil alone must be considered as well as *overall failure mechanisms* involving both the overlying fill and the soft soil foundation. These are described in Chapters 11 and 12.

7.3 Serviceability limit states

Analysis to estimate the *expected deflections* in reinforced soil structures at the end of construction, and during the remaining design life of the structure is strongly recommended for design.

The simplest form of analysis for serviceability is to adopt a limiting *maximum allowable elongation* (strain) in the reinforcement, from which the *serviceability strength* of the reinforcement can be found corresponding to the design time and temperature (Section 6.4.1). The internal and overall equilibrium calculations may then be repeated, using the *design values* for *serviceability*, to demonstrate that equilibrium can be achieved without exceeding the serviceability strength.

7.3.1 Bounds to likely deflection

The working equilibrium in soil reinforced by geotextiles occurs most frequently with the soil mobilising a significant proportion of its available peak shearing resistance. In broad terms, this is because the stress-strain response of soil is relatively *stiff* (the shearing resistance is mobilised with relatively little tensile strain) with respect to the load-elongation properties of geotextiles.

As a result, it is possible to estimate the limits to the *expected equilibrium* as follows:

- *Upper limit*: the highest likely reinforcement force (and elongation) may be found by assuming the lowest likely shearing resistance in the soil is mobilised, namely the 'at rest' angle of friction.
- *Lower limit*: the lowest likely reinforcement force may be found by assuming that the highest likely shearing in the soil is mobilised, namely the peak angle of friction.

These two limits are illustrated in Figure 7.7 for the case of a steep reinforced slope, and using the compatibility curve introduced in Section 4.3. The maximum gross *required force* for equilibrium in the slope is found from the most critical mechanism passing through the toe, the one requiring the greatest force for *internal equilibrium* (Figure

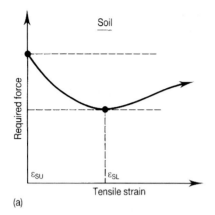

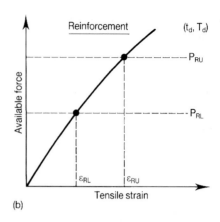

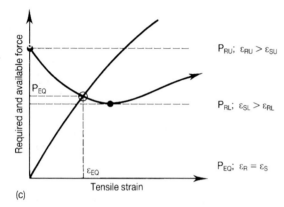

Figure 7.7 *Limits to the expected equilibrium shown on a compatibility curve: (a) soil behaviour, (b) reinforcement behaviour, and (c) the expected equilibrium*

7.7a). Assuming that the tensile strain in the reinforcement develops with tensile strain in the soil, the *available force* from the intersected reinforcement layers increases as tensile strain develops in the soil and the reinforcement (Figure 7.7b).

The upper and lower values of likely gross reinforcement force P_{RU}, P_{RL}, and the corresponding tensile strain in the soil ε_{SU}, ε_{SL}, and tensile elongations in the reinforcement, ε_{RU}, ε_{RL}, are marked on Figure 7.7a and 7.7b.

The *expected equilibrium* is where there is both force equilibrium ($P_{EQ} = P_{Required} = P_{Available}$) and compatibility of tensile strain ($\varepsilon_{EQ} = \varepsilon_R = \varepsilon_S$), as shown in Figure 7.7c.

The *expected equilibrium* is usually found within the above range, $P_{RU} \geq P_{EQ} \leq P_{RL}$, because of the influence of the compatibility between tensile strain and elongation in the soil and the reinforcement. At the *upper limit*, $\varepsilon_{RU} > \varepsilon_{SU}$, while at the *lower limit* the reverse normally applies, $\varepsilon_{SL} \geq \varepsilon_{RL}$ (Figure 7.7c). This serves to emphasise the important role of *strain compatibility* in determining the *stress equilibrium* in reinforced soil.

The above approach to bracketing the expected working equilibrium in reinforced soil is illustrated in Chapter 10 for reinforced soil walls and in Chapter 12 for embankments on soft soil.

7.4 Synopsis of Chapter 7

(1) The design analysis for reinforced soil is conveniently expressed in terms of the *required stresses* (or *forces*) for equilibrium in the soil and the *available stresses* (or *forces*) provided by the reinforcement.

(2) Suitably pessimistic *design values* for the soil properties, the loadings and the reinforcement properties are used in the *ultimate limit state* calculations to find an arrangement of reinforcement so that, for the case of slopes and walls,

$$Available\ stress \geq Required\ stress$$

(3) In the design of reinforced slopes and walls, the above equality must be satisfied for the analysis of *internal equilibrium*, which usually gives the greatest required stresses in the soil, and for *overall equilibrium*, which considers potential failure mechanisms passing through both the unreinforced backfill and the reinforced soil.

(4) *External equilibrium* must be examined also to check that there is sufficient *capacity* in the foundation beneath the reinforced zone, and that there is adequate stability on deep-seated failure mechanisms passing entirely around the reinforced zone.

(5) The expected values of the soil properties, reinforcement properties and the loadings are used to check *the equilibrium for serviceability*.

8   Steep reinforced slopes

A steep slope may be defined as one in which the factor of safety would be less than unity, $FS_s < 1.00$, in the absence of the reinforcement. In other words, the stability of a steep slope depends critically on the reinforcement.

Reinforcement is also used to increase the stability of slopes which are already stable, $FS_s \geq 1.00$. An example is the reinforcement of the side slopes of clay embankments to prevent shallow slips from forming (Chapter 9).

It is conventional to refer to very steep reinforced slopes as retaining walls. There is little difference, however, between a steep slope at an angle $\beta = 80°$ to the horizontal, and one with $\beta = 90°$. The main distinction is that the bearing capacity of the underlying foundation soil, the resistance of the structure to applied loading, and the effect of deformation on the design of the facing, are all more critical factors in the design of near-vertical reinforced soil structures (Chapter 10).

The three main categories of slope reinforcement are summarised in Figure 8.1. The general principles described in this chapter apply to all three cases.

The focus in this chapter is the analysis for steep reinforced slopes (Figure 8.2). *Design charts* are given for steep slopes with a level crest, and are useful for many practical applications (Figures 8.21 to 8.23). The principles described apply to complex slope geometries, but these require more general methods of analysis which are discussed at the end of the chapter.

8.1 Internal equilibrium: idealised case

It is helpful to identify three distinct *zones* in a steep reinforced fill (Figure 8.3). Large reinforcement forces are required in *zone 1* to maintain stability across a series of

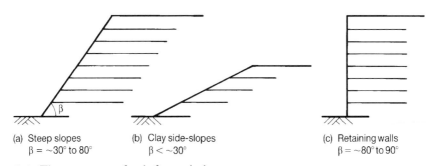

| (a) Steep slopes | (b) Clay side-slopes | (c) Retaining walls |
| $\beta = \sim30°$ to $80°$ | $\beta < \sim30°$ | $\beta = \sim80°$ to $90°$ |

Figure 8.1 *Three types of reinforced slope*

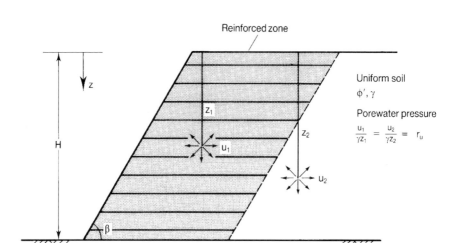

Figure 8.2 *Steep slope definitions*

critically inclined slip surfaces such as *AE*. The reinforcement layers must have a *design strength* and *spacing* sufficient to maintain the equilibrium on such *internal* failure mechanisms.

The reinforcement extends beyond *zone 1* (bounded by the surface AB) to a depth in the slope which defines *zone 2* (Figure 8.3). This allows the reinforcement to intercept and maintain equilibrium on potential *overall* failure mechanisms (such as the surface OGI) passing through *zone 2* and the unreinforced backfill (*zone 3*), and ensures sufficient bond between the reinforcement and the soil to enable the design forces to be mobilised in *zone 1*.

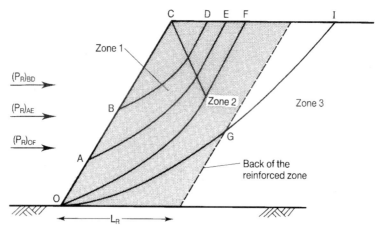

Figure 8.3 *Three zones in a steep reinforced slope:* zone 1, *bounded by AB,* zone 2, *to end of reinforcement, and* zone 3, *the unreinforced backfill*

8.1.1 Idealised equilibrium

The idealised equilibrium is one in which the reinforcement layers support a constant force in *zone 1*, maintained through to the face, which reduces through *zone 2* reaching zero at the boundary with *zone 3* (Figure 8.4).

The starting point for design is the internal equilibrium in *zone 1*. The magnitude of the *required stresses* for equilibrium, and the extent of *zone 1*, depend on: the slope height H; the slope angle, β; backfill sloping above the crest at an angle, i; the soil shearing resistance, ϕ'; the pore-pressure ratio, r_u; and the applied vertical surcharge, q_{sv} (Figure 8.5).

Because of the *similarity* between critical slip surfaces such as OF, AE and BD (Figure 8.3), the gross maximum required force for equilibrium in *zone 1* caused by self-weight

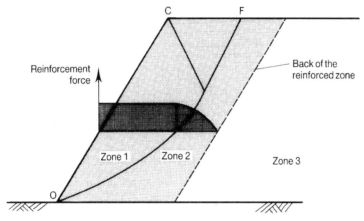

Figure 8.4 *Idealised equilibrium with uniform reinforcement force in* zone 1 *decreasing to zero at the back of* zone 2

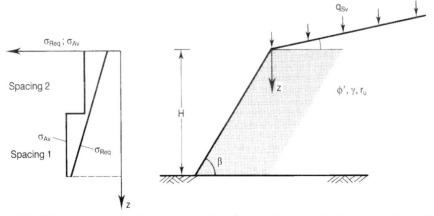

Figure 8.5 *Maximum required stress in the soil exceeded everywhere by the available stress from reinforcement arranged at two spacings*

loading, P_R, increases with the square of the slope height. (The role of similarity in earth pressure problems was discussed by Terzaghi, 1943.) Thus the need for reinforcement may be represented by a linearly increasing *maximum required stress*, σ_{Req} (Figure 8.5).

The variation of *required stress* with depth in the slope indicates how the reinforcement should be distributed to satisfy equilibrium most efficiently. A reinforcement layer with a *design strength*, P_d, placed with a vertical and horizontal spacing, s_v, s_h, provides an *available stress* in the soil, $\sigma_{Av} = P_d/s_v s_h$.

For balanced equilibrium the available stress should exceed the required stress at every depth in the slope. A shortfall in the provision of reinforcement at any depth could result in local over-loading in the reinforcement layer above its design strength. A typical pattern of linearly increasing maximum required stress in a steep slope, and the available stresses from reinforcement arranged in two zones is illustrated in Figure 8.5.

The concept of a required stress for equilibrium in a steep reinforced slope is similar to the Rankine earth pressure acting on a gravity retaining wall. But rather than providing the required stress *externally* by means of a retaining structure, the stresses in a reinforced slope are transmitted back into the soil, into *zone 2*, by the tensile force in the reinforcement layers.

8.1.2 Analysis for required stress

The idealised equilibrium in *zone 1* for a steep slope can be illustrated by the stress field found from the method of characteristics (Figure 8.6), as discussed by Wroth (1972).

This suggests that the required stresses for equilibrium in *zone 1* may be determined from existing earth pressure coefficients, such as those published by Caquot *et al.* (1973). The appropriate value of 'wall roughness' must be used to correspond with the horizontal direction of the reinforcement, $\delta_w = 90 - \beta$ (Figure 8.6).

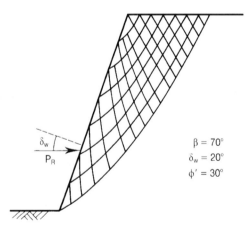

$\beta = 70°$
$\delta_w = 20°$
$\phi' = 30°$

Figure 8.6 *Stress characteristics illustrating balanced equilibrium in* zone 1. *(After Houlsby, 1989)*

The range of slopes to which existing earth pressure coefficients can be applied in reinforced soil design is restricted by the limits $\delta_w/\phi \leq 1$ or $\beta \geq (90° - \phi)$, and zero porewater pressure, $r_u = 0$. New analysis is required for other cases.

8.1.3 Limit equilibrium analysis

Two limit equilibrium methods which are suited to the analysis of reinforced slopes are a full two-part wedge analysis (Figure 8.7) and a logarithmic spiral analysis (Figure 8.8). The two-part wedge analysis has the advantage that it can reproduce the potential for failure to pass between reinforcement layers, while the logarithmic spiral analysis is a rigid-body mechanism which does not require assumptions to be made about interslice forces (Section 8.8.1).

Both analyses give earth pressure coefficients to within a few percent of the existing solutions over the applicable range (Jewell, 1989). They are also in close agreement for

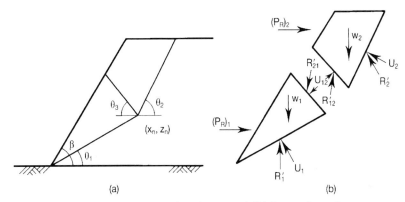

Figure 8.7 (a) Two-part wedge mechanism and (b) boundary forces

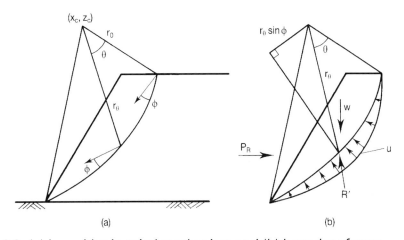

Figure 8.8 (a) Logarithmic spiral mechanism and (b) boundary forces

other slope cases, including those with porewater pressure ($r_u > 0$). In general, the logarithmic spiral mechanism gives the slightly more critical results, especially for flatter slopes (i.e. the maximum required force for equilibrium calculated from the logarithmic spiral analysis slightly exceeds that from the two-part wedge analysis).

Earth pressure coefficients from the above analysis for simple slope geometries are summarised in design charts (Figures 8.21 to 8.23). The coefficients agree with those derived independently by Leshchinsky and Boedecker (1989), using logarithmic spiral analysis (for $r_u = 0$). The earth pressure coefficients may be used to find the envelope of maximum required stress for steep slopes.

8.2 Overall equilibrium

Once the provision of reinforcement to satisfy the *internal equilibrium* in *zone 1* has been determined, it is necessary to proportion *zone 2* to maintain equilibrium on deeper-seated potential failure surfaces, such as *OGI* in Figure 8.3. Investigations then show that the choice of a *constant reinforcement length* generally provides an efficient and practical arrangement.

The analysis for *overall equilibrium* is illustrated in Figure 8.9. The reinforcement must extend sufficiently into the slope to maintain equilibrium on potential failure mechanisms which only intersect some of the reinforcement layers lower in the slope.

A relatively wide range of combinations of reinforcement strength, spacing and length can provide equilibrium in a steep slope. An optimum solution, one that balances reinforcement spacing and length, is one in which the reinforcement spacing is chosen to satisfy the required stresses for *internal equilibrium*, and then the layers are extended sufficiently into the slope to satisfy *overall equilibrium*.

The solution for the minimum reinforcement length for overall stability given in the design charts was found by assuming that all the available force could be mobilised in the intersected reinforcement layers, as indicated by the shaded region in Figure 8.10. The need for a bond length at the end of the reinforcement layer invalidates the

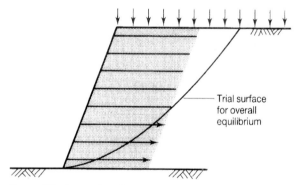

Figure 8.9 *Overall equilibrium check on the required reinforcement length*

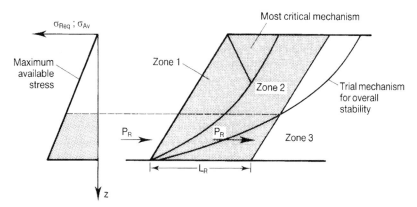

Figure 8.10 *Maximum available reinforcement force,* P_R*, to maintain overall equilibrium*

assumption, but this is corrected by a simple adjustment in the design procedure (Section 8.2.1).

In a limit equilibrium analysis of a specific slope design, the mobilised forces including the effect of bond would be used (Figure 8.9).

8.2.1 Allowance for bond

A bond length is needed at the end of each reinforcement layer so that the design strength of the reinforcement can be mobilised without pullout. The bond length, L_b, needed to support the design force, P_d, may be found from

$$P_d = (2W_r L_b)(\sigma'_n \alpha_b \tan \phi') \qquad \qquad ...(8.1)$$

where W_r is the width of the reinforcement, L_b is the bond length, $2W_r L_b$ is the nominal area of contact over which bond develops between the soil and the reinforcement, σ'_n is the effective stress acting normal to the reinforcement surface, and $\alpha_b \tan \phi'$ is the bond shearing resistance, governed by the bond coefficient, α_b, and the shearing resistance of the soil, $\tan \phi'$.

The required bond length at the base of a steep slope, L_B, for horizontal reinforcement layers on which the normal effective stresses are $\sigma'_n = \sigma'_v$ and $\sigma'_v = \gamma H(1 - r_u)$, is found, from Equation (8.1), i.e.:

$$\frac{L_B}{H} = \left(\frac{P_d}{2W_r \gamma H^2} \right) \left(\frac{1}{1 - r_u} \right) \left(\frac{1}{\alpha_b \tan \phi'} \right) \qquad ...(8.2)$$

The variation of the required bond length with depth below the crest in a reinforced soil wall is shown in Figure 8.11 ($\beta = 90°$, $i = 0°$, $q_{sv} = 0$). The available reinforcement force on a typical two-part wedge mechanism is reduced by bond, so that the gross force, P_b, is less than the maximum possible value, P_R (Figure 8.11).

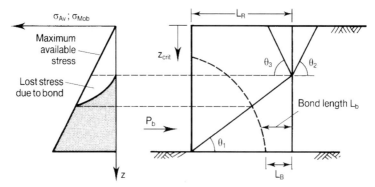

Figure 8.11 *Required bond length and loss of available force*

Examination of trial wedges through the toe of the slope shows that the influence of bond is to reduce the available force in the reinforcement by an almost constant proportion, $P_b/P_R \cong constant$, for wedges in the range $(45° + \phi/2) \geq \theta_1 \geq 0°$. This loss in available force can be expressed (slightly conservatively) in terms of the bond length at the base of the slope, L_B, and the length of the reinforcement, L_R,

$$\frac{P_b}{P_R} \approx \frac{L_R - L_B}{L_R} = 1 - \frac{L_B}{L_R} \qquad ...(8.3)$$

8.2.2 Allowance for load-shedding

Bond reduces the mobilised reinforcement force available to maintain *overall equilibrium*. Additional reinforcement layers must be included in the slope, surplus to those required for the ideal equilibrium in *zone 1*, to compensate for this shortfall.

Since the loss of reinforcement force is approximately a constant proportion of the maximum available reinforcement force, it may be remedied simply by increasing the provision of reinforcement throughout the slope by the same factor. This can be thought of as a *load-shedding allowance* because the requirement for reinforcement force which is not met where bond is a problem will be shed down the failure surface to where the extra reinforcement layers are intersected.

The minimum provision of reinforcement in *zone 1*, defined by the earth pressure coefficient K_{Req}, should be increased by a constant factor to compensate exactly for the effect of bond and the choice of reinforcement length,

$$K_d = \frac{K_{Req}}{1 - L_B/L_R} \qquad ...(8.4)$$

where K_d is the design earth pressure coefficient (Figure 8.12). The reinforcement length, L_R, is the value reported in the design charts calculated assuming perfect bond (Section 8.2). Thus the effect of poorer reinforcement bond capacity (Equation 8.2) is mitigated by the inclusion of extra reinforcement layers in the slope (Equation 8.4). The

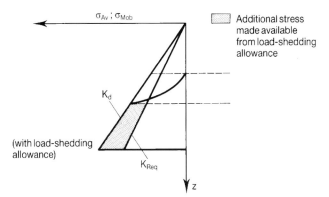

Figure 8.12 *Additional reinforcement, $K_d > K_{Req}$, to mitigate loss of available force due to bond*

practical effect of this is small, however, for steep slopes with granular fill reinforced by geotextiles or polymer grids.

Bond is a more significant factor where the reinforcement force per unit width is greater, P_d/W_r, and where the bond coefficient (α_b) is less, as is the case for smooth reinforcement strips, for example.

8.3 Internal equilibrium: practical corrections

8.3.1 Allowance for bond

The increased provision of reinforcement described above compensates for bond on potential failure mechanisms through the toe of the slope. However, the effect of bond on potential failure mechanisms higher in the slope, such as the slip surface *EF* in Figure 8.3, must also be considered.

One way to mitigate the effects of bond on *internal equilibrium* is to define a minimum required stress so as to increase the amount of reinforcement at the top of the slope. Wedge analysis (Figure 8.13) then shows that a suitable minimum stress, σ_{min},

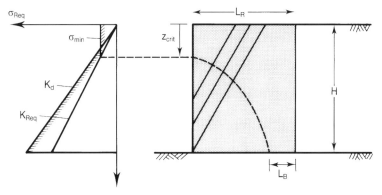

Figure 8.13 *Additional reinforcement, σ_{min}, to allow for bond near the crest of a steep slope*

may be defined in terms of a critical depth, z_{crit}, where the bond length is equal to the length of the reinforcement, $L_b = L_R$ (Equation 8.1). From Equation (8.2)

$$\frac{z_{crit}}{H} = \frac{L_B}{L_R} \qquad \qquad ...(8.5)$$

and the minimum required stress is,

$$\sigma_{min} = \gamma_d Z_{crit} K_{Req}\ \gamma_d H(L_B/L_R)K_{Req} \qquad ...(8.6)$$

The allowance for bond at the crest of the slope is illustrated in Figure 8.13. The practical effect of this on reinforcement quantities is usually small.

8.3.2 Allowance for compaction stresses

The potential influence of compaction is to lock force into the reinforcement. It is prudent to ensure that the reinforcement can support the lateral stress caused by compaction to avoid the risk of damage caused by temporary over-loading.

Compaction theory is well developed through Broms (1971), Ingold (1979), Duncan and Seed (1986) and Bolton (1990). The analysis by Bolton sets bounds to the *maximum horizontal stress* in the soil caused by compaction. This lateral stress, σ_{comp}, is defined in terms of the total maximum force per unit length of the roller Q, imposed by the joint action of gravity and cyclic acceleration, and the unit weight of the soil, γ,

$$0.9\sqrt{Q\gamma} \geq \sigma_{comp} \geq 0.45\sqrt{Q\gamma} \qquad ...(8.7)$$

Typical compaction procedures for granular soil result in a lateral stress of the order 10 to 30kN/m². The final, or residual, stress that remains in the soil on removal of the compactor depends on the amount of *elastic* rebound.

For example, a middle-range vibrating roller might have a mass per unit width, 2000kg/m, and a dynamic force factor, 2, delivering $Q = 40$kN/m. This would generate a maximum residual compaction stress in the range $25 \geq \sigma_o \geq 12$kN/m².

In standard construction procedures for reinforced soil, only relatively light, hand-operated compaction plant is allowed near a slope or wall face. The maximum likely stress that such compaction would induce in the soil is of the order $\sigma_{comp} = 15$kN/m².

Some practical considerations are as follows:

1. the compaction stress, σ_{comp}, normally exceeds the minimum stress at the slope crest, σ_{min}, needed to compensate for bond (Section 8.3.1)
2. practical factors in steep slope design usually result in an over-provision of reinforcement at the top of the slope so that, $\sigma_{Av} \geq \sigma_{comp}$, in any case
3. compaction induced stresses will reduce with time if any creep occurs in the reinforcement.

8.4 External equilibrium

The undesirable design situations for equilibrium are foundation failure beneath the reinforced zone or possible slip passing entirely around the reinforced structure. These design situations were introduced in Chapter 7 and illustrated in Figures 7.5 and 7.6. There are four main checks for external equilibrium:

1. Direct outward sliding of the reinforced zone over the foundation.
2. Bearing capacity failure in the foundation beneath the reinforced zone.
3. Excessively eccentric loading at the base of the reinforced zone.
4. External failure on slip mechanisms passing around the reinforced zone.

8.4.1 Direct sliding

Direct sliding is a critical aspect of design for all reinforced slopes. Slip surfaces may develop preferentially across the surface of a reinforcement layer at a reduced shearing resistance, $\alpha_{ds} \tan \phi$, where α_{ds} is the coefficient of direct sliding (Section 4.5).

A two-part wedge mechanism is generally used for the analysis of direct sliding (Figure 8.14). The most critical direct sliding mechanisms often occur at the base of the slope. As slopes are flattened, $\beta < 90°$, the weight of soil resisting direct sliding reduces, and hence the required reinforcement length at the base of the slope increases (see the design charts, Figures 8.21 to 8.23).

At foundation level, direct sliding can occur by the reinforcement sliding over the underlying foundation soil, as well as by the fill sliding over the underlying reinforcement layer.

A single minimum value for the coefficient of direct sliding, $\alpha_{ds} = 0.8$, was used to derive the design charts. This value should be satisfied by many reinforcement materials, and a correction may be applied where $\alpha_{ds} < 0.8$. *Note that the design charts assume that the shearing resistance of the foundation soil is at least as great as the backfill material.*

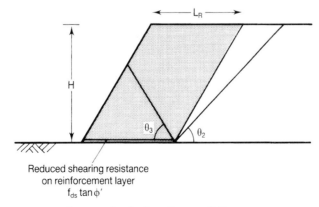

Figure 8.14 *Two-part wedge analysis for direct sliding*

The design curves for direct sliding (Figures 8.21 to 8.23) are shown with a chain-line boundary: no instability could be found using potential direct sliding mechanisms in the area to the left of this line. This suggests that stability is governed solely by overall and external stability considerations. Care is urged in the design of slopes falling within this range.

8.4.2 Bearing capacity

In steep reinforced slopes, where $\beta \geq 70°$ for example, it is desirable to check the local bearing capacity of the foundation immediately beneath the reinforced zone. This is additional to the analysis of external stability on slip surfaces passing through the foundation soil beneath the reinforced zone.

To complete a bearing capacity check at the base of the reinforced zone, the disturbing forces acting on the reinforced zone have to be evaluated, namely the thrust from the unreinforced backfill, externally applied loads, and the self-weight loading of the reinforced zone. For very steep slopes it is reasonable to calculate the backfill thrust using earth pressure coefficients. For example, it may be assumed that level backfill exerts a horizontal thrust on the reinforced zone, in which case the earth pressure coefficients given in the design charts may be used.

Once the forces have been evaluated, the magnitude and location of the resultant thrust acting on the base of the reinforced zone may be calculated. Conventional bearing capacity theory is then applied to check the foundation bearing capacity, and to ensure that the resultant thrust acts within the central third of the base of the reinforced zone. The usual remedial actions are to increase the length of the reinforcement at the base of the slope or to increase the embedment of the reinforced zone.

The equations for the analysis of bearing capacity are given in Sections 5.4 and 5.5. Their application is illustrated in detail for the retaining wall example in Chapter 10. The design example in this chapter (Section 8.7) assumes a competent foundation.

8.4.3 External stability

Conventional methods of limit equilibrium analysis, such as the method of slices, may be used to check the stability on slip surfaces passing entirely around the reinforced zone and through the foundation soil beneath the reinforced zone. This check is critical for all reinforced slopes, irrespective of the slope angle.

8.5 Design charts for steep reinforced slopes

The design charts in this chapter (Figures 8.21 to 8.23) apply to the case of a steep reinforced slope, $90° > \beta > 30°$, with a level crest, $i = 0°$, and resting on a competent foundation (Figure 8.2). Porewater pressures in the slope are defined in terms of a pore-pressure ratio, r_u (see below). The same soil properties and porewater pressures apply to both the reinforced fill and the unreinforced backfill. A uniform vertical surcharge may be applied on the slope crest.

The design charts are for polymeric reinforcement products, with a bond coefficient, α_b. A fixed value for the coefficient of direct sliding, $\alpha_{ds} = 0.8$, has been assumed in the charts, and this should be exceeded by most reinforcement products. A correction may be applied in cases where $\alpha_{ds} < 0.8$.

Design *values* for the input parameters should be selected following the guidance in Chapter 6. Both *ultimate* and *serviceability limit states* may be investigated using the appropriate combination of design values for each case.

Judgement on the maximum acceptable elongation in the reinforcement is required when selecting the *serviceability strength, P_s* (Section 6.4.1). A maximum allowable elongation of the order 3 to 5% is appropriate for most steep reinforced slopes, although greater elongation in the reinforcement may be acceptable for flatter slopes.

The pore-pressure ratio, r_u, identifies the magnitude of the porewater pressure at depth simply as a function of the vertical overburden pressure, $u = \gamma z r_u$, Figure 8.2 (Bishop and Morgenstern, 1960). Although this does not give an ideal description of the pattern of porewater pressure in a slope that might develop with infiltration, it is the only non-dimensional parameter available for use in charts.

Where flow into the reinforced slope is envisaged, a representative pore-pressure ratio should be chosen so that the predicted porewater pressure at each point in the slope exceeds or equals that given by the flow net. The case for a simple phreatic surface is illustrated in Figure 8.15.

8.6 Steps for using the design charts

Step 1: Values from the charts
Select design values and determine the required reinforcement length:
1.1 Select *design values* for the input parameters as described in Chapter 6. Determine K_{Req} and L_R/H from the design charts, Section 8.5. A linear interpolation between the charts is sufficient for intermediate cases.

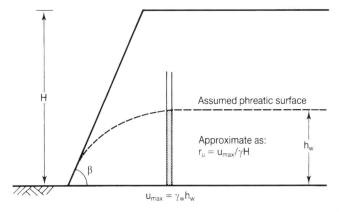

Figure 8.15 *Choice of pore-pressure ratio to allow for a phreatic surface*

1.2 Ensure that the required length $(L_R/H)_{ds}$ is valid by checking the direct sliding coefficient, $\alpha_{ds} \geq 0.8$. If this is not the case, *increase* the required reinforcement length at the base of the slope, $(L_R/H)_{ds}$, by the factor $0.8/\alpha_{ds}$.

1.3 Select the reinforcement length arrangement as follows.

(a) Where $(L_R/H)_{ovrl} > (L_R/H)_{ds}$ choose reinforcement with a constant length $L_R/H = (L_R/H)_{ovrl}$.

(b) Where $(L_R/H)_{ds} > (L_R/H)_{ovrl}$

either: choose reinforcement with a constant length $L_R/H = (L_R/H)_{ds}$,

or: choose reinforcement with a length varying uniformly from $(L_R/H)_{base} = (L_R/H)_{ds}$ at the base to $(L_R/H)_{crest} = (L_R/H)_{ovrl}$ at the crest.

1.4 Determine the *bond length* at the base of the slope L_B/H from Equation (8.2), Section 8.3.1.

Step 2: Envelope of maximum required stress in the soil

Construct the envelope of *maximum* required stress in the slope, Figure 8.16a:

2.1 The basic *required stress* for the equilibrium is determined from the depth below the slope crest, z and the required earth pressure coefficient, K_{Req},

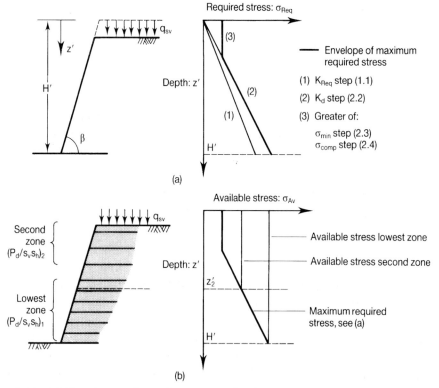

Figure 8.16 *(a) Envelope of maximum required stress, and (b) locus of maximum available stress in a steep reinforced slope*

$$\sigma_{Req} = \gamma_d z K_{Req}$$

2.2 A greater provision of reinforcement is needed, however, to allow for the effect of reinforcement bond on overall stability (Section 8.2.1). Calculate the *bond allowance* (1 − L_B/L_R), and increase the *design required stress* throughout the slope by increasing the design earth pressure coefficient

$$K_d = \frac{K_{Req}}{1 - L_B/L_R}$$

2.3 Additional reinforcement is needed near the crest of the slope to allow for the influence of bond on local equilibrium close to the face (Section 8.3.1). Calculate the critical depth $z_{crit}/H = L_B/L_R$, to determine the *minimum required stress* at the crest of the slope

$$\sigma_{min} = \gamma_d z_{crit} K_{Req} = \gamma_d H(L_B/L_R) K_{Req}$$

Step 2.3 may be omitted during preliminary design.
2.4 Estimate the stress induced by compaction (Section 8.3.2).
A value, $\sigma_o = 15\text{kN/m}^2$, may be assumed for preliminary design.

Step 3: Locus of available stress from the reinforcement
Construct the locus of *maximum available* stress in the slope, Figure 8.16b:
3.1 Devise a reinforcement layout so that the *minimum available stress* at every depth, z, exceeds the envelope of *maximum required stress* calculated in *Step 2*. The *available stress*, $\sigma_{av} = P_d/(s_v s_h)$, depends both on the reinforcement design strength and spacing. Either or both of these may be changed at different elevations in the slope.
3.2 Two zones of reinforcement at constant spacing are often used. The maximum provision of reinforcement is set by the lowest layer in any zone. The lowest zone extends to the base of the slope where the reinforcement strength and spacing must satisfy the inequality

$$P_d/(s_v s_h) \geq \gamma_d H K_d$$

3.3 If the spacing or reinforcement material is to be changed at a higher elevation in the slope, at a depth, z_2, below the slope crest, the above inequality must be satisfied but using the depth, z_2, rather than the slope height, H, and the appropriate design strength for the reinforcement.
3.4 It is usually convenient to determine the elevations for the reinforcement graphically. First construct the locus of *available stress*, marking on the maximum depths, such as z_2, at which the reinforcement or spacing will be changed (Figure 8.16b). Now mark in the positions of the reinforcement layers working from the

base of the slope and only changing the reinforcement arrangement above the maximum depth for that zone, such as z_2 in Figure 8.16b.

3.5 The following limits to the maximum vertical spacing are recommended

$$(s_v)_{max} \leq Minimum \ of \ (H/5, \ 1m)$$

Where only limited deformation in a steep slope with a wrap around face is acceptable, a reduced maximum spacing is recommended $(s_v)_{max} \leq 0.5m$.

Allowance for uniform vertical surcharge

Uniform vertical surcharge, q_{sv}, at the slope crest is allowed for by using an artificially greater *effective height, H'*, in the design procedure

$$H' = H + \frac{q_{sv}}{\gamma_d}$$

Design proceeds exactly as before (*Step 1 to 3* above) but using H' instead of H for the slope height, and an effective depth, $z' = z + q_{sv}/\gamma_d$, instead of z. The provision of reinforcement is simply terminated at the physical crest of the slope, H, which occurs at an effective depth $z' = q_{sv}/\gamma_d$.

This procedure is approximate but reproduces closely the *required stresses,* while being conservative for the *required reinforcement length.* It is recommended for surcharges up to $H'/H \leq 1.3$.

8.7 Design example

The design example illustrates the selection of design values and the use of the design charts. The example has been simplified for reasons of length.

8.7.1 Project data and design values

Slope details

A 7.5m high noise barrier with an angle $\beta = 80°$, and a 10m wide crest, is needed for an environmental protection scheme. The reinforced slope will extend to 0.5m below ground level, giving an effective height 8m. An available free-draining granular fill, polymer grid reinforcement and a wrap-around facing will be used. The existing ground conditions provide a competent foundation for the slope.

The range for the unit weight measured for the fill is 19kN/m^3 when lightly compacted to a maximum 21kN/m^3 when heavily compacted. The expected unit weight under field compaction is 20kN/m^3.

Direct shear tests on the fill compacted to the expected field density gave peak angles of friction in the range 39° to 45°, under applied vertical stresses 100 to 200kN/m^2. The large strain or critical state angle of friction was measured to be between 30.5° and 34°.

When completed there will be access to the top of the barrier, which will not carry traffic or utilities (e.g. water pipes): it is therefore considered adequate to design for zero surcharge, $q_{sv} = 0\text{kN/m}^2$, and because the fill is free-draining, zero porewater pressure, $(r_u)_d = 0$.

The following *design values* are selected for the *ultimate limit state* analysis (Chapter 6): slope height, $H = 8.0\text{m}$; unit weight of fill, $\gamma_d = 21\text{kN/m}^3$; critical state strength of the soil, $\phi'_d = 31°$; vertical surcharge, $q_{sv} = 0\text{kN/m}^2$, hence $H' = H$; and pore-pressure ratio, $(r_u)_d = 0$.

A higher mobilised angle of friction and the expected soil unit weight would be appropriate for the *serviceability limit state* analysis (Chapter 6), the remaining *design values* staying the same: expected unit weight, $\gamma_d = 20\text{kN/m}^3$; and, based on a cautious estimate of the peak strength, $\phi'_p = 41.5°$, a design angle of friction, $\phi'_d = 35°$ (Equation 6.1).

Reinforcement details

The slope is situated in Northern Europe and has a required design life of 60 years, giving the design conditions, $t_d = 60$ years and $T_d = 20°\text{C}$.

A series of polymer grids with *index strengths* in the range 110 to 35kN/m are to be considered. The skin friction on the solid surfaces of the grids is tan $\delta = 0.6$ tan ϕ'. The grids all have a similar geometry with a solid area ratio $\bar{a}_s = 0.4$, and transverse members spaced to give $S/\bar{a}_b B = 20$ (Sections 4.5 and 4.6).

The coefficient of direct sliding may be calculated as $\alpha_{ds} = 0.24 + 0.60 = 0.84$, from Equation (4.3). The first component is from shear on the solid grid surfaces and the second component is from soil to soil shear through the grid apertures.

For *ultimate limit state* conditions, the bearing stress ration in the fill is $\sigma'_b/\sigma'_n = 6.3$, from Equation (4.8) with $\phi'_d = 31°$. This gives a coefficient of bond for the grids $\alpha_b = 0.24 + 0.26 = 0.50$, from Equation (4.6); the first component stems from surface shear, and the second component from bearing stress.

The manufacturer of the reinforcement grids recommends the following allowances for damage and environmental degradation in the reinforcement, $f_d = 1.2$ and $f_{env} = 1.1$, for the envisaged soil and environmental conditions at the project site (Sections 2.5 and 6.4). These are relatively small allowances because of the benign conditions in this case. The material properties test data have to be extrapolated by 1 $\log_{10}$ cycle of time to reach the design life (i.e. there are stress-rupture data for up to 6 years of continuous loading) and the appropriate material factor for design is then $f_m = 1.5$ (Table 6.1). The manufacturer's data define characteristic values for the reinforcement grids as summarised in Table 8.1.

The expected cumulative elongation in the reinforcement grids for the design conditions in the slope, carrying a force equal to the design strengths given in Table 8.1, in just less than 3.5% in each case.

Table 8.1 Characteristic strength of the reinforcement grids in kN/m. (t_d = 60 years and T_d = 20 °C)

Index strength kN/m	Reference strength $(P_{Ref})_{t_dT_d}$	Field strength $(P_{Field})_{t_dT_d}$ eqn. (6.3)	Design strength P_d eqn. (6.4)
110	66	50	33
80	48	36	24
55	33	25	16.5
35	21	16	10.5

Notes: Characteristic index and reference strength from manufacturer.
 Field strength for degradation f_d = 1.2 and f_{env} = 1.1.
 Material factor f_m = 1.5 for $\log_{10}$ cycle of extrapolation.

Limit states

Deformation in the environmental barrier is not a critical factor and a maximum allowable elongation over the life of the slope 5% is chosen for the serviceability limit. Since this elongation is greater than that caused by a force equal to the design strength (3.5%, from above), it implies that the *serviceability strength* for the reinforcement is greater than the *design strength* ($P_s > P_d$). Since more advantageous design values are assumed for the serviceability analysis, the design will be governed by the *ultimate limit state* case (see Section 6.4.1.).

8.7.2 Design steps

The following analysis is for the *ultimate limit state* condition which governs the design, as discussed above. The step numbers refer to those in Section 8.6.

Step 1.1 The required earth pressure coefficient, K_{Req} = 0.23, and the required reinforcement lengths, $(L_R/H)_{ovrl}$ = 0.53, and $(L_R/H)_{ds}$ = 0.25, may be determined from the charts for the design values $(r_u)_d$ = 0, β = 80° and ϕ'_d = 31°.

Step 1.2 The required length at the base of the slope is valid since α_{ds} = 0.84 ≥ 0.80.

Step 1.3 As $(L_R/H)_{ovrl}$ ≥ $(L_R/H)_{ds}$, the minimum required reinforcement length has a constant value L_R = 0.53 × 8 = 4.3m.

> *There are two ways to proceed. The first approach is to ignore the corrections for bond in preliminary design: the design process must then be repeated, based on the preliminary layout but now allowing for bond, and modifying the reinforcement layout as necessary. The second approach (adopted here) is to select a reinforcement material and spacing at the outset and to allow for bond immediately.*

Step 1.4 Make a preliminary selection for the reinforcement. For example, by assuming a constant spacing s_v = 0.5m throughout the slope, the maximum required stress at the base of the slope would be σ_{Req} = $K_{Req}\gamma_d H$ = 39kN/m². The grid reinforcement with an index strength 80kN/m, and design strength 24kN/m, would provide sufficient available stress at the base of the slope, σ_{Av} = 24/0.5 = 48kN/m² (Table 8.1). The bond length at the base of the wall for this reinforcement grid would be, L_B/H = 0.03, from Equation 8.2 and W_r = 1m, α_b = 0.5, and ϕ' = ϕ'_d = 31°.

Step 2.1 The basic required stress for equilibrium is shown in Figure 8.17.

Step 2.2 From the values L_R/H = 0.53 (*Step 1.3*) and L_B/H = 0.03 (*Step 1.4*), the ratio L_B/L_R = 0.06 and the bond allowance $(1 - L_B/L_R)$ = 0.94. The design earth pressure coefficient, allowing for bond, is then K_d = 0.23/0.94 = 0.24 (Equation 8.4).

Step 2.3 The minimum required stress to allow for bond at the crest, for L_B/L_R = 0.06, is σ_{min} = 2.3kN/m² (Equations 8.5 and 8.6). This is a minimal value as expected for polymer grid material (Figure 8.17).

Step 2.4 A prescriptive value for the maximum stress induced by compaction is assumed for design, σ_o = 15kN/m² (Figure 8.17). This value must be checked once the compaction equipment has been selected.

Step 3.1 The reinforcement to provide a suitable locus of *available stress* may be devised graphically (adopted here) or by calculation.

If a single spacing is used, s_v = 0.5m, and a reinforcement design strength P_d = 24kN/m were adopted, then n = 8/0.5 = 16 layers would be required. The reinforcement layout in Figure 8.18a has the first layer placed at foundation level.

Steps 3 Economies might be achieved by using less strong reinforcement near the crest of the slope where there is an excess of available stress (Figure 8.18a).

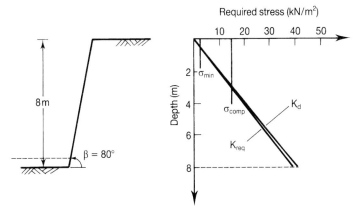

Figure 8.17 *Envelope of maximum required stress for the design example*

For example, choosing the weaker grid in Table 8.1 $(P_d)_2 = 10.5\text{kN/m}$, but keeping the same spacing, $s_v = 0.5\text{m}$, would provide an available stress, $(\sigma_{Av})_2 = 21\text{kN/m}^2$. This reinforcement arrangement would be acceptable above a depth, $z_2 = P_d/(s_v\gamma_dK_d) = 4.1\text{m}$, and allow the top six layers of the stronger reinforcement grid to be replaced (Figure 8.18b).

Use of the intermediate grid with $P_d = 16.5\text{kN/m}$ would reduce the provision of reinforcement further. For this grid, $\sigma_{Av} = 33\text{kN/m}^2$, which is permissible above a depth below the slope crest, $z_3 = 6.5\text{m}$.

Step 3.4 The reinforcement layout using all three grids would have a constant spacing $s_v = 0.5\text{m}$, and five layers each of the two stronger reinforcement grids with six layers of the lightest grid near the top (Figure 8.19).

The three alternative designs are summarised in Table 8.2, where relative material costs for the reinforcement are indicated. The optimum design will depend on the project details. While a more sophisticated layout minimises reinforcement material costs, other cost factors, such as construction control and material supply arrangements, can make the simpler reinforcement layouts most cost-effective overall.

8.8 General methods of stability analysis

More general methods of slope stability analysis are being adapted for the design of reinforced soil. These will enable more complex slopes to be designed, and allow independent checking on slopes designed using charts, but they are not yet generally available.

Conventional slope stability methods should be used routinely to check the *external equilibrium* of reinforced slopes against potential failure on slip surfaces passing entirely around the reinforced zone.

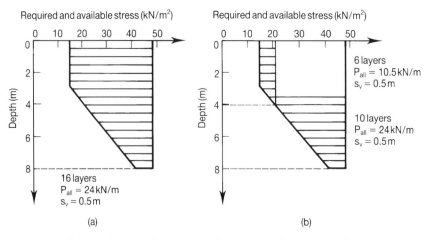

Figure 8.18 *Provision of available stress for the design example*

8.8.1 Comment on the method of slices

The local force equilibrium at the intersection of a failure surface through soil and the reinforcement material it contains was discussed in Section 4.1.

In the analysis with rigid body mechanisms, such as a single wedge or logarithmic spiral surface, there is no need for assumptions about the internal force equilibrium within the sliding mass. As soon as the sliding block is sliced, however, assumptions about the forces in the reinforcement layers crossing the slice boundaries have to be made. Even in the two-part wedge analysis, these assumptions significantly affected the calculated results (Jewell, 1989). More detailed study on the application of the method of slices to the analysis of reinforced soil is urgently required.

The common approach when adapting a method of slices to reinforced soil analysis has been to allocate the reinforcement force to the slice at the point of intersection

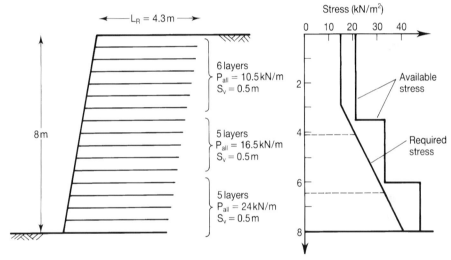

Figure 8.19 *Cross-section for the design example using all three reinforcement grids*

Table 8.2 Comparison of costs for reinforcement layouts

Index strength kN/m	Design 1 layers	Design 2 layers	Design 3 layers
80	16	10	5
55			5
35		6	6
Relative unit cost:	80	68	63
Saving over design 1:	0%	15%	21%

Note: Reinforcement costs are 5, 4 and 3 units respectively.

between the slip surface and the reinforcement layer (Figure 8.20). The effect of reinforcement layers crossing inter-slice boundaries is then ignored, and conventional assumptions are made as if the soil was unreinforced. As stated above, it is not yet known whether such assumptions are satisfactory.

Another point of difference is in the variety of ways that a *factor of safety* may be evaluated. To be consistent with the approach in this book, it is recommended that *design values* for the input parameters should be chosen and used directly in the analysis. This includes design values for the available reinforcement force, which is the lesser of the design strength or mobilised force due to bond. The objective is to ensure that equilibrium can be achieved on all potential failure mechanisms subject to the design loadings, and mobilising the design resistances.

By not seeking to evaluate a single 'lumped' factor of safety, the effect of inconsistencies caused by the different positions for the reinforcement force in the equilibrium equation is much reduced. In this book the reinforcement forces are considered to *increase the resistances* in the equilibrium equation rather than either (a) reducing the disturbing forces, or (b) being split between these two effects.

It is essential, therefore, that any analysis of reinforced soil by the method of slices should state clearly the assumptions made for:

- the allocation of reinforcement forces to slices
- the force equilibrium on the inter-slice boundaries
- the definition of any factor of safety (preferably computed using *design values* for the soil and the reinforcement properties, and the loadings), and
- the position of the reinforcement terms in the equilibrium equation (preferably they should *increase the resistances*).

8.9 Synopsis of Chapter 8

(1) The *steep slopes* considered in this chapter could not remain in equilibrium without reinforcement. The reinforcement of clay side-slopes to prevent shallow slips is considered in Chapter 9, and the case of near-vertical slopes, $\beta \geq 80°$, and retaining walls is considered in Chapter 10.

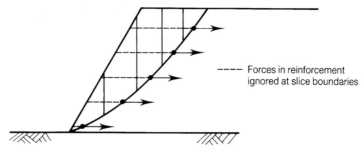

Forces in reinforcement
ignored at slice boundaries

Figure 8.20 *Illustration of the method of slices applied to reinforced soil*

(2) The *internal equilibrium* in a steep slope determines the *maximum required stresses* which govern the reinforcement strength and spacing.

(3) The reinforcement layers must extend sufficiently into the slope to maintain equilibrium on potential *overall* and *direct sliding* failure mechanisms, and these govern the reinforcement length.

(4) Reinforcement *bond* characteristics influence the internal and overall equilibrium, while *compaction stresses* influence the internal equilibrium. Allowance for these must be made.

(5) A separate analysis of *external equilibrium* for potential slip surfaces passing entirely around and beneath the reinforced soil zone is required.

(6) In very steep slopes, a separate analysis of *the bearing capacity* in the foundation immediately beneath the reinforced zone is required. This is illustrated in Chapter 10.

(7) A design procedure using *design charts* for steep reinforced slopes with a level crest, and resting on a level, competent foundation soil, has been described. The design charts are given in Figures 8.21 to 8.23 inclusive.

(8) More complex slopes require individual stability analysis using limit equilibrium methods. Care is needed in the assumptions made about the action of the reinforcement forces in the slope, and in the definition of safety factors.

Key references

Bishop, A.W. and Morgenstern, N. (1960). Stability coefficients for earth slopes. *Géotechnique*, Vol. 10, 129–150.

Jewell, R.A. (1989). Revised design charts for steep reinforced slopes. *Proc. Symp. Reinforced Embankments: Theory and Practice in the British Isles*. Thomas Telford, Cambridge.

Leshchinsky, D. and Boedecker, R.H. (1989). Geosynthetic reinforced soil structures, *ASCE Journal of Geotechnical Engineering*, Vol. 115, No. 10, October, 1459–1478.

Wroth, C.P. (1972). General theories of earth pressures and deformations. General Report. *Proc. 5th Int. Conf. on Soil Mechanics and Foundation Engineering*, Madrid, Vol. 2, 33–52.

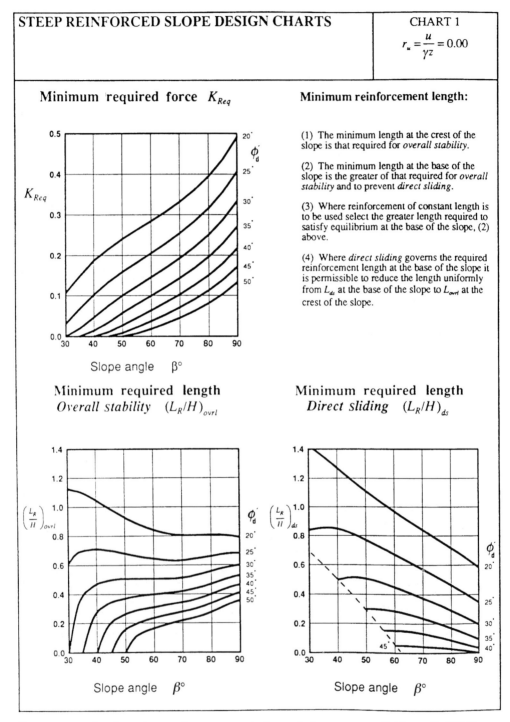

Figure 8.21 *Design chart 1 for steep reinforced slopes,* r_u = 0 *(Jewell, 1990)*

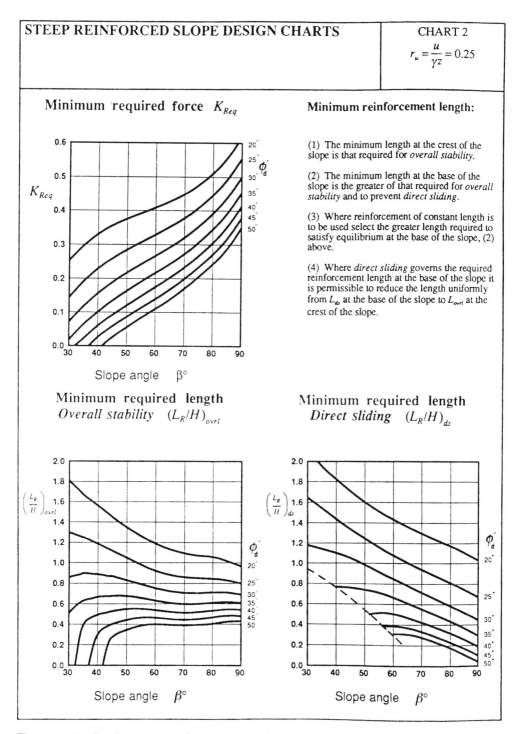

| STEEP REINFORCED SLOPE DESIGN CHARTS | CHART 2 $r_u = \dfrac{u}{\gamma z} = 0.25$ |

Minimum required force K_{Req}

Minimum reinforcement length:

(1) The minimum length at the crest of the slope is that required for *overall stability*.

(2) The minimum length at the base of the slope is the greater of that required for *overall stability* and to prevent *direct sliding*.

(3) Where reinforcement of constant length is to be used select the greater length required to satisfy equilibrium at the base of the slope, (2) above.

(4) Where *direct sliding* governs the required reinforcement length at the base of the slope it is permissible to reduce the length uniformly from L_{ds} at the base of the slope to L_{ovrl} at the crest of the slope.

Slope angle $\beta°$

Minimum required length
Overall stability $(L_R/H)_{ovrl}$

Minimum required length
Direct sliding $(L_R/H)_{ds}$

Slope angle $\beta°$

Slope angle $\beta°$

Figure 8.22 *Design chart 2 for steep reinforced slopes,* $r_u = 0.25$ *(Jewell, 1990)*

STEEP REINFORCED SLOPE DESIGN CHARTS	CHART 3
	$r_u = \dfrac{u}{\gamma z} = 0.50$

Minimum required force K_{Req}

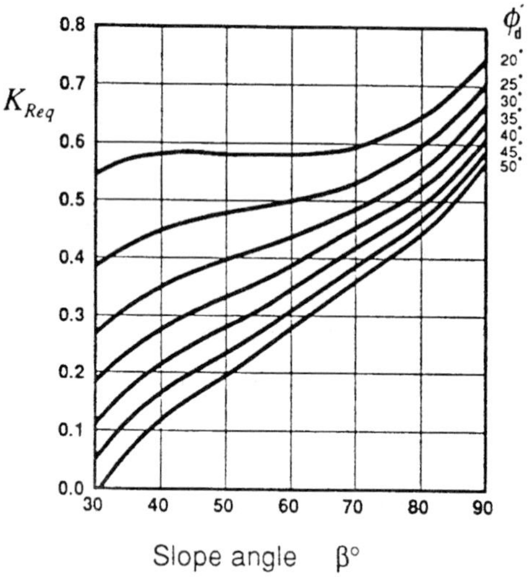

Slope angle $\beta°$

Minimum reinforcement length:

(1) The minimum length at the crest of the slope is that required for *overall stability*.

(2) The minimum length at the base of the slope is the greater of that required for *overall stability* and to prevent *direct sliding*.

(3) Where reinforcement of constant length is to be used select the greater length required to satisfy equilibrium at the base of the slope, (2) above.

(4) Where *direct sliding* governs the required reinforcement length at the base of the slope it is permissible to reduce the length uniformly from L_{d_s} at the base of the slope to L_{ovrl} at the crest of the slope.

Minimum required length
Overall stability $(L_R/H)_{ovrl}$

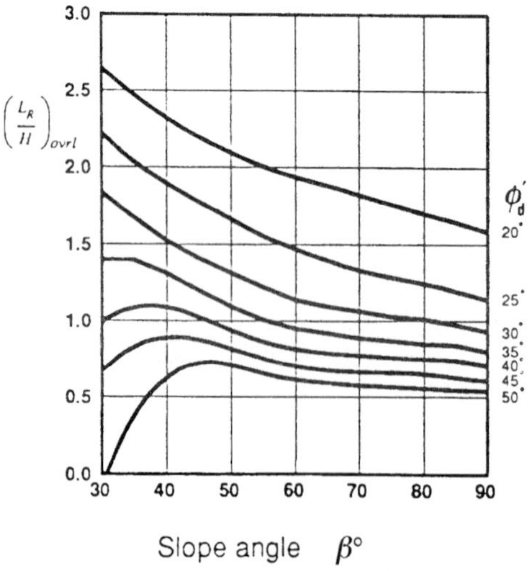

Slope angle $\beta°$

Minimum required length
Direct sliding $(L_R/H)_{ds}$

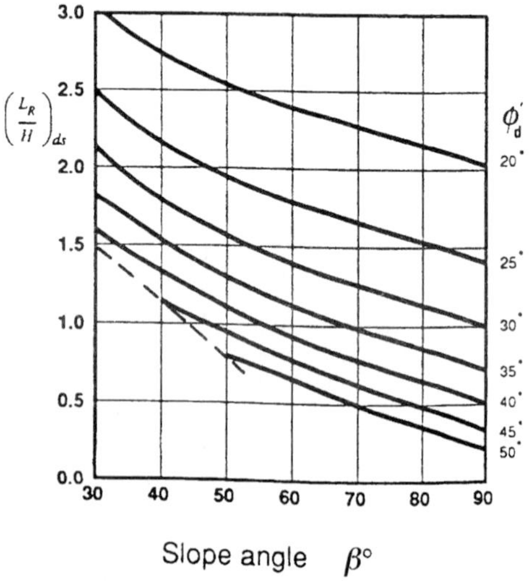

Slope angle $\beta°$

Figure 8.23 *Design chart 3 for steep reinforced slopes,* r_u = 0.50 (Jewell, 1990)

9 Reinforcement of shallow slips in clay embankments

The relatively widespread occurrence in the United Kingdom of shallow slope failures in highway embankments and cuttings formed from overconsolidated clays has been documented by Parsons and Perry (1985) and Perry (1989). These generally translational slides take place on shallow slip surfaces of the order 1.5m below the slope face (Figure 9.1a).

Two factors contribute to this instability. First, positive porewater pressures develop in the near-surface soil due to the ingress of water (Figure 9.1b). Second, the shearing resistance of the clay soil at low effective stress, after swelling with time, reduces progressively toward the fully softened or critical state strength. The effective field strength is significantly less than the values found from linear extrapolation of routine test data at higher stresses (Figure 9.1c).

Conventional limit equilibrium analysis allowing for these factors shows that much flatter (unreinforced) slopes would be required if the incidence of shallow slips is to be

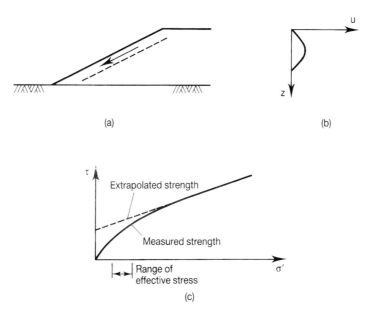

(a)   (b)

(c)

Figure 9.1 *Shallow slope failures in clay slopes: (a) slip surface, (b) near-surface porewater pressures, and (c) reduced shearing resistance at low effective stress*

reduced. This accords with the empirical recommendations based on field observation by Perry (1989).

Rather than adopt flatter side-slopes, an alternative is to improve the equilibrium at shallow depth, either by increasing the shearing resistance with reinforcement, or by reducing the near-surface porewater pressures through drainage measures.

It is the former solution, the use of geotextile reinforcement in the side-slopes of clay embankments, which is described in this chapter. The reinforcement is either included during construction, or incorporated during reconstruction following a slip.

Reinforcement may also be used to strengthen or stabilise cuttings, for example by installation of reinforcement *in situ*, known as soil nailing. This technique is not considered below because metal bars rather than geotextiles are currently used for soil nailing. It is to be expected, however, that the techniques and the materials for *in-situ* reinforcement will continue to be developed in the future and find application in the stabilisation of cuttings and slopes of the type discussed in this chapter.

The factors which control the long-term instability on shallow slip surfaces in clay embankments are considered in this chapter, and an analysis is introduced to take these into account. The focus is on London Clay slopes because much of the detailed field observation and laboratory test data at low effective stress are for this soil. Typical design layouts for geotextile reinforcement in the shoulders of clay embankments are then derived, and preliminary design charts given for standard cases.

The shallow instability in clay embankment shoulders considered here differs from the use of reinforcement in steep slopes described in Chapter 7. Clay embankment slopes are generally much flatter, typically $\beta < 30°$, and the critical instability is on shallow slip surfaces, and results from positive porewater pressures in the top 1 to 2m of soil and from progressive softening in the near-surface soil at low effective stress.

9.1 Factors causing instability

The high incidence of shallow slips in cuttings and embankments within 20 years of construction has been documented by Perry (1989). A rate of failure within 20 years of construction of the order 50% has been observed in Gault clay embankments higher than 5m and built with a side-slope $1:2.5$. The rate of failure for similar London Clay embankments is about 25%.

There are two main difficulties in predicting these long-term shallow slips.

1. Lack of data on the magnitude of porewater pressures in the near-surface zone of the slope at the point of instability, which is caused mainly by sustained moisture ingress from rainfall and from surface run-off.
2. Lack of knowledge about the strength characteristics of both *in-situ* and recompacted overconsolidated clays brought to failure at low effective stress after being allowed to swell.

There are other unknowns which might also contribute to long-term instability, including the effect of weathering on the properties of the clay soil in the upper 1 to 2m of the slope, the influence of fissuring on the clay strength, the role of 'progressive' failure, and construction aspects such as layering of the fill, the topsoil, the vegetation and the performance of slope drainage.

9.1.1 Porewater pressures

Greenwood *et al.* (1985) report details from some long-term slips in Gault and London clay embankments in Eastern England. Unlike slips in cuttings, embankment slips are rarely observed as they develop because embankment batters generally cannot be seen from the roadway. However investigation soon after failure typically reveals a very wet slipped mass with extremely soft soil in the back scarp. Slips are often found close to sources of water in highway embankments, such as leaking discharge pipes from carriageway drainage, or where the road sub-base extension intersects and drains into the embankment slope.

Measurement of the moisture content in the clay with depth at a slip in a Gault clay embankment slope showed relatively high moisture contents to a depth of 1.5m, coinciding with the observed planar slip surface (Greenwood *et al.*, 1985). Measurements of porewater pressure in a nine year-old London Clay embankment in which slip failure occurred indicated positive porewater pressures to some 1.5 to 2m below the slope surface (Atkinson and Farrar, 1985). Significant negative porewater pressure was measured in the remaining body of overconsolidated clay in the embankment. Similar distributions of porewater pressure have been found by Anderson and Neale (1980a and 1980b) and Crabb *et al.* (1987).

These field observations strongly suggest that in an ageing clay embankment there is a near-surface zone up to 2m thick which is thoroughly wetted and saturated after periods of sustained rainfall. In highway embankments, additional water may be supplied from carriageway drainage arrangements. Slips usually occur immediately following periods of sustained wet weather, often in the Spring, and are likely to be driven by positive porewater pressures.

9.1.2 Shearing resistance at low effective stress

Very low normal effective stresses of the order 15 to $30kN/m^2$ apply on shallow slip planes only 1 to 2m deep. This is much less than the range of stresses examined in standard laboratory testing.

There are few measurements on the shear strength of stiff clays which have been allowed to swell at very low effective stress. Such triaxial testing on London Clay has been carried out by Atkinson and Farrar (1985), with further results reported in Crabb and Atkinson (1991). Recompacted samples were tested under constant total stress while being subject to gradually increasing porewater pressure, to approximate the stress path followed in the side-slope of a clay embankment. The London Clay samples were obtained from a 12m high embankment with a $1:2$ side slope in Denham, Buckinghamshire, which had suffered shallow slip failures over 38% of its length within nine years of construction.

The measured envelope of peak shearing resistance was found to be highly non-linear at low effective stress (Figure 9.2). Shown for comparison is the linear Mohr-Coulomb envelope described by conventional parameters, $c' = 25\text{kN/m}^2$ and $\phi' = 16°$, determined by the standard drained triaxial compression testing for the project. The strength envelope measured by Atkinson and Farrar (1985) at low stress is similar to that deduced for London Clay by Bishop *et al.* (1965).

9.2 Analysis for shallow slips

9.2.1 Assumed porewater pressure

The measured porewater pressure distribution which develops with time in clay embankments, follows a pattern of a wetted zone in which increasing positive porewater pressures may act up to 1 to 1.5m below the slope surface, below which the porewater pressures reduce to zero by a depth of 2.5 to 3m at most. The rest of the overconsolidated clay fill in the embankment continues to experience negative porewater pressures.

The magnitude and distribution of the maximum porewater pressures measured at Denham could be described by a pore-pressure ratio in the range $r_u \approx 0.15$ to 0.20, where r_u is the ratio of the porewater pressure to the total vertical stress. Measured porewater pressures of the magnitude are reported by Anderson and Neale (1980a).

It is not clear whether higher transient porewater pressures might occur at shallow depth immediately following periods of sustained rainfall. Anderson and Neale (1980a) report tension cracks in embankment slopes filled with water following sustained rainfall, and this may be the case at failure. Vaughan *et al.* (1978) have measured higher maximum seasonal porewater pressures up to $r_u \approx 0.3$ to 0.4 in the near-surface zone of

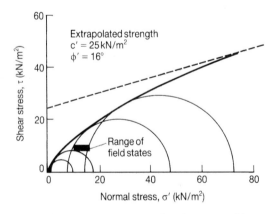

Figure 9.2 *Measured shearing resistance for London Clay at low effective stress (after Atkinson and Farrar, 1985)*

clay slopes, but only in the much flatter downstream slopes of embankment dams.

For the purpose of analysis, the porewater pressure distribution may be subdivided into three parts and described using the pore-pressure ratio r_u (Figure 9.3).

- constant r_u to a depth z_1
- linearly decreasing r_u with depth below z_1 reducing to zero at depth z_2
- constant and zero porewater pressure below z_2.

The field measurements on highway slopes indicate that a pore-pressure ration $r_u = 0.20$ gives a reasonably pessimistic assumption of the maximum porewater pressures at failure, varying with depth as $z_1 = 1.5$m and $z_2 = 2.5$m (Figure 9.3).

9.2.2 Slip surface geometry

The geometry of the slip surface assumed for the analysis is shown in Figure 9.4, and is similar to that used by Anderson and Neale (1980b). A tension crack filled with water is assumed to be present at the crest of the slope. The maximum depth of the water is assumed to be 1.5m or the depth of the crack, whichever is the lesser. The effective thrust on the vertical boundary with the lower wedge is assumed to act horizontally.

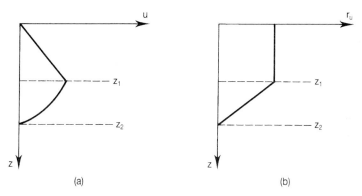

Figure 9.3 *(a) Maximum porewater pressure distribution in clay embankment side-slopes and (b) the idealisation for analysis*

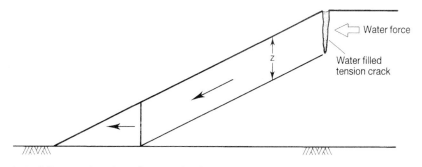

Figure 9.4 *Slip mechanism for analysis*

Comparative analyses show that the calculated factor of safety is relatively insensitive to the precise assumptions made in the limit equilibrium analysis. For example, the assumption of a horizontal exit angle for the toe wedge has only a second-order effect on the calculated factor of safety. Shallow *slip circles* between the base of the tension crack and the toe of the slope give almost identical results to the wedge mechanism. Thus the simple geometry shown in Figure 9.4 is considered adequate for the analysis of shallow translational slips.

9.3 Results for shallow slips

A standard case of a London Clay embankment with a $1:2$ side slope is examined by way of example. This case was selected because of the high incidence of failure within 10 to 20 years of construction for such embankments and because the measurements of soil strength at low effective stress are for London Clay. An embankment height of 6m is examined, but design charts are presented for slopes in the range 5 to 10m high.

9.3.1 Unreinforced case

The variation with depth of the mobilised shearing resistance required to just maintain equilibrium in the embankment slope (unreinforced) is summarised in Figure 9.5. The mobilised angle of friction, ϕ'_m, required to maintain equilibrium with depth in the slope is given for different values of mobilised effective cohesion ($c' = 0, 2, 4$ or $6kN/m^2$). This shows that a relatively small cohesion is sufficient to lower the most critically stressed zone in the soil to a depth of 1 to 2m.

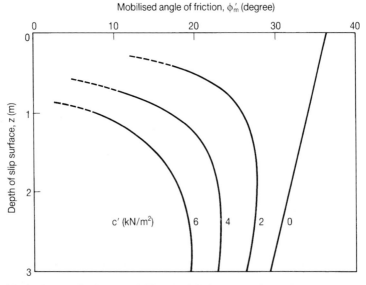

Figure 9.5 *Variation of the mobilised friction angle with depth to maintain equilibrium in a clay side-slope (6m high, 1:2 side slope, $r_u = 0.2$, $z_1 = 1.5m$, $z_2 = 2.5m$)*

The required shearing resistance for equilibrium in the slope may be represented as a 'resistance' envelope on a Mohr-Coulomb diagram. The two resistance envelopes shown in Figure 9.6 are of a maximum pore-pressure ratio, r_u = 0.2 (the standard case), and for a higher porewater pressure, r_u = 0.4, both varying with depth as before, (z_1, z_2).

The peak shearing resistance for the London Clay at low effective stress measured by Atkinson and Farrar (1985), and the fully softened or critical state shearing resistance, ϕ'_{cs} = 23°, are shown for comparison. The results show that the shearing resistance to maintain equilibrium in the clay (under the assumed conditions) is somewhat greater than the fully softened, critical state strength but less than the peak strength measured in short-term laboratory tests. This is reasonable because of the swelling and the weathering in the near-surface clay which are expected to reduce the shearing resistance with time.

In a recent paper, Crabb and Atkinson (1991) have used a simpler analysis than the one above to examine a wider range of observed shallow slip failures in clay embankments. They conclude that failure may occur simply through the clay softening to the critical state strength, with little or no positive porewater pressure.

9.3.2 Reinforced case: slip repair

The precise combination of the shear strength and the porewater pressure distribution in shallow slips is usually not known. It is sensible for design to examine a range of likely combinations of these to give failure in the *unreinforced* slope. A reinforcement layout may then be designed to boost the factor of safety by a desired amount. A factor of safety

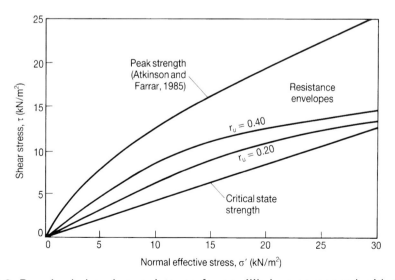

Figure 9.6 *Required shearing resistance for equilibrium compared with the peak and critical state shearing resistance of London Clay*

of the order $FS_s \approx 1.2$ to 1.3 in the *reinforced* side-slope (compared with $FS_s = 1.00$ without the reinforcement) is probably sufficient to guarantee the long-term stability on otherwise critical shallow slip surfaces (i.e. the reinforcement is included to secure equilibrium in the slope while only mobilising a shearing resistance, $\tan \phi'_m = \tan \phi'_f/FS_s$, where ϕ'_f is the mobilised value at failure in the unreinforced slope).

The results in Table 9.1 record the gross required reinforcement force per unit length of slope (a unit 1m width of the 6m high slope) needed to boost the factor of safety from unity in the *unreinforced* slope to $FS_s = 1.2$ or 1.3 in the *reinforced* slope. The analysis was carried out exactly as described above, and the results are for a 6m high embankment with a 1:2 slope. The soil strength in the *unreinforced* slope was found by scaling down the measured peak envelope for the London Clay (Figure 9.6) to achieve a minimum *unreinforced* factor of safety equal to unity for the chosen pore-pressure ratio. The gross required reinforcement force to boost the factor of safety in the *reinforced* slope was then calculated (Table 9.1). The unit weight of the soil was assumed to be $\gamma = 18\text{kN/m}^3$.

Comparing the results in Table 9.1 for $r_u = 0.2$ and 0.4, shows that the amount of reinforcement depends much more on the *degree of improvement* in stability than on the exact combination of soil shear strength and porewater pressure that caused failure in the unreinforced slope.

The corresponding required reinforcement lengths are reported in Table 9.2. These were calculated by assuming that the reinforcement must extend sufficiently into the

Table 9.1 Gross required reinforcement force (kN/m slope) to provide a factor of safety $FS_s = 1.2$ and 1.3

Porewater pressure	$r_u = 0.2$	$r_u = 0.4$
$FS_s = 1.2$	19.7kN/m slope	18.4kN/m slope
$FS_s = 1.3$	27.3kN/m slope	26.1kN/m slope

Soil strength adjusted so that $FS_s = 1.00$ with no reinforcement
Case examined 1:2 slope of 6m height

Table 9.2 Required reinforcement length to provide a factor of safety $FS_s = 1.2$ and 1.3

Porewater pressure	$r_u = 0.2$	$r_u = 0.4$
$FS_s = 1.2$	4.5m	4m
$FS_s = 1.3$	6m	5m

Soil strength selected so that $FS_s = 1.00$ with no reinforcement
Case examined 1:2 slope of 6m height

slope to intersect the deepest slip surface on which the *unreinforced* factor of safety was less than the minimum required factor of safety (FS_s = 1.2 or 1.3).

9.4 Design charts for side-slope reinforcement

A procedure to design reinforced side-slopes and slip repairs is to allow for the most pessimistic combination of soil shear strength and porewater pressure that could reasonably occur over the lifetime of the slope, and then select a reinforcement arrangement to just maintain equilibrium should the design situation actually arise.

No additional safety margin is introduced. The safety in the slope resides in the difference between the expected shearing resistance in the clay as opposed to the fully softened strength, and between the assumed porewater pressures and those which would normally apply. In the event that the clay should soften fully (in spite of the presence of reinforcement), and the assumed porewater pressures develop, the reinforcement would still just maintain the equilibrium.

Results to illustrate this design procedure are given in Figures 9.7 and 9.8. These are for standard 1:2 embankment slopes, a maximum pore-pressure ratio r_u = 0.20, a soil unit weight γ = 18kN/m^3, and slopes between 5 and 10m high.

Assuming a critical state strength ϕ'_{cs} = 23° for the London Clay, the results in Figures 9.7 and 9.8 indicate a required reinforcement force and length comparable with those giving a conventional factor of safety FS_s = 1.3 (Section 9.3.2).

The results may be used as preliminary design charts for standard 1:2 clay embankment slopes in the United Kingdom where the choice of a pore-pressure ratio

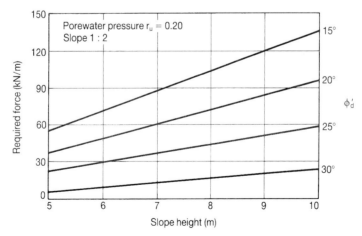

Figure 9.7 *Gross required reinforcement force for combinations of slope height and design angle of friction (slope 1:2, r_u = 0.2, z_1 = 1.5m, z_2 = 2.5m)*

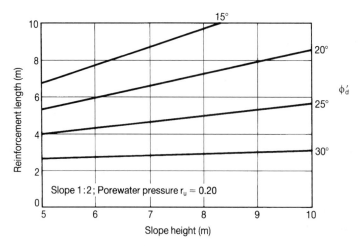

Figure 9.8 *Required reinforcement length for combinations of slope height and design angle of friction (slope 1:2, r_u = 0.2, z_1 = 1.5m, z_2 = 2.5m)*

r_u = 0.2 should be sufficiently pessimistic for most cases. The charts are expressed in terms of a design angle of friction for the clay which should be selected by considering the effects of progressive softening and weathering in the clay soil at shallow depth. (The fully softened, critical state strength is recommended for most cases.)

The limit equilibrium wedge analysis may be repeated for other embankment slope angles and porewater pressure conditions.

9.4.1 Contrast with steep slopes

The differences between the reinforcement of clay embankment side-slopes described above, and the reinforcement of steep slopes discussed in Chapter 8 need to be highlighted.

The main differences are (1) the slope angle, typically $\beta < 30°$ for clay embankment side-slopes while $\beta > 30°$ for steep slopes, and (2) the distribution of porewater pressure, which is positive only near the slope surface in embankment side-slopes while it is assumed to develop throughout the soil fill in steep slopes. A water-filled tension crack is included in the analysis of embankment side-slopes.

The most critical feature is the relatively shallow depth over which positive porewater pressures develop in embankment side-slopes. This confines the instability to relatively shallow slip mechanisms, whereas more deep-seated slips occur in steep slopes. The net effect is that the gross required reinforcement force and the required reinforcement length to maintain equilibrium in clay embankment side-slopes (Figures 9.7 and 9.8) are much less than those required in equivalent steep slopes with the same slope angle, design angle of friction and maximum pore-pressure ratio.

9.5 Selection of reinforcement

9.5.1 Reinforcement types and materials

Polymer grids and woven geotextiles are both suitable types of reinforcement to carry long-term load and provide adequate bond with the clay soil in an embankment shoulder. The procedures described in Chapter 6 to determine the long-term design strength for the reinforcement should be followed. This requires the influence of time under load and exposure to the environment to be taken into consideration, together with the mechanical damage to the reinforcement caused by construction. The design strength is likely to be a relatively small proportion of the short-term index strength for the material.

When design is based on a fully softened strength in the clay, the maximum acceptable elongation in the reinforcement is governed by serviceability considerations. A maximum allowable reinforcement elongation of the order 5% should result in outward face deflections no greater than 100 to 150mm for typical slopes.

9.5.2 Reinforcement layout

It is recommended that the reinforcement in embankment shoulders should be uniformly distributed, as equally spaced layers of uniform strength. The reason is that the required reinforcement force for equilibrium increases (approximately) linearly with the height of the slipping slope for shallow, planar slips at an approximately fixed depth. This is in marked contrast to the steep-slope case where the volume of slipping soil, and the magnitude of required reinforcement force to maintain equilibrium on critical slip surfaces, increases in proportion to the square of the slope height. In the latter case the reinforcement should be more closely spaced with depth in the slope for a balanced design.

A practical vertical spacing for reinforcement layers in embankment side-slopes is of the order 0.3 to 1m, and at least five layers of reinforcement should normally be used in a slope. Intermediate, short layers of less strong reinforcement may be included at the face at closer spacing, to boost the available reinforcement force near the slope face which is restricted by the low effective streses in the soil (Figure 9.9). The use of such intermediate layers is more practical for construction compared with a wrap-around

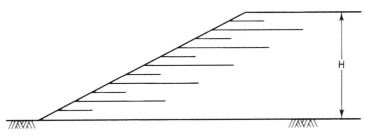

Figure 9.9 *Typical reinforcement arrangement in a clay embankment side-slope*

facing. Closely spaced reinforcement at the slope face may also improve the compaction which can be achieved.

9.5.3 Reinforcement bond

The variation of the required and maximum available reinforcement force in a clay side-slope is illustrated in Figure 9.10. The results are for the standard 6m high embankment with 1:2 side-slope analysed previously, strengthened by six layers of reinforcement extending 6m into the slope.

The variation of the required force along the reinforcement is calculated by dividing equally the gross required reinforcement force on trial slips at different depths between the six reinforcement layers. The available bond force in each layer was calculated assuming a bond coefficient $\alpha_b = 0.7$.

The results in Figure 9.10a are for the case where $r_u = 0.2$ and a factor of safety $FS_s = 1.3$ (Table 9.1), and in Figure 9.10b for the same porewater pressure conditions but with the fully softened shearing resistance in the clay $\phi_{cv} = 23°$, and no additional factor of safety (i.e. the design chart case with $\phi'_d = \phi'_{cs}$).

There is an excess of available bond in the reinforcement under the combination of parameters in the first analysis (Figure 9.10a), but when the fully softened strength of the clay is assumed to act, and for the chosen vertical spacing 1.0m, bond becomes a critical

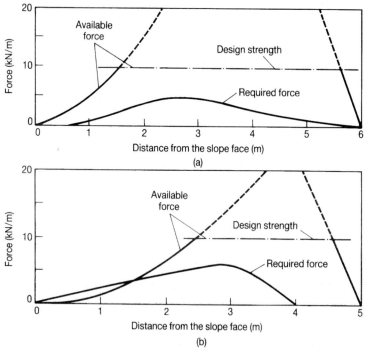

Figure 9.10 *Envelopes of required and available force in reinforcement layers for a 1:2 side-slope*

factor in the initial 1.5m length of reinforcement close to the face of the slope (Figure 9.10b). However, this is remedied simply by (a) adopting a closer spacing for the reinforcement, as $s_v = 1.0$m is at the top of the recommended range (Section 9.5.2), or (b) including intermediate short lengths of reinforcement at the face (Figure 9.9).

9.6 Construction expedients

To repair a shallow slip in the side-slope of a clay embankment using reinforced soil, it is often necessary to choose a sequence of excavation and reinstatement to minimise the risk of triggering further slip failures, and to improve the wet clay soil for handling and compaction purposes.

Murray (1985) has described methods to deal with these problems. Overall stability can be maintained by excavating and reinstating the slipped soil mass sequentially in strips, each perhaps 5 to 10m wide, minimising soil handling by using the excavated material from the 'next' strip for the reinstatement of the 'current' strip. The excavation is generally cut in steps. Where environmentally acceptable, quicklime can be effective when intermixed with set clay soil to improve handling and compaction, but may lead to a more rapid chemical degradation in polymer reinforcement materials.

9.7 Design example

Use the preliminary design charts to select a reinforcement layout to prevent the development of shallow slips in the shoulder of an 8.5m high embankment to be built from London Clay with a 1 : 2 side slope. The required design life for the slope is 50 years.

The fully softened shearing resistance for the clay may be assumed to be $\phi'_{cv} = 23°$, and the maximum porewater pressure in the slope is given by the pore-pressure ratio, $r_u = 0.2$, acting to a depth 1.5m, and reducing to zero by a depth 2.5m, as described in Section 9.2.

A polymeric grid reinforcement is to be used with an extrapolated rupture strength, $P_{Ref_{t_d},T_d} = 10$kN/m, at 50 years and 20°C. The reinforcement is compatible with the soil environment at the site. Allowing for mechanical damage, $f_d = 1.2$, environmental degradation, $f_{env} = 1.1$, and a material factor, $f_m = 1.5$, leads to a design strength $P_d = 5$kN/m (Section 6.4). If this design force were supported for 50 years at 20 °C the resulting cumulative elongation in the reinforcement would be approximately 6%.

Pullout tests on the reinforcement indicate that the bond between the reinforcement and the clay exceeds 70% of the shearing resistance of the clay. A value for the bond coefficient $\alpha_b = 0.7$ is assumed for design.

For a slope of height 8.5m, and clay fill with a design angle of friction $\phi'_d = 23°$, the gross required reinforcement force for equilibrium is $P_{Req} = 60$kN/m, from Figure 9.7. The required reinforcement length is $L_R = 6$m, from Figure 9.8.

The design cross-section in Figure 9.11 contains 12 uniformly spaced layers of the polymeric reinforcement at a vertical spacing s_v = 0.7m (i.e. 12 × 5kN/m = 60kN/m and 8.5m/12 = 0.7m).

If a cheaper reinforcement material were to be considered then 21 layers spaced at s_v = 0.4m would demand a design strength at the end of the design life just less than P_d = 3kN/m.

9.8 Synopsis of Chapter 9

   (1) Shallow slip failures which develop some years after construction have been identified as a significant problem for clay embankment side-slopes constructed in highway earthworks in the United Kingdom.
   (2) Two likely causes of such instability are (a) significant positive porewater pressure in the top 1 to 2m of clay below the slope surface, and (b) relatively low shearing resistance in the near-surface zone due to progressive weathering and softening of the clay.
   (3) Reinforcement provides an effective solution which can maintain equilibrium without requiring the slope angle to be reduced. The reinforcement may be included as part of the earthworks construction, to prevent subsequent instability, or in the repair of slips.
   (4) Design charts are provided for 1 : 2 embankment side-slopes and for the typical porewater pressures which have been observed. Separate limit equilibrium analysis is required for other combinations of slope angle and porewater pressure.
   (5) Similar shallow instability takes place in cuttings in uniform stiff clays. Reinforcement provides an effective solution for the repair of such slips. Design should take into account the specific geometry of the cutting, the lithology of the cut soil and the porewater conditions in the slope. These are likely to be more complex than the typical embankment case considered in this chapter.

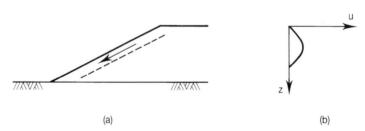

(a)   (b)

Figure 9.11 *Reinforcement layout for the design example*

Key references

Atkinson, J.H. and Farrar, D.M. (1985). Stress path tests to measure soil strength parameters for shallow landslips, *Proc. XII Int. Conf. on Soil Mechanics and Foundation Engineering*. San Francisco, Vol. 4, pp 983–986.

Crabb, G.I. and Atkinson, J.H. (1991). Determination of soil strength parameters for the analysis of highway slope failures, *Slope Stability Engineering*. Thomas Telford, London.

Greenwood, J.R., Holt, D.A. and Herrick, G.W. (1985). Shallow slips in highway embankments constructed of overconsolidated clay. *Failures in Earthworks*. Thomas Telford, London, pp. 79–92.

Perry, J. (1989). A survey of slope condition on motorway earthworks in England and Wales. *Research Report 199*. Transport and Road Research Laboratory, Crowthorne.

10   Retaining walls

The combination of metal strips and good quality granular fill used to build retaining walls faced with concrete panels first established reinforced soil as a successful technique.

Polymer reinforcement materials were introduced to mitigate corrosion, but their lower stiffness and tendency to creep initially cast doubt on their applicability for reinforced soil wall construction. However, *polymer grid* and encased *polyester strip* reinforcement soon found application in wall projects and gained Agrément certification. More recent developments include walls combining modular block facing and grid reinforcement, and open faced 'loop-anchor' walls (Figure 10.1).

Steel-strip reinforced walls provided the focus for the early research. The design methods that were developed for such structures have been gradually reappraised with the increasing use of polymer reinforcement and as knowledge of reinforced soil behaviour has improved. Today, for example, the fundamental influence of the reinforcement's extensibility is much more clearly understood. The design calculations presented in this chapter build on well established principles, but are intended for polymer reinforcement materials, and are presented in the format used throughout this book.

The reinforcement layout found from such analysis for a wall, with a level crest and resting on a competent foundation, is essentially identical to that found for the equivalent 'vertical slope' following the design procedures in Chapter 8. It is the influences of

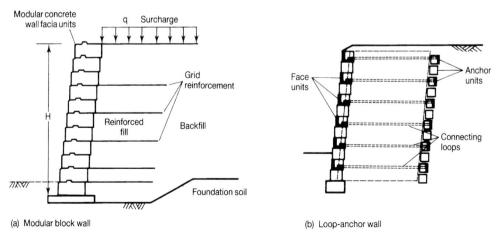

(a) Modular block wall   (b) Loop-anchor wall

Figure 10.1 *Two examples of reinforced soil wall systems*

externally applied concentrated-loads, of the foundation bearing capacity, and of structural deformation at the wall face that provide the focus for the design of polymer-reinforced soil walls. Also, the consequences of failure in a retaining wall are likely to be more serious than for a steep slope (Section 6.1.2).

The case of walls with a level crest, retaining level backfill and supporting vertical surcharge loads, is considered first (Figure 10.2). Design equations and solutions for wall displacement can be derived for these structures, as indicated in the text. The extension of the analysis to allow for concentrated loads and inclined backfill is then described.

A more complex nomenclature is required to allow different soils for the reinforced fill, the retained backfill and the foundation soil (Figure 10.2). For each soil there will be a peak angle of friction, ϕ'_p, a large strain angle of friction, ϕ'_{cv}, and an angle of friction selected for design, ϕ'_d (see Chapter 5).

However, only the design angle of friction is utilised in the equations below, denoted as ϕ'_{rd}, ϕ'_{bd} and ϕ'_{fd} for the *reinforced* fill, the *backfill* and the *foundation* soil respectively. The active earth pressure coefficient corresponding to the design angle of friction is denoted by the symbol, K_{ar}, for the *reinforced* fill, and, K_{ab}, for the *backfill*.

10.1 Summary of design steps

Design follows the sequence described for steep reinforced slopes (Figure 10.3). Typically, the wall *stability* is considered first (the *ultimate* limit state calculations), after which the *expected deformations* are checked (the *serviceability* limit state calculations).

As described in Chapter 7, the routine calculation for serviceability is made by choosing a *maximum allowable elongation* in the reinforcement from which a

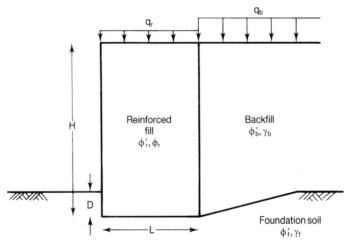

Figure 10.2 *Definitions for reinforced soil walls*

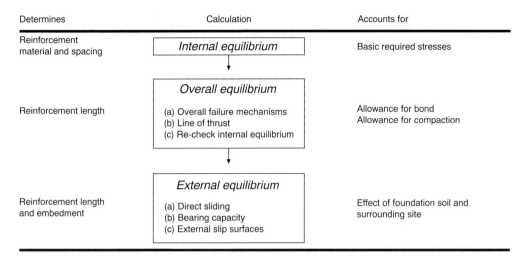

Determines	Calculation	Accounts for
Reinforcement material and spacing	**Internal equilibrium**	Basic required stresses
Reinforcement length	**Overall equilibrium** (a) Overall failure mechanisms (b) Line of thrust (c) Re-check internal equilibrium	Allowance for bond Allowance for compaction
Reinforcement length and embedment	**External equilibrium** (a) Direct sliding (b) Bearing capacity (c) External slip surfaces	Effect of foundation soil and surrounding site

Figure 10.3 *Summary of steps in the design of reinforced soil walls*

serviceability strength can be found (Section 7.3). The equilibrium analysis is repeated to demonstrate a satisfactory equilibrium when the *design values* for *serviceability* apply. As indicated above, the wall deflection due to elongation of the reinforcement layers may be estimated using chart solutions for walls with a level crest.

In this book, *internal equilibrium* is examined first to determine the selection of the reinforcement material and the spacing (assuming an adequate length). The minimum required length of the reinforcement is then found by considering *overall equilibrium* on potential failure mechanisms passing through the reinforced fill and the unreinforced backfill.

The ability of the foundation soil to support the inclined and eccentric loading at the base of the reinforced zone is then checked. If found to be inadequate, the reinforced zone may be embedded deeper into the foundation soil and/or the reinforcement length increased. More complex solutions such as ground modification or piling may be needed where such measures are insufficient.

A final check is required on potential failure mechanisms passing entirely around the reinforced zone. Problems with *external equilibrium* may be caused by changes in the site geometry, or groundwater conditions, due to the reinforced soil construction.

Once an adequately stable reinforced soil wall has been found, the expected deflections may be estimated. These develop during construction and subsequently from progressive creep and settlement during the life of the structure.

Three factors which contribute to face deflections are:

1. deformation in the reinforced zone caused by elongation in the reinforcement layers

2. deflections caused directly by construction activities, including 'slackness' in the reinforcement or connections
3. displacement and consolidation settlement in the foundation caused by the fill loading.

Construction methods and foundation displacements can be as great a cause of wall deflection as elongation in the reinforcement.

10.2 Internal equilibrium: idealised case

For walls with a level backfill, subject to uniform vertical surcharge but no concentrated loads, and where the wall facing panels do not contribute to the stability (the standard design assumption, Section 10.7.3), then *stress analysis* after the fashion of Rankine (1857) and *wedge analysis* as in Coulomb (1773) lead to exactly the same solution for the required stresses for internal equilibrium (Figure 10.4). This is for the case where equilibrium in the soil is maintained by horizontal reinforcement layers.

For this case, the *most critical mechanism* through the toe (for internal equilibrium) is a plane wedge at an angle, $\theta = 45 + \phi'_{rd}/2$ to the horizontal, which defines a region of high reinforcement forces behind the wall face, *zone 1*, the area *OCF* in Figure 10.4c. The gross, maximum required force for internal equilibrium above a depth, z, is

$$(P_{Req})_z^i = K_{ar}\left(\frac{\gamma_r z^2}{2} + q_r z\right) \qquad\qquad ...(10.1)$$

where the unit weight, γ_r, the design angle of friction, ϕ'_{rd}, and the active earth pressure coefficient, $K_{ar} = (1 - \sin \phi'_{rd})/(1 + \sin \phi'_{rd})$, are for the reinforced fill, and there

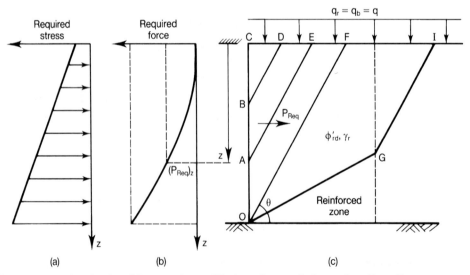

Figure 10.4 *Analysis of internal equilibrium in a reinforced soil wall*

are no porewater pressures in the soil. Equation (10.1) defines a required stress, σ_{Req}, which increases linearly with depth in the fill (Figure 10.4a).

For a balanced equilibrium, the vertical and horizontal reinforcement *spacing*, (s_v, s_h), and *design strength*, P_d, should be selected to provide an *available stress*, $\sigma_{Av} = P_d/s_v s_h$ which exceeds the maximum *required stress* at every depth in the soil (Figure 10.5).

10.3 Overall equilibrium

While *internal equilibrium* sets the maximum required stresses to be resisted by the reinforcement, *overall equilibrium* governs the required reinforcement length. The three main considerations for *overall equilibrium* are described below.

10.3.1 Overall failure mechanisms

The reinforcement must have sufficient length to maintain stability on potential overall failure mechanisms passing through the reinforced zone into the retained backfill (Figure 10.6a). The two-part wedge mechanism shown, with a smooth, vertical inter-wedge boundary coinciding with the back of the reinforced zone, is suitable for the analysis of overall equilibrium (Section 10.7.1). The gross *required* and *available reinforcement forces* determined on such trial mechanisms may be plotted opposite the point of intersection with the back of the reinforced zone (Figure 10.6b).

The *design values* of the parameters are used in the analysis (Section 6.1.2). The lesser of the *design strength* or the maximum force allowed by *bond* (in the bond length) should be used for each reinforcement layer, depending on the point where the reinforcement is intersected by the potential slip surface (see Figures 10.6 and 10.7).

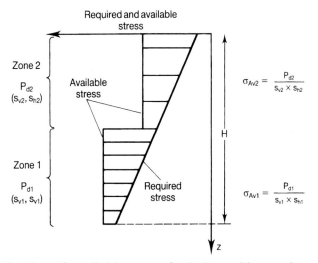

Figure 10.5 *Distribution of available stress for balanced internal equilibrium*

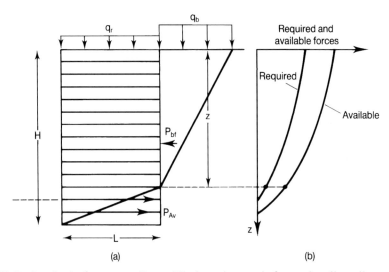

Figure 10.6 *Analysis for overall equilibrium in a reinforced soil wall*

The analysis of mechanisms passing through the toe of the wall normally yields the most critical results. However, overall failure mechanisms passing through the face of the wall at other elevations should be considered. (Potential failure mechanisms passing behind and below the reinforced zone are checked when examining *external equilibrium*, Section 10.5.)

The forces acting in the two-part wedge analysis of overall equilibrium are summarised in Figure 10.8. It is assumed that the unreinforced backfill attains a uniform active state, and that the resultant thrust, P_{bf}, acts horizontally on the back of the reinforced zone. The equations for this analysis are given in Section 10.3.3.

10.3.2 Allowance for bond and load-shedding

The bond length at the end of each reinforcement layer means that a lesser force than the *design strength* is mobilised in the layers intersected in the bond length (Figure 10.7). As

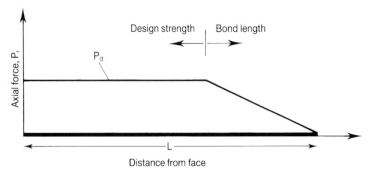

Figure 10.7 *Maximum available force in a reinforcement layer*

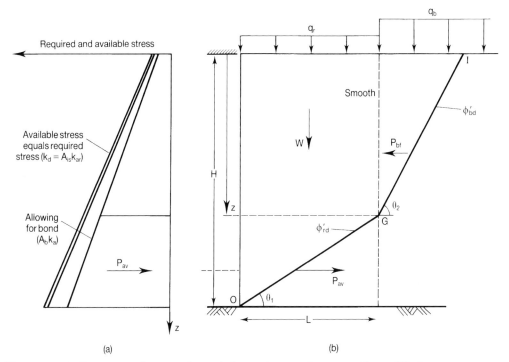

Figure 10.8 *Forces acting on the reinforced zone for overall equilibrium*

described for steep slopes (Section 8.2.1), the net effect of bond on overall equilibrium is to reduce the maximum available reinforcement force (number of layers intersected multiplied by the design strength) by an almost constant proportion, irrespective of the angle, θ_1, of the trial wedge mechanism. The lesser available force allowing for bond may be defined as $P_{Av} = A_b P_R$, where P_R is the gross available force (ignoring bond), and the coefficient, A_b (≤ 1), is the bond allowance.

A simple, slightly conservative expression for the bond allowance is, $A_b = 1 - L_B/L_R$, where, L_R, is the reinforcement length and, L_B, is the bond length for the layer at the base of the wall. This equation was introduced in Section 8.2.1, where the bond length, L_B, was defined by Equation (8.2), repeated below in terms of the wall height, H, rather than the effective height, $H' = H + q_r/\gamma_r$,

$$\frac{L_B}{H} = \left(\frac{P_d}{2W_r\gamma_r H^2 (1 + q_r/\gamma_r)} \right) \left(\frac{1}{1 - r_u} \right) \left(\frac{1}{\alpha_b \tan \phi'_{rd}} \right) \quad \text{...(8.2 bis)}$$

Although they have been allowed for, porewater pressures are typically assumed to be negligible in the free-draining granular fill commonly used for wall construction, $r_u = 0$.

Compared to a satisfactory reinforcement layout found without consideration for bond, either the reinforcement length has to be increased, or the reinforcement spacing has to be reduced, to maintain the same level of overall stability when allowing for bond.

The latter approach is often convenient, and the reinforcement spacing is selected to provide a higher design stress, $K_d = A_{ls}K_{ar}$, than strictly needed for *internal equilibrium*. The basic required stress for *internal equilibrium* is, K_{ar}, and the coefficient, A_{ls} (≥ 1), is called the load-shedding (or load-sharing) allowance (Figure 10.8). In this approach, the detrimental effect of bond can be compensated by a load-shedding allowance, $A_{ls} = 1/A_b$, so that the reinforcement length can be set equal to the value found from an analysis for *overall equilibrium* which ignores bond.

The advantage of this approach is that charts for reinforcement length can be derived which apply irrespective of the bond characteristics of the reinforcement material, as in the charts for steep slope design (Section 8.3.1). The detrimental effects of bond are compensated for by reducing the required spacing of the reinforcement layers. Also, it allows reasonably simple analytical expressions to be given for the required reinforcement length for *overall equilibrium* (see below).

The coefficients for the bond and the load-shedding allowances, A_b and A_{ls}, have been included in the design equations for walls (Equation 10.4) to allow other, alternative solutions to the one described above to be investigated. In the case above, $A_bA_{ls} = 1$.

10.3.3 Equations for overall equilibrium

Although the forces acting on a trial mechanism (as in Figure 10.8) are well defined, an analytical solution which gives the most critical mechanism directly has not been found, and a numerical search is still needed. Thus equations for the *required* and the *available forces* on trial mechanisms through the toe (intersecting the back of the reinforced zone at depth z), must be used to find, by trial and error, a reinforcement length to give an acceptable overall equilibrium at all depths (Figure 10.6b). This can be simply accomplished on a spreadsheet, for example.

The *required* reinforcement force for equilibrium on the wedge mechanism *OGI* in Figure 10.8 (for example) must resist the load exerted by the unreinforced backfill, P_{bf}, and maintain equilibrium on the plane wedge *OG*, subject to the vertical load from the soil self-weight and applied surcharge $(W + q_rL) \tan(\theta_1 - \phi'_{rd})$. The resulting expression for the gross *required force* for equilibrium on a trial wedge at an angle to the horizontal, ϕ_1, is

$$\left(\frac{P_{Req}}{\gamma_r H^2}\right)_{ovrl} = K_{ab}\frac{z}{H}\left(\frac{1}{2}\frac{\gamma_b}{\gamma_r}\frac{z}{H} + \frac{q_b}{\gamma_r H}\right)$$

$$+ \frac{L}{H}\left(\frac{1}{2}\left(1 + \frac{z}{H}\right) + \frac{q_r}{\gamma_r H}\right)\tan(\theta_1 - \phi'_{rd}) \qquad ...(10.2)$$

where the subscript, $()_{ovrl}$, indicates the case for *overall stability*, and where

$$\tan \theta_1 = \left(\frac{1 - z/H}{L/H}\right) \qquad \text{...(10.3)}$$

The gross *available force* is

$$\left(\frac{P_{Av}}{\gamma_r H^2}\right)_{ovrl} = A_b A_{ls} K_{ar}\left(1 - \frac{z}{H}\right)\left(\frac{1}{2}\left(1 + \frac{z}{H}\right) + \frac{q_r}{\gamma_r H}\right) \qquad \text{...(10.4)}$$

The above forces should be checked over the full range of possible values, θ_1, to find a reinforcement length to satisfy the design requirement

$$\left(\frac{P_{Av}}{P_{Req}}\right)_{min} \geq 1.0 \qquad \text{...(10.5)}$$

as discussed in Chapter 7 (Figure 10.6b). As usual, the design values for all the parameters should be used in the analysis.

10.3.4 Line of thrust in the reinforced zone

In more detailed analysis, the line of thrust within the reinforced zone should be examined for trial mechanisms of the type illustrated in Figure 10.8, to demonstrate that satisfactory moment equilibrium can be achieved in the reinforced zone.

The forces and the eccentricity of the resultant thrust, R, acting on the base of a trial wedge through the reinforced soil are shown in Figure 10.9 for a wall with no surcharge.

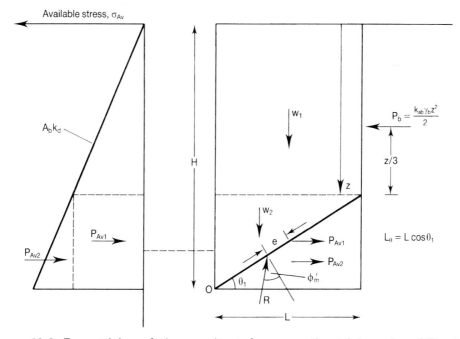

Figure 10.9 *Eccentricity of the resultant force on the trial wedge OG, at an angle θ*

The conventional criterion for satisfactory equilibrium is adopted, that the resultant thrust should remain within the central (or middle) third of the base of any trial wedge.

The general equations for moment equilibrium may be derived from the forces shown in Figure 10.9. Unfortunately, these do not produce a simple closed form, and the pattern of results is shown in Figure 10.10, for the case of zero porewater pressure, and equal properties in the reinforced fill and backfill.

The eccentricity of the resultant force, R, for a wall with no surcharge, is plotted in Figure 10.10a as a function of the depth, z, of the trial wedge (Figure 10.9), and for a range of trial reinforcement lengths, L/H. The results are for the case $\phi'_{rd} = \phi'_{bd} = 35°$.

The eccentricity is expressed in terms of the length of the inclined trial wedge, L_θ, and the permissible range is $+1 \geq 6e/L_\theta \geq -1$. The line of thrust for the case of the minimum required reinforcement length to meet the central third criterion, ($L/H = 0.52$), is illustrated in Figure 10.10b.

The finding is that eccentricity (or moment equilibrium) is most critical at the base of the reinforced zone, $\theta_1 = 0°$ (Figure 10.10b). But the eccentricity also reaches a limiting value on plane wedges through the toe which do not intersect the back of the reinforced zone, such as the plane OJ in Figure 10.10b.

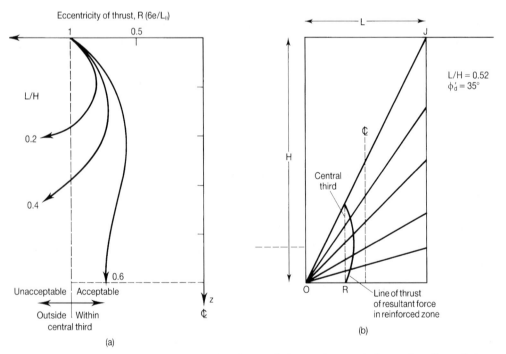

Figure 10.10 *Results to illustrate the line of thrust in a reinforced soil wall (case with $\phi'_d = 35°$ and no surcharge)*

For a level backfill, and equal reinforced fill and backfill properties, and for zero surcharge and zero porewater pressure, the minimum required length to meet the central third criterion is

$$(L/H)_{min} = \sqrt{K_{ab}} \qquad\qquad ...(10.6)$$

which happens to equal exactly the required reinforcement length to just contain the most critical wedge mechanism for *internal equilibrium*, $\theta_1 = 45 + \phi'_{rd}/2$, which may be expressed as

$$(L/H)_{min} = \sqrt{K_{ar}} \qquad\qquad ...(10.7)$$

In the general case, allowing for surcharge loads and different properties in the reinforced fill and backfill, the minimum required reinforcement length to meet the central third criterion is

$$\left(\frac{L}{H}\right)^2_{ecc} = K_{ab}\left(\frac{\gamma_b}{\gamma_r} + \frac{3q_b}{\gamma_r H}\right)\bigg/\left(1 + \frac{q_r}{\gamma_r H}\right) \qquad\qquad ...(10.8)$$

The worst case is when the surcharge above the reinforced zone is set to zero $q_r = 0$, and this is the usual design assumption.

10.3.5 Minimum required length for overall equilibrium

To illustrate the analyses above, some results comparing the minimum required length for *overall equilibrium* (Section 10.3.3) and *moment equilibrium* (Section 10.3.4) are illustrated in Figure 10.11. The case is for a wall with a level backfill, zero porewater pressure, equal soil properties in the reinforced fill and the backfill, $\phi'_{rd} = \phi'_{bd} = \phi'_d$, and a reinforcement spacing chosen to balance exactly the influence of bond and load-shedding, $A_{ls} = 1/A_b$ (Section 10.3.2). The effect of any surcharge on the backfill is expressed in terms of the non-dimensional parameter, $q_b/\gamma_r H$.

Where the foundation stability permits, satisfactory overall equilibrium can be achieved with shorter reinforcement lengths than given in Figure 10.11a. This is done by including much more reinforcement in the wall than strictly required for internal equilibrium, in other words using a high load-shedding allowance, $A_{ls} \gg 1/A_b$. However, the results in Figure 10.11b show that reduction of the reinforcement length in this way leads quickly to unsatisfactory moment equilibrium with implied tension on inclined planes towards the base of the reinforced zone.

Practically, there is often much less control on the backfill soil used and its compaction, but this influences significantly the *overall equilibrium*. The results in Figure 10.12 illustrate the point, and apply for walls with a level backfill, but now the design angle of friction in the backfill has a value 5° less than in the reinforced fill, $\phi'_b = \phi'_{rd} - 5°$. The effect of surcharge loading on the backfill is indicated.

In summary, the results indicate for reinforced soil walls comprising granular fill and backfill that the minimum reinforcement length for *overall and moment equilibirum* is of the order, $0.7 \geq L/H \geq 0.5$.

10.4 Internal equilibrium: practical corrections

Two practical corrections to the idealised *internal equilibrium* are required to allow for *bond* and *compaction stresses*, as described previously for steep slopes (Section 8.3). The same corrections apply for walls and, again, it is the minimum required stress to

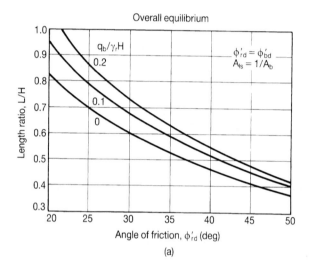

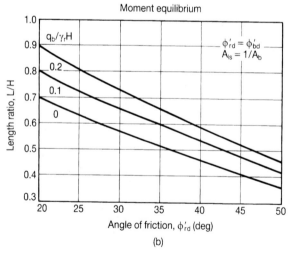

Figure 10.11 *Minimum reinforcement length for balanced equilibrium (case: $\theta'_{bd} = \theta'_{rd}$, $\gamma_b = \gamma_r$, level backfill, and $A_{ls} = 1/A_b$)*

allow for compaction that usually dominates the internal equilibrium at shallow depth (Equation 8.7). A prescriptive value, $\sigma_{comp} = 15kN/m^2$, for the minimum stress for internal equilibrium is recommended. The value to be used may be checked once the compaction equipment has been selected using Equation 8.7.

Although it can be argued that with time polymeric reinforcement materials may creep and hence relieve any locked-in compaction stresses, it is normally not onerous to satisfy the 'short-term' required stress due to compaction. Practical factors influence the choice of the reinforcement material and spacing near the crest of reinforced soil wall, which often leads to sufficient reinforcement near the crest of the wall to resist the effects of

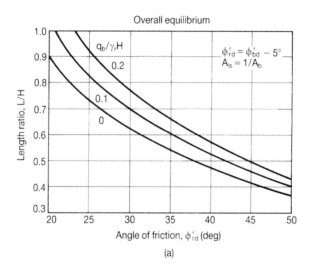

Overall equilibrium

(a)

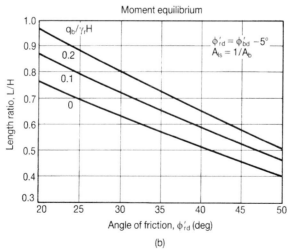

Moment equilibrium

(b)

Figure 10.12 *Minimum reinforcement length for balanced equilibrium (case: $\theta'_{bd} = \theta'_{rd} - 5°$, $\gamma_b = \gamma_r$, level backfill, and $A_{ls} = 1/A_b$)*

bond and compaction without any further adjustment. This is illustrated in the design example (Section 10.8).

In the case where external concentrated loads are applied directly to the reinforced zone, it is necessary to carry out a separate wedge analysis to check the internal equilibrium, as described in Section 10.9.

10.5 External equilibrium

The undesirable design situations for external equilibrium are foundation failure beneath the reinforced soil wall and possible slip failure entirely around the reinforced structure. These were outlined in Chapter 7 (Figures 7.5 and 7.6), and lead to the four main checks on external equilibrium:

1. direct outward sliding of the reinforced zone over the foundation
2. excessively eccentric loading at the base of the reinforced zone
3. bearing capacity failure in the foundation beneath the reinforced zone
4. external failure on slip mechanisms passing around the reinforced zone.

10.5.1 Direct sliding

The required reinforcement length to prevent *direct sliding*, $(L/H)_{ds}$, for a wall with a level backfill (Figure 10.13) is

$$\left(\frac{L}{H}\right)_{ds} = \frac{K_{ab}}{\alpha_{ds} \tan \phi'_d} \left(\frac{\gamma_b}{2\gamma_r} + \frac{q_b}{\gamma_r H}\right) \qquad \qquad ...(10.9)$$

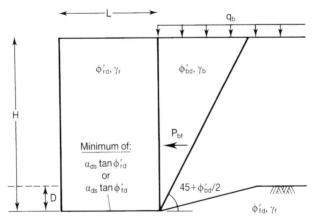

Figure 10.13 *Direct sliding at foundation level*

where *design values* for the parameters are used, and the active earth pressure coefficient $K_{ab} = (1 - \sin \phi'_{bd})/(1 + \sin \phi'_{bd})$. The lesser resistance of the fill, ϕ'_{rd}, and the foundation, ϕ'_{fd}, is adopted for the resistance to direct sliding, $\tan \phi'_d$. An appropriate value for the coefficient, α_{ds}, should be used for direct sliding between the reinforcement and the fill or the foundation soil.

The above analysis is recommended even where the reinforced zone is embedded in the foundation to a depth, D. Any lateral (passive) resistance that could be provided is disregarded to allow for the risk of a trench being dug adjacent to the toe of the wall.

Where the required length to resist direct sliding is greater than that for a balanced overall equilibrium (Section 10.3), the longer length, $(L/H)_{ds}$, must be adopted lower in the wall. The reinforcement length may be reduced higher in the wall to the lesser value found for overall equilibrium. However, the depth, z/H, at which the reinforcement length may be reduced must be chosen (a) to avoid direct sliding higher in the wall, and (b) to guard against a combined mechanism involving direct sliding over a shorter length at the base of the wall (Figure 10.14).

To avoid direct sliding in the reinforced fill where the reinforcement length is reduced to L/H, the change should be made no deeper than

$$\left(\frac{z}{H}\right)_1 = \frac{2\alpha_{ds} \tan \phi'_{rd}}{K_{ab}} \frac{\gamma_r}{\gamma_b} \left(\frac{L}{H}\right) - \frac{2q_b}{\gamma_b H} \qquad ...(10.10)$$

To resist the combined mechanism involving direct sliding on the shorter length, L/H, at the base of the wall (Figure 10.14) the reinforcement length should be reduced at a depth less than

$$\left(\frac{z}{H}\right)_2 = \sqrt{1 - \frac{2\alpha_{ds} \tan \phi'_d}{A_b K_d} \frac{(L_{ds} - L)}{H}} \qquad ...(10.11)$$

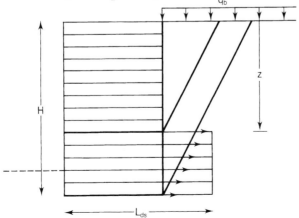

Figure 10.14 *Possible direct sliding mechanisms when* $L_{ds} > L$

Equation (10.11) is suitable for preliminary design purposes, but the influence of bond on the equilibrium in this case may be greater than determined from the standard bond allowance, A_b (Section 10.3.2). In detailed design, the bond allowance should be found by considering each individual reinforcement layer intersected.

Direct sliding on clay foundation soils
When a reinforced soil wall is founded on clay soil, possible direct sliding at the *end of construction due to undrained shear* across the surface of the foundation soil should be considered (the *drained case being analysed* as described above). Equation (10.9) is modified in this case,

$$\left(\frac{L}{H}\right)^u_{ds} = \frac{K_{ab}}{\alpha_{ds}}\left(\frac{\gamma_b H}{2s_{ud}} + \frac{q_b}{s_{ud}}\right) \qquad \qquad ...(10.12)$$

where s_{ud} is the design value for the undrained shear strength of the foundation, and the superscript, $(\ )^u$, represents the *undrained analysis*.

10.5.2 Excessive eccentricity
To satisfy *overall equilibrium*, the reinforcement length was chosen to maintain the resultant thrust at the base of the reinforced zone within the central third. This ensures satisfactory moment equilibrium for the foundation (Section 10.3.4).

10.5.3 Bearing capacity
The bearing capacity at the base of a reinforced soil wall may be analysed as an equivalent strip footing of effective width, $\bar{L}$ (Figure 10.15). The force resultants which

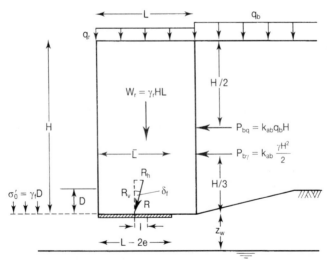

Figure 10.15 *Equivalent foundation for the analysis of bearing capacity*

act on the foundation are due to the surcharge and self-weight loading in the fill, and from the thrust of the retained backfill. As usual, *design values* for all the properties and loadings should be used.

The loading can be fully described in terms of the resultant vertical force, R_v, and horizontal force, R_h, which act at an eccentricity, e, from the centreline. The combined loading acts at an inclination, $\tan \delta_f = R_h/R_v$.

The equations for the analysis of foundation bearing capacity are given in Section 5.4. The loading at the base of the reinforced zone (Figure 10.15) may be compared with that on a strip footing (Figure 5.18). For the case of a reinforced soil wall with level backfill and uniform surcharge load (Figure 10.15), the forces acting at the base of the reinforced zone are:

$$\frac{R_v}{\gamma_r HL} = 1 + \frac{q_r}{\gamma_r H} \qquad \qquad ...(10.13)$$

$$\frac{R_h}{\gamma_r HL} = \frac{K_{ab}}{(L/H)} \left(\frac{q_b}{\gamma_r H} + \frac{1}{2} \frac{\gamma_b}{\gamma_r} \right) \qquad ...(10.14)$$

$$\frac{e}{H} = \frac{K_{ab}}{2(L/H)} \frac{((q_b/\gamma_r H) + (\gamma_b/3\gamma_r))}{(1 + (q_r/\gamma_r H))} \qquad ...(10.15)$$

$$\tan \delta_f = \frac{K_{ab}}{(L/H)} \frac{((q_b/\gamma_r H) + (\gamma_b/2\gamma_r))}{(1 + (q_r/\gamma_r H))} \qquad ...(10.16)$$

Two of the limiting cases discussed earlier may be found from the above equations. The reinforcement length for the limiting eccentricity, $e/L = 1/6$, (Equation 10.8), may be recovered from Equation (10.15). Similarly, the reinforcement length for incipient direct sliding, $\tan \delta_f = \alpha_{ds} \tan \phi'_d$, (Equation 10.9), may be found from Equation (10.16).

The analysis for bearing capacity is illustrated by the design example in Section 10.8.

Undrained bearing capacity for clay

For a reinforced soil wall on a clay foundation, the short-term, *undrained* bearing capacity should be considered in addition to the long-term, *drained* bearing capacity. The same loads act on the foundation (Equations 10.13 to 10.16) and the equations for undrained bearing capacity are given in Section 5.5.

In broad terms, *the undrained* case should be carefully considered where $\gamma_r H/s_{ud} > 2$, while *drained* bearing capacity would normally govern where, $\gamma_r H/s_{ud} < 2$.

10.5.4 External stability

Conventional methods of stability analysis are used to examine the equilibrium on potential slip mechanisms passing entirely around the reinforced zone. The analysis for *external stability* is needed to check that the planned earthworks will not disturb the general stability, and a variety of possible failure mechanisms should be examined using conventional slope stability methods.

The analysis also provides an additional check on foundation bearing capacity when potential failure mechanisms of the form shown in Figure 10.16a are examined. These may be compared with the mechanism implied by the analysis of local bearing capacity described in Section 10.5.3 (Figure 10.16b).

10.6 Deformation of walls

Progress has been made in the analysis of deformation in reinforced soil walls caused by the elongation in the reinforcement, and for the progressive horizontal and vertical displacements at the crest of a reinforced soil wall due to creep in the reinforcement.

However, wall displacements can be influenced significantly by other factors, such as the immediate and consolidation deformation in the foundation, and the analysis for these other components of displacement is beyond the scope of this book.

10.6.1 Deformation of the reinforced fill

Charts for estimating the deformation in reinforced soil walls caused by elongation of the reinforcement layers were derived by considering the *internal* and the *overall* equilibrium described in the previous sections. The analysis and the resulting charts for horizontal and vertical wall displacements may be found in Jewell and Milligan (1989). The charts agree reasonably well with the field measurements where sufficient data allows back analysis, and with the behaviour of the instrumented walls reported by Jarrett and McGown (1988).

The latter walls enabled a second source of displacement caused by the incremental nature of wall construction to be identified. During construction, initially unstressed layers of reinforcement higher in the wall are incorporated into an already deforming structure. In other words, the initial position of the ends of the unstressed reinforcement

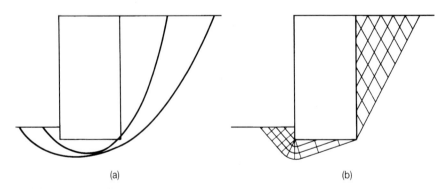

(a)   (b)

Figure 10.16 *Check on foundation stability: (a) bearing capacity analysis, and (b) analysis of external slip mechanisms*

layers is not on the initial (planned) alignment of the face. (The exception is the wall built with a full-height facing panel that is firmly propped during filling, thereby controlling the initial position of the reinforcement layers, Section 10.7.3.)

In practice, the *influence of construction* is counteracted by initially tilting the facing panels backward towards the fill. The exact measures and construction procedures adopted significantly affect the face deflection.

The analytical solutions for wall displacement due to reinforcement elongation are useful (a) to assess the need for construction measures, such as the tilting of facing panels, to provide good alignment of the wall face, and (b) to estimate the progressive wall displacements caused by creep in the reinforcement, or subsequent loading by surcharge.

A simplified chart of *maximum horizontal displacement* for walls built with granular fill, $\phi'_{cv} = 32°$, and uniformly spaced reinforcement, is given in Figure 10.17. The maximum horizontal displacement, δ_{max}/H, is expressed in terms of a maximum reinforcement elongation, P_{base}/J, and the mobilised angle of friction in the fill, ϕ'_{rm}. The mobilised reinforcement force at the base of the wall is defined as,

$$P_{base} = (K_{ar})_m s_v s_h (\gamma_r H + q_r) \qquad ...(10.17)$$

where $(K_{ar})_m$ is the active earth pressure coefficient in the reinforced fill for the mobilised angle of friction. The secant stiffness for the reinforcement, J, should reflect the time period over which it has been subject to load (Section 2.3.2).

Limits to the likely wall displacements can be found by examining different mobilised shearing resistances in the fill, as discussed in Section 7.3.1. For granular fill, the

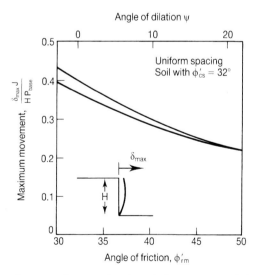

Figure 10.17 *Chart for maximum horizontal movement in reinforced soil walls (after Jewell, 1990)*

maximum likely displacements are found by assuming that only the critical state angle of friction is mobilised, $\phi'_{rm} = \phi'_{cv}$, while the *minimum* likely displacements would occur if the peak shearing resistance of the fill were mobilised, $\phi'_{rm} = \phi'_p$.

Calculation of deflection

To calculate the displacement due to elongation in the reinforcement, chose a mobilised angle of friction for the fill and determine the value, $\delta_{max}J/HP_{base}$, from Figure 10.17. The maximum wall deflection, δ_{max}/H, depends on the secant stiffness of the reinforcement, J, and the mobilised reinforcement force, P_{base}, calculated from Equation (10.17).

To evaluate the creep displacement, simply calculate the deflection for two values of reinforcement stiffness, J, to represent conditions at the beginning and end of the loading period. The difference between the two calculated deflections is the displacement due to creep. (In practice, the strain in the soil caused by creep in the reinforcement could enable a higher soil friction angle to be mobilised, and thereby reduce the required reinforcement force and the corresponding additional elongation below that envisaged above.)

If an increment of uniform vertical surcharge, Δq_r, is applied to the wall, the resulting increase in reinforcement force will cause a corresponding displacement at the wall face. Again, the incremental displacement is found from the difference between the total displacement with and without the surcharge loading.

Only the maximum horizontal displacement is given in Figure 10.17, but the corresponding maximum settlement, δ_y/H, at the crest of the wall (due to elongation in the reinforcement) is normally of the same order as, or just less than, the horizontal displacement, δ_{max}/H. More detailed analysis of both horizontal and vertical displacement may be made using the charts given in Jewell and Milligan (1989).

10.6.2 Deformation caused by foundation movement

Conventional methods of assessing foundation displacement need to be used, such as the analysis for foundations on granular soils by Burland and Burbidge (1984). The influence of short-term undrained displacements and consolidation settlements should be considered for loading on clay foundations.

The consolidation settlement at the back of the reinforced zone can exceed the settlement at the toe of the wall, the edge of the loaded region (Figure 10.18). This can cause the face of the wall to 'tip backward' into the fill, as discussed by Jones and Edwards (1980).

It is important to recognise that the final vertical alignment of the face of a reinforced soil wall depends on at least four separate factors, namely:

1. the deformation caused by elongation in the reinforcement
2. the deformation caused by alignments during construction
3. the immediate, undrained displacement in the foundation, and

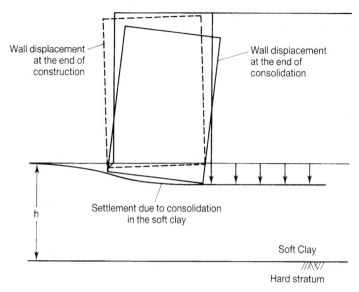

Figure 10.18 *Resultant wall displacements following consolidation*

4. the consolidation settlement in the foundation caused by the loading from the reinforced fill and the backfill.

10.7 Practical aspects influencing design

10.7.1 Thrust from the backfill

In the analysis for walls it has been assumed that the backfill exerts a horizontal thrust on the back of the reinforced zone, equivalent to the thrust on a smooth retaining wall. In most cases, allowing for roughness on this boundary, so that the thrust from the backfill would be angled *downward*, would enhance the equilibrium. But equally, if the thrust from the backfill were angled *upward* it would lead to a more critical equilibrium (O'Rourke and Jones, 1990).

The assumption of a horizontal thrust is made for two main reasons.

First, the assumption of a thrust from the backfill angled *downward* implies that the backfill soil moves downward with respect to the reinforced zone. But as shown from the analysis of foundation displacement, it is far from clear that this should be the case, *a priori*, particularly once the influence of consolidation settlement in the foundation is considered (Section 10.6.2, Figure 10.18). Likewise, the foundation might contain a layer of compressible soil deeper beneath the back of the reinforced zone than at the toe, again implying a 'backward' rotation caused by consolidation settlement.

Second, the analysis for reinforced soil using a full two-part wedge mechanism (Section 8.1) shows the critical planes are angled from the vertical, and that the *assumption* of a vertical inter-wedge boundary is a simplification for design.

Given these uncertainties, it is prudent not to rely on a more advantageous inclination of the thrust from the backfill than the horizontal direction. Indeed a detailed justification should be given if a more advantageous assumption is to be made.

10.7.2 Connections

There is a need to connect the reinforcement to the facing in most reinforced soil walls, whether multiple panels, modular blocks or full-height facing units are used. Two important design considerations are (a) an allowance for *relative vertical displacement* between the settling reinforced fill and the facing (which is often relatively incompressible and stiffened at the base by a small footing), and (b) detrimental factors reducing the *strength or durability* of the connection with the face. These considerations are inter-related, since the development of a stress concentration at the connection due to relative settlement could cause rupture in the reinforcement.

In general, the reinforced soil zone will settle to some extent with respect to the wall facing, and the connection should allow for adequate relative vertical displacement. This may be achieved with a sliding connection, and a variety of connection details are available (Jones, 1988). An alternative is to allow the face to 'settle' with the fill by incorporating compressible materials in joints between facing units, to allow them to 'concertina' together.

The reinforcement strength may be reduced locally at the connection with the facing. This could be caused by mechanical damage, for example at the frictional/shear connection of reinforcement with modular blocks (Figure 10.19a), or stress concentration where a joint is made with the reinforcement material wrapped around a shear connector (Figure 10.19b).

Because of the variable influence of construction, it is not considered reliable in design to assume that the force in the reinforcement at the connection with the face will always be less than at some distance away from the face. Indeed, any relative settlement

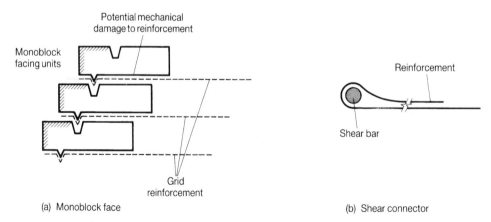

(a) Monoblock face   (b) Shear connector

Figure 10.19 *Connections at the face (a) Monoblock face (b) Shear connector*

between the fill and the face potentially could cause a 'stress concentration' in the reinforcement at the connection with the face. Thus whatever detail is used, the appropriate *design strength* used in the calculation of *internal equilibrium* should be the lesser of the strength at the joint or in the main reinforcement material.

10.7.3 Full-height facing

The use of a full-height facing can significantly affect the behaviour of reinforced soil walls compared with walls with flexible facing, such as panel or 'wrap-around' facing.

First, if a full-height face is propped externally while the reinforced fill is being placed and compacted, the props only being removed near the end of filling, this largely eliminates the component of displacement due to construction (Section 10.6.1).

Second, full-height facing normally has a significant rigidity and strength to inhibit potential failure mechanisms passing out through the face of the wall. Stresses from the fill can be transmitted to the face causing significant vertical and horizontal forces to be transmitted through the face to the underlying foundation soil (Figure 10.20). These forces can greatly increase stability, thereby reducing the amount of force that must be provided by the reinforcement layers.

Thus full-height facing can provide a structural role and contribute to the stability of reinforced soil. However, to perform such a structural role, special measures must be taken to ensure that the necessary forces can be transmitted reliably from the face to the foundation. Unless such measures are taken, the possibility that a trench may be dug adjacent to the toe of the wall should always be considered (Figure 10.20). The reinforcement would have to support the extra load caused by the loss of support for the face.

In general, the appropriate assumption for ultimate limit state design is to ignore the contribution to stability derived from the face. However, account can be taken in

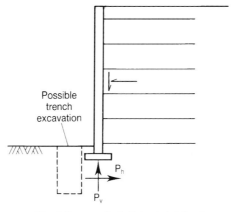

Figure 10.20 *Forces transmitted through full-height facing*

serviceability calculations of the extra stiffness provided by the face. This applies equally to reinforced soil walls with other facings.

10.8 Design example for a retaining wall

10.8.1 Data and design values

Note that while the calculated results have been rounded-off to an appropriate accuracy, the underlying value, rather than the rounded-off value, has been carried forward in the calculation (i.e. as in a spreadsheet). This can cause small discrepancies between the quoted results and those calculated using the rounded-off values.

Slope details

A retaining wall up to 5m high is to be included in the landscaping of a housing development. A stone-faced (modular block) wall has been chosen to provide an attractive finish. The facing blocks are 200mm high, 500mm wide and 400mm deep and are designed to stack at a gradient $10:1$, $\beta = 84°$. The soil will be reinforced by polymer grids, and the structure is to be designed as a vertical wall. The 5m height includes for embedding the wall 0.3m, so that the base of the monoblock face, and of the reinforced backfill, is 0.3m below final ground level.

Site investigation reveals a predominantly medium dense, sandy Thames gravel. SPT values of 27 to 40 blows/300mm, and direct shear tests on samples recompacted to the field density, indicate that the peak strength of the gravel is about $48° \geq \phi'_p \geq 45°$. The large strain angle of friction measured in direct shear tests is $\phi'_{cv} \approx 33°$.

The large strain angle of friction is selected to represent the strength of the foundation soil for *ultimate limit state* calculations, $\phi'_{fd} = 33°$. (This gives a similar mobilised angle of friction for design as would apply if a conventional factor of safety, $FS_s = 1.5$, were applied to a representative peak angle of friction for the soil, $\phi'_p = 45°$, as discussed in Section 5.2.2.) The minimum expected unit weight of the foundation soil is $\gamma_f = 19\text{kN/m}^3$, and the highest estimated water table is at 10m below ground level. Both these parameters are used directly in design.

An imported granular fill will be used for construction. Compaction to 95% of the maximum dry density gives an expected bulk density for the fill, $\gamma = 21\text{kN/m}^3$. Compacted by this amount in a shear box, the peak angle of friction was measured to be $49° \geq \phi'_p \geq 46°$ for applied stresses in the range $150\text{kN/m}^2 \geq \sigma'_v \geq 50\text{kN/m}^2$, relevant to the reinforced fill and backfill. The large strain angle of friction was measured to be not less than $\phi'_{cv} = 33°$.

For *ultimate limit state* calculations, the critical state angle of friction for the fill is selected for design, $\phi'_{rd} = 33° = \phi'_{bd}$, together with a slightly higher than expected soil density, $\gamma_r = \gamma_b = 22\text{kN/m}^3$.

A nominal uniform surcharge $q_r = q_b = 10\text{kN/m}^2$ is assumed for design to allow for temporary over-filling, and other variable surcharges. A prescriptive allowance for compaction stress is assumed, $\sigma_{comp} = 15kN/m^2$, and the compaction equipment will be chosen not to exceed this value (Section 10.4).

Reinforcement details

A design life of 50 years is chosen for the wall, and a design temperature *in the ground* 20°C is considered appropriate. Polymer reinforcement grids are to be used, and a partly frictional, partly dowelled connection for the reinforcement between the facing blocks, coupled with protection measures for the reinforcement, allows the full *design strength* in the reinforcement to be developed at the facing.

Three grids are offered, and the manufacturer recommends the following allowances for degradation, $f_d = 1.35$ and $f_{env} = 1.15$, to allow for the soil, and the effects of construction and the environmental conditions at the site (Sections 2.5 and 6.4). Extrapolation of the material properties data by 1 $\log_{10}$ cycle of time is required to reach the design life, and a material factor, $f_m = 1.50$, is chosen following the guidance in Table 6.1. The characteristic value of the *index* and *reference strength* supplied by the manufacturer for each product and the *resulting design strength* are summarised in Table 10.1.

When the grids are subjected to a force equal to the design strength (Table 10.1) for a 20-day period they exhibit a cumulative elongation of about 2%. The estimated total cumulative elongation under this load by the end of the design life is 3%. The appropriate values for the reinforcement stiffness for serviceability are given in Table 10.2.

The constituent material of the polymer grids has a coefficient of skin friction, $\tan \delta = 0.6 \tan \phi'$, and all three grids have a similar geometry, $\bar{a}_s = 0.35$, and, $S/\bar{a}_b B = 30$, (Section 4.4). The coefficient of direct sliding may be calculated as, $\alpha_{ds} = 0.21 + 0.65 = 0.86$, from Equation (4.3). The bearing stress ratio in the reinforced fill is, $\sigma_b'/\sigma_n' = 8.8$, from Equation (4.8), and the bond coefficient is, $\alpha_b = 0.21 + 0.19 = 0.40$, from Equation (4.6).

Table 10.1 Characteristic strengths for the reinforcement grids in kN/m. ($t_d = 50$ years and $T_d = 20°C$)

Index strength kN/m	Reference strength $(P^{Ref}_{lim})_{t_d T_d}$	Field strength $(P_{field})_{t_d T_d}$	Design strength P_d
70	42	27	18
50	30	19	12.5
30	18	11.5	7.5

Notes: Characteristic index and reference strength from manufacturer.
Field strength for degradation $f_d = 1.35$ and $f_{env} = 1.15$.
Material factor $f_n = 1.50$ for 1 $\log_{10}$ cycle of extrapolation.
Strengths rounded-down to nearest 0.5kN/m.

Table 10.2 Characteristic stiffnesses of the reinforcement grids in kN/n. (t_d = 50 years and T_d = 20°C)

Index strength kN/m	End of construction $J_{500 \text{ hours, } 20°C}$	Design life $J_{50 \text{ years, } 20°C}$
70	900	600
50	640	430
30	390	260

Notes: Stiffness is serviceability strength over cumulative elongation.
Stiffness rounded to nearest 10kN/m.

Limit states

Deformation for this wall is not critical and a maximum allowable elongation in the reinforcement, 5%, over the design life of the structure is considered acceptable for serviceability. This elongation is greater than would be caused by a force equal to the design strength (3%, see above) and so the *serviceability strength* for the reinforcement is limited by the *design strength*. Thus the reinforcement layout will be governed by the *ultimate* limit state analysis (see Section 6.4.1).

The expected deformations for the wall will be calculated using the reinforcement stiffness values listed in Table 10.2.

The main design steps below follow the flow chart in Figure 10.3.

10.8.2 Design steps (*ultimate limit state*)

Internal equilibrium

Earth pressure coefficient   The earth pressure coefficient for the reinforced fill is K_{ar} = 0.295, Equation (10.1).

There are various ways to proceed with design. In this example, the effects of bond and load-shedding will be matched, A_{ls} = $1/A_b$, as recommended in Section 10.3.2. The bond allowance is normally quite small for grid reinforcement, and thus only a nominal value for the load-shedding allowance, A_{ls} = 1.1 will be assumed initially. Once the reinforcement layout has been selected, the bond allowance can be checked to insure that sufficient load-shedding has indeed been allowed. The design can be revised if necessary.

A provisional value for the load-shedding allowance, A_{ls} = 1.1, is assumed initially (see above). The design value for the earth pressure coefficient is then, K_d = $A_{ls}K_{ar}$ = 0.324.

Required stress   The distribution of *required stress* for internal equilibrium is shown in Figure 10.21, allowing for the surcharge,

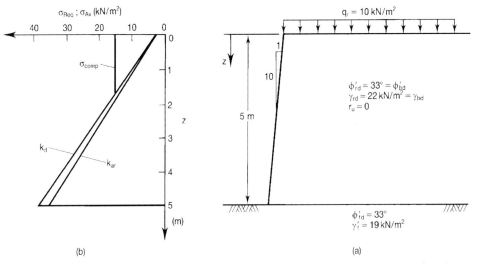

(b)   (a)

Figure 10.21 *Design example: wall details and required stresses for internal equilibrium*

Reinforcement selection

$q_r = 10\text{kN/m}^2$, and the minimum stress due to compaction, $\sigma_{comp} = 15\text{kN/m}^2$.

The maximum required stress at the base of the wall is $(\sigma_{Req})_{max} = 0.324 \times (5 \times 22 + 10)$ or $(\sigma_{Req})_{max} = 38.9\text{kN/m}^2$. The 200mm high facing units set the possible vertical spacings for the reinforcement $s_v = 0.2\text{m}, 0.4\text{m}$ and 0.6m. The range of *available design stress* provided by the reinforcement grids at these spacings, and the depth z_{max} below the slope crest to which the spacings apply, are summarised in Table 10.3.

Table 10.3 Available stress from reinforcement, σ_{Av} in kN/m^2, and the maximum permissible depth for each reinforcement below the crest, z_{max} in m

Index strength P_{index}	Spacing $s_v = 0.2\text{m}$		Spacing $s_v = 0.4\text{m}$		Spacing $s_v = 0.6\text{m}$	
	σ_{Av}	z_{max}	σ_{Av}	z_{max}	σ_{Av}	z_{max}
70	90.1	12.1	45.1	5.8	30.0	3.7
50	64.4	8.5	32.2	4.0	21.4	2.5
30	38.6	4.9	19.3	2.2	12.8	1.3

Notes: Design strength from Table 10.1.
Available stress P_d/s_v, for continuous layers.
Maximum allowable depth $z_{mm} = (P_d/K_d\gamma_v s_v) - (q_r/\gamma_r)$.
Available stresses and maximum depths rounded-down.

Trial layout

A practical choice is to use one reinforcement material at different spacings to match the required and available stresses. The reinforcement layout can be found by drawing, starting from the base of the wall. The grid with the intermediate strength, P_{index} = 50kN/m, would require a layout with the first seven layers spaced at s_v = 0.2m, the next four layers at s_v = 0.4m and the final three layers at s_v = 0.6m, giving a total 14 layers (Figure (10.22a).

In a detailed design study, the benefits of other reinforcement arrangements would be examined. For example, the use of the stronger grid, P_{index} = 70kN/m, would require a layout with five layers spaced at s_v = 0.4m, and five more layers spaced at s_v = 0.6m (Figure 10.22b).

Bond length

The bond length at the base of the wall for the reinforcement with an index strength, P_{index} = 50kN/m, with uniform width, W_r = 1m, is L_B/H = 0.044, from Equation (8.2) (Section 10.3.2).

Overall equilibrium
Overall failure mechanisms

The design charts for steep slopes described in Chapter 8 may be used for an initial assessment of the minimum length for overall stability (Figure 8.21). For a design angle of friction,

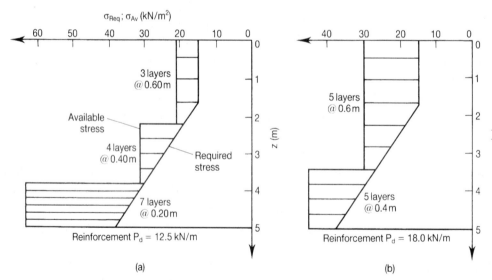

Figure 10.22 *Design example: trial reinforcement layout to provide the required stresses (a) one reinforcement material (b) use of stronger grid at base*

$\phi'_d = 33°$, the minimum length for overall stability is, $L/H = 0.56$. This may be found also from Figure 10.11a, for the case with no surcharge, $q_b/\gamma_r H = 0$.

When allowance is made for the surcharge, $q_b/\gamma_{rd}H = 0.1$, but ignoring the beneficial influence of surcharge on the reinforced fill, $q_r/\gamma_{rd}H = 0$, the results in Figure 10.11a indicate a greater minimum length for overall stability, $(L/H)_{ovrl} = 0.62$.

Eccentricity at the base
The minimum length to maintain satisfactory moment equilibrium can be found from Equation (10.8) or Figure 10.11b. Again, accounting for the surcharge on the backfill but disregarding that on the reinforced zone, gives a minimum length for moment equilibrium, $(L/H)_{ecc} = 0.62$.

Practical effects on internal equilibrium
The main external factor affecting internal equilibrium is compaction, and a prescribed minimum required stress, $\sigma_{comp} = 15\text{kN/m}^2$, is used to allow for compaction (Section 10.8.1).

Summary
The above analyses for *overall* equilibrium indicate a minimum required reinforcement length, $L/H = 0.62$.

External equilibrium

Direct sliding
Assuming that direct sliding occurs beneath the lowest reinforcement layer and the underlying foundation soil, $\phi'_{fd} = 33°$, the minimum length to resist direct sliding is $(L/H)_{ds} = 0.31$, from Equation (10.9). (Recall, $\alpha_{ds} = 0.86$.)

Drained bearing capacity
The minimum required length for overall equilibrium is, $L/H = 0.62$. Assuming this length, the equivalent foundation loading and dimensions at the base of the reinforced zone can be found from the Equations (10.13) to (10.16) in Section 10.5.3: $R_v/\gamma_r HL = 1.09$, $R_h/\gamma_r HL = 0.28$, $\tan \delta_f = 0.26$ and $e/H = 0.092$.

Stress at the base of wall
The equivalent footing width at the base of the wall is then $\bar{L}/H = 0.62 - 2 \times 0.092 = 0.435$, or $\bar{L} = 2.18\text{m}$. The average vertical bearing stress is then
$\sigma_f = R_v/\bar{L} = 1.09 \times 22 \times 5 \times 3.12/2.18\text{kN/m}^2$, or $\sigma_f = 171\text{kN/m}^2$.

Bearing capacity factors
The bearing capacity factors for the foundation soil, $\phi'_{fd} = 33°$, and $N_q = 26.1$ and $N_\gamma = 35.2$, from Table 5.3. The reduction factors for load inclination, for $\tan \delta_f = 0.26$, are $i_q = 0.55$ and $i_\gamma = 0.41$, from Equations (5.23) and (5.24) respectively.

Allowable bearing stress	Ignoring the benefit of embedment, assuming $D = 0\text{m}$, the allowable vertical bearing stress from Equation (5.19) is $\sigma'_{bc} = 0.5 \times 0.41 \times 35.2 \times 2.18 \times 19 = 298\text{kN/m}^2$. The *design value* of foundation bearing capacity, $\sigma_{bc} = 298\text{kN/m}^2$, is more than sufficient to support the *design value* of applied vertical stress at the base of the wall, $\sigma_f = 171\text{kN/m}^2$. (Recall that both the bearing stress and the bearing capacity have been calculated with pessimistic *design values* for the loadings and resistances, and that no additional factor of safety is required, Chapter 6.)
External stability	A general slope stability analysis for potential slip mechanisms passing entirely around the reinforced zone indicates satisfactory external stability.
Summary	The reinforcement length for design is governed by overall equilibrium rather than external equilibrium. The provisional reinforcement length for design is then, $L/H = 0.62$, or $L = 3.1\text{m}$.

Check for bond

Check the bond allowance	In the analysis above, an additional allowance of 10% on the required reinforcement stresses was included to counterbalance the effects of bond (i.e. a load-shedding allowance, $A_{ls} = 1.1$, was assumed).
Required load-shedding allowance	For the reinforcement used, the bond length at the base of the slope is, $L_B/H = 0.044$ (see *the results above for internal equilibrium*, bond length). The reinforcement length is, $L/H = 0.62$, giving a bond ratio, $L_B/L = 0.044 \div 0.62 = 0.071$, and a bond allowance, $A_b = 1 - L_B/L = 0.93$.

As discussed in Section 10.3.2, the required load-shedding allowance to exactly balance the effect of bond is $A_{ls} = 1/A_b$, so that the required load-shedding allowance is $A_{ls} = 1.08$. Since a greater allowance has been assumed, $A_{ls} = 1.1$, the design is satisfactory (i.e. it includes a marginally greater provision of reinforcement than required).

10.8.3 Check on serviceability

The simplified chart for wall deflection (Figure 10.17) was derived for the case of reinforcement at constant spacing. In the present design, the lower part of the wall is reinforced by seven layers spaced at 200mm, and four layers spaced at 400mm. The displacement due to elongation in the reinforcement will be calculated assuming all the reinforcement is at one or the other of these spacings. The maximum deflection for the actual reinforcement layout should fall within this range.

Two values of mobilised angle of friction in the reinforced fill will be used, $\phi'_{rm1} = 33°$ and $\phi'_{rm2} = 45°$, to represent the limits to the likely value (Section 10.6.1). The deflection both at the end of construction and at the end of the design life will be calculated, using the reinforcement stiffness, $J_c = 640\text{kN/m}$ and $J_d = 430\text{kN/m}$, for the two cases respectively (Table 10.2).

No permanent surcharge is expected, $q_r = q_b = 0\text{kN/m}^2$, and the expected bulk density of the reinforced fill is, $\gamma_r = 21\text{kN/m}^3$.

The calculation of the maximum deflection for the wall is summarised in Table 10.4 (Section 10.6.1).

The maximum wall deflections are all relatively small, the largest value being 56mm. As discussed in Sections 7.3 and 10.6, the expected equilibrium is most likely to occur once the soil has mobilised a relatively high proportion of the peak shearing resistance. In the design example, the seven layers at the closer 0.20m spacing are expected to dominate the deformation response of the wall. Allowing for these factors, an appropriate estimate for the likely deflection in the wall would be of the order: $\delta_{max} = 14\text{mm}$ at the end of construction, increasing to $\delta_{max} = 21\text{mm}$ at the end of the design life, implying creep during the design life $\delta_{max} = 7\text{mm}$.

The deflections due to reinforcement elongation could, in practice, be smaller still if forces are transmitted through the modular block facing of the wall to the foundation (Section 10.7.3). This mechanism increases stability, thereby relieving the reinforcement of some load.

Table 10.4 Summary of displacement calculations for the design example

S_v	ϕ'_m	$\left(\dfrac{\delta_{max}J}{HP_{base}}\right)$	P_{base}	End of construction $J = 640\text{kN/m}$		End of design life $J = 430\text{kN/m}$		Creep during design life
				$\dfrac{\delta_{max}}{H}$	δ_{max}	$\dfrac{\delta_{max}}{H}$	δ_{max}	δ_{max}
m	deg		kN/m		mm		mm	mm
0.20	33°	0.39	6.2	0.0037	19	0.0056	28	9
0.20	45°	0.25	3.6	0.0014	7	0.0021	11	4
0.40	33°	0.39	12.4	0.0075	38	0.0112	56	19
0.40	45°	0.25	7.2	0.0028	14	0.0042	21	7

Notes: $\delta_{max}J/HP_{base}$ values from Figure 10.17
P_{base} from Equation (10.17)
Displacements rounded to nearest mm.

It is important to emphasise, however, that the deflections discussed above are due to elongation in the reinforcement only. Other causes of wall movement can be just as significant, such as any tilting caused by immediate or consolidation settlement in the foundation (including differential settlement along the wall), construction-induced movements or effects due to temperature changes, for example (Section 10.6).

10.8.4 Design cross-section

The wall cross-section is shown in Figure 10.23. Note the practical details such as a levelling pad for the facing blocks and the coarser gravel included behind the face, connected to the toe drainage arrangements. Also note the collector drain at the crest of the wall to minimise water infiltration into the wall.

10.9 Point loads

Point loads may be applied to the ground surface, either on the reinforced fill or the backfill, due to traffic loading or abutment forces, for example. These forces are simple

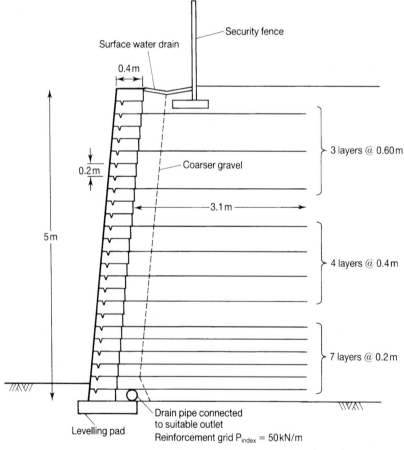

Figure 10.23 *Design example: final cross-section*

to incorporate into a plane wedge analysis of *internal equilibrium*, and a two-part wedge analysis of *overall equilibrium*. But there is no simple stress analysis for this case, such as given for the walls described in Sections 10.2 and 10.3. Approximations have to be introduced (which are consistent with the results of wedge analysis) to allow for the effects of point loads on the *required stresses* for equilibrium in the soil.

10.9.1 Internal equilibrium

It is conventional to separate the vertical and horizontal components of the applied loading (BSI, 1991; DTp, 1978). When the applied load bears eccentrically, it is also conventional to calculate the effective width of the loaded area, B, and the distance, X, from the edge of the crest (Figure 10.24).

An important plane-wedge mechanism is the one at the critical inclination for self-weight loading, $\theta = 45° + \phi'_{rd}/2$, which just contains the loaded area, $\bar{B}$ (Figure 10.24). The additional required force for equilibrium on this critical wedge, caused by the point loading, is

$$\Delta P_{Req} = Q_h + \sqrt{K_{ar}}Q_v \qquad \qquad ...(10.18)$$

It is conventional to distribute the first component, the horizontal force, Q_h, as an additional required stress reducing linearly from a maximum value at the crest of the slope to zero at the point of intersection between the critical wedge and the wall face, at a depth, $h_c = (X + \bar{B}/2)\tan(45 + \phi'_{rd}/2)$ (Figure 10.25). The maximum additional stress at the crest due to the horizontal loading is, $\Delta(\sigma_{Req})_h = 2Q_h/h_c$.

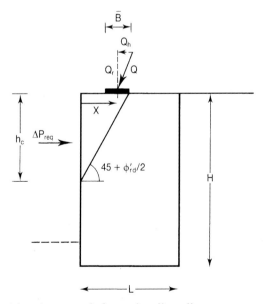

Figure 10.24 *Inclined load on a reinforced soil wall*

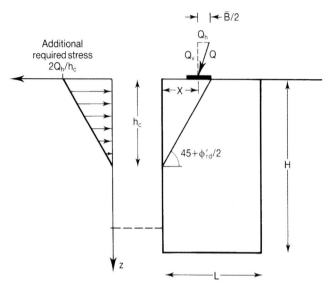

Figure 10.25 *Additional required stress due to a horizontal point load*

Following this approach, the additional required stress for *internal equilibrium* due to the vertical point load, Q_v, may be taken equal to a uniform stress, $\Delta(\sigma_{Req})_v = (Q_v\sqrt{K_{ar}})/h_c$, which acts over the same depth, h_c (Figure 10.26).

Vertical loading on the reinforced zone may influence the required stresses lower in the wall, below the depth h_c. The approximation of a load-spreading of vertical stress

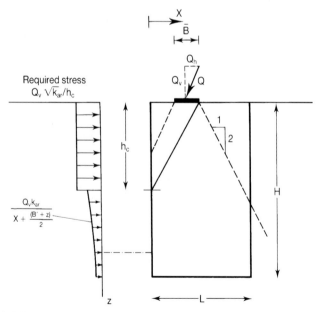

Figure 10.26 *Additional required stress due to a vertical point load*

through the fill provides an alllowance for this (BSI, 1991). Load-speading at $2:1$ would cause an additional vertical stress in the reinforced fill, for $z > h_c$, equal to $\Delta\sigma_v = Q_v/(X + \bar{B}/2 + z/2)$. The corresponding increase in the required stress for internal equilibrium for, $z > h_c$, would be, $\Delta(\sigma_{Req})_v = K_{ar}\Delta(\sigma_v)$, as illustrated in Figure 10.26.

If the applied loads act only over a limited length of the wall, for example as would apply for the support of a bridge deck on an abutment, then the benefit of load-spreading in the second direction, along the length of the wall, may also be considered.

The above components of required stress for a wall with uniform vertical surcharge subject to an inclined line loading behind the crest are illustrated in Figure 10.27. Note the required stresses to resist point loads are additive to the required stresses due to self weight and vertical surcharge (Figure 10.27), but do not add to the stress induced by compaction (which itself is caused by a moveable, vertical point load). Only if it is greater than the stress caused by point loading would the compaction stress still govern at shallow depth.

10.9.2 Allowance for bond

While the above stress analysis may be used to proportion the reinforcement layout, a separate wedge analysis must be carried out to determine whether the reinforcement has sufficient bond to resist the applied point loads (Figure 10.28). Plane wedges may be used, intersecting the front face of the wall at a variety of elevations, usually just above a reinforcement layer. A wide range of possible wedge angles θ should be checked.

As before, *design values* for the soil and the reinforcement parameters should be used in the analysis. The *available force* in the reinforcement layers intersected will be determined by the lesser of the design strength or the mobilised bond force, as appropriate (Figure 10.7).

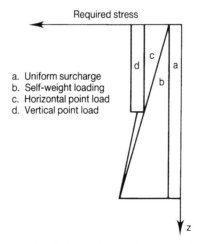

a. Uniform surcharge
b. Self-weight loading
c. Horizontal point load
d. Vertical point load

Figure 10.27 *Required stress for internal equilibrium with point loading*

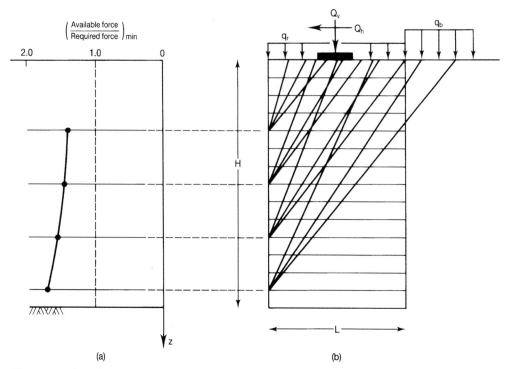

Figure 10.28 *Wedge analysis to check internal equilibrium*

One aspect of design not yet resolved is how to allow for any increased bond capacity due to the imposed point loading. It is recommended that when vertical point loading is continuously present, the increased normal effective stress acting on the reinforcement (estimated by means of load-spreading) should be allowed when calculating bond. Care is needed, however, when sudden or repeated loading is applied. Here it is usual to check that the reinforcement bond is adequate when not allowing for the increase in vertical stress that occurs under the sudden (rapid) load (i.e. use the pre-existing effective stresses). In cases of cyclic applied loading, the possibility of a degradation of the bond capacity (below that prior to the applied loading) should be considered, and special analysis will be required.

The results may be summarised on a plot of the minimum ratio, (P_{Av}/P_{Req}), found for potential wedges intersecting the wall face at each depth (Figure 10.28a).

10.9.3 Overall and foundation equilibrium
Where point loads are applied to the backfill behind the reinforced zone, the most critical angle for the back-wedge (in a two-part wedge analysis) will depend on factors such as the position, inclination and magnitude of the loads. It is necessary to carry out separate wedge analysis to find the variation with depth of the required force for overall

equilibrium (i.e. it is not possible simply to modify the equation given in Section 10.3.3).

If the point loads are applied only to the reinforced zone, the expression for the required force for overall equilibrium given earlier can be modified (Section 10.3.3).

These statements apply equally to the assessment of the worst loading acting at the base of the reinforced zone, for the analysis of foundation stability.

10.10 Sloping fill

Reinforced soil walls may include sloping fill above or behind the reinforced zone (Figure 10.29). The wedge analysis for *overall stability* and *internal stability* can be carried out as before simply allowing for the sloping fill geometry.

The higher stresses in the soil beneath sloping fill may also be calculated from the active earth pressure coefficients given in Figure 10.30. When a sloping fill at an inclination, i, to the horizontal extends to the edge of the crest, the appropriate active earth pressure coefficient for the stress analysis of *internal equilibrium* would be the value, $(K_{ar})_i$ (Figure 10.30). If the backfill slopes up for a considerable distance behind the reinforced zone, a similar active earth pressure coefficient, $(K_{ab})_i$, may be used for the backfill loading.

If the sloping backfill only rises a short distance, to a level plateau at a height, H_p, the resulting horizontal stresses acting on the back of the reinforced zone, L, may be estimated using the approximation shown in Figure 10.31. To a certain depth the horizontal stress at the back of the reinforced zone is governed by the *sloping fill* and the higher active earth pressure coefficient, $(K_{ab})_i$, (Figure 10.30). At greater depth, the

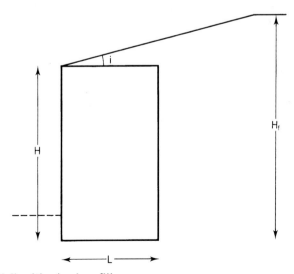

Figure 10.29 *Wall with sloping fill*

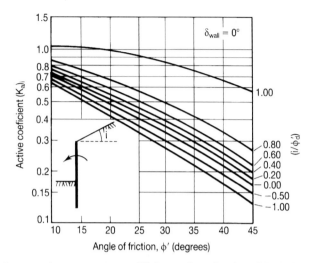

Figure 10.30 *Active earth pressure coefficients for sloping fills (after Caquot et al., 1973)*

stress may be considered due to an equivalent level backfill of height, H_p, exerting the standard active earth pressure K_{ab}. The depth at which the change occurs, z_i, below the crest of the wall (Figure 10.31), is

$$\frac{z_i}{H} = \frac{K_{ab}}{((K_{ab})_i - K_{ab})} \left(\frac{H_p}{H} - 1 - \frac{L}{H} \frac{(K_{ab})_i}{K_{ab}} \tan i \right) \qquad \text{...(10.19)}$$

The additional required stress for internal equilibrium within the reinforced zone, and the additional disturbing stresses applied to the back of the reinforced zone (due to a sloping backfill) may be incorporated into the equations given earlier. Sloping backfills also affect the external equilibrium which should be checked carefully.

10.11 'Loop-anchor' walls

In a loop-anchor wall (Figure 10.1b) the reinforcement bond is provided entirely by bearing stresses acting on the anchor unit. The design procedures described above can still be used, subject to the following comments and recommendations.

The reinforcement length should be defined as the distance between the back of the facing units and the face of the anchor units, where the bearing stress is mobilised, Figure 10.32a. The bond-allowance, A_b, may then be taken equal to unity. The available bearing stress on the anchor may be estimated as described previously (Section 4.6), assuming the full, vertical overburden pressure from the fill (Figure 10.32c). Normally it is assumed that there is no bond between the anchor loops and the soil.

The maximum available force in the reinforcement layers for *ultimate* limit state design is the lesser of the *design strength* of the straps or the *bond capacity* for the anchor. For *serviceability* it would be the lesser of the *serviceability strength* and the

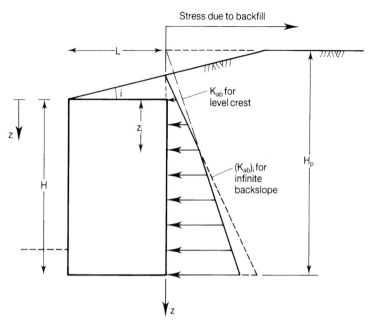

Figure 10.31 *Approximation for backfill stresses due to a broken slope*

bond capacity, in this case calculated using the expected (rather than design) values of parameters.

The direct sliding resistance on horizontal planes through loop-anchor reinforced soil can be assumed to be unaffected by the reinforcement loops (Figure 10.32). The direct sliding resistance may be taken to equal unity, $\alpha_{ds} = 1$.

10.12 Synopsis of Chapter 10

(1) The *internal equilibrium* in a reinforced soil wall governs the *maximum required stress* for equilibrium, and hence what is required from the reinforcement (in terms of strength and spacing).

(2) *Overall equilibrium*, including the analysis for the *line of thrust* in the reinforced zone, determines the *required reinforcement length.*

(3) Depending on the foundation conditions, a greater reinforcement length may be required lower in the wall to prevent either *outward direct sliding* at the interface between the reinforcement and the fill, or foundation soil, or *bearing capacity failure,* or both.

(4) Consideration of the *external equilibrium* of potential failure mechanisms passing entirely around the reinforced zone is required to check that the reinforced soil structure can remain in satisfactory equilibrium with the surrounding site.

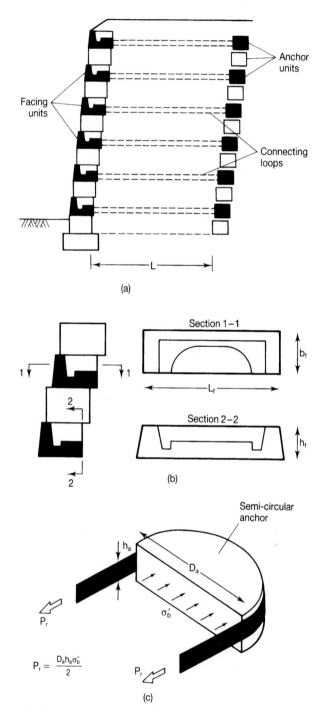

$$P_r = \frac{D_a h_a \sigma'_b}{2}$$

(c)

Figure 10.32 *Details for loop-anchor walls*

(5) Allowance should be made for the effect of any future excavation at the toe of the wall, such as for drains, by assuming no passive resistance at the base of the face.

(6) In the analysis of simple wall structures with level backfill, not subject to point loads, both *stress analysis* after the fashion of Rankine, and *wedge analysis* after the fashion of Coulomb, lead to the same design result.

(7) With sloping fills and point loads only approximate stress anlysis is possible, and it is desirable that both types of analysis are used when making a design for a reinforced soil wall.

(8) The displacement at the face of a reinforced soil wall stems from (a) the elongation of the reinforcement, (b) the influence of the construction method and procedures, (c) the immediate settlement and lateral displacement in the foundation, and (d) the consolidation settlement in the foundation.

Key references

British Standards Institution (1991). *Code of Practice for Strengthened/Reinforced Soils and Other Fills*, Draft Code BS 8006, BSI, London, issued for public comment. British Standards Institution, London.

Department of Transport (DTp) (1978). *Reinforced earth retaining walls and bridge abutments for embankments*, Technical memorandum BE 3/78. DTp, London.

Jewell, R.A. and Milligan, G.W.E. (1989). Deformation calculations for reinforced soil walls. *Proc. 12th Int. Conf. on Soil Mechanics and Foundation Engineering*. Rio de Janeiro, Vol. 2, 1257–1262.

Jones, C.J.F.P. (1988). *Earth reinforcement and soil structures*, 2nd edn. Butterworth, London.

11   Embankments on soft soil

The use of geotextiles to improve embankments over soft soil is an effective and well-tried form of reinforced soil construction. Geotextiles may improve the embankment stability, allow a more controlled construction over very soft or difficult foundation soils, and ensure more uniform settlement of the embankment. Embankment stability usually needs to be improved only while the foundation consolidates, and in such cases the long-term durability of the geotextile reinforcement is of secondary concern.

'Soft ground' construction may be defined in terms of an imposed loading that is sufficient to stress a significant volume of the foundation soil beyond the preconsolidation pressure (Ladd, 1991). This occurs most frequently in embankment construction over normally consolidated or lightly overconsolidated clays, examples of which are embankments for transportation facilities and flood-control levées built in estuarine or marsh areas.

The embankments considered in this chapter typically have side slopes less than $1:2$, or an angle to the horizontal less than $\beta \le 27°$. 'Soft clay' foundations in this context generally have an undrained shear strength, $s_u \le 30\text{kPa}$, and are lightly over-consolidated, $OCR \ge 3$, within 10m of the ground surface. Often there is a relatively thin crust at ground level in which the strength and overconsolidation greatly exceed the values cited above, usually caused by desiccation.

Reinforcement in an embankment on soft soil is most effective when placed at or close to the foundation surface (Figure 11.1a). If the reinforcement were absent, the factor of safety at the end of construction would usually fall to below unity (i.e. the desired cross-section could not be built without the reinforcement) before increasing once more as the strength in the foundation improved with consolidation (Figure 11.1b). Thus the

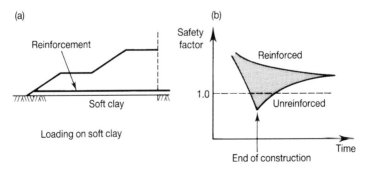

Figure 11.1 *Reinforcement improving stability during construction and foundation consolidation*

reinforcement is needed only to improve the stability during construction and subsequent consolidation.

Methods of stability analysis which allow for reinforcement in embankment design are relatively well established. Agreement has been found between limit equilibrium, finite element and plasticity methods of analysis for reinforced embankments on soft soil. But, as in the case of unreinforced embankments, care is needed to determine whether imposed loading will cause a drained, partially drained or an undrained failure. One source of uncertainty for reinforced embankment design is the link between the reinforcement stiffness properties and the embankment deformation behaviour, and empirical guidelines are often followed to allow for this aspect of behaviour.

The way that reinforcement improves the stability of an embankment on soft soil is reviewed first in terms of stress and force equilibrium (Section 11.1), and then in terms of deformation and failure mechanisms (Section 11.2). The aim is to illustrate the fundamental mechanics which apply. The link between embankment stability, the rate of construction and the dissipation of excess porewater pressures is then discussed (Section 11.3), where the influence of the loading conditions on the clay shearing resistance is examined.

11.1 Stress and force equilibrium

The main loading from an embankment on soft soil is due to the vertical self-weight of the embankment fill (Figure 11.2a). The second important loading is from the outward

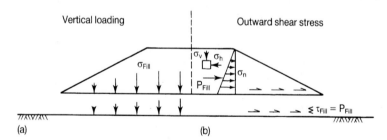

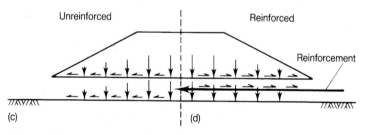

Figure 11.2 *Disturbing forces in an unreinforced embankment, with reinforcement supporting outward shear stress*

directed lateral force, P_{Fill}, caused by horizontal stress in the fill (Figure 11.2b). The resulting outward shear stress which acts on the foundation surface reduces the foundation bearing capacity (Figure 11.2c). The primary role for the reinforcement, therefore, is to support the outward shear stress and relieve the foundation of this critical loading (Figure 11.2d).

The detrimental influence of outward shear stress on bearing capacity was described previously for drained and undrained loading (Sections 5.4 and 5.5), and is illustrated in Figure 11.3 for a surface footing on clay of uniform undrained strength, s_u. The bearing capacity factor, $N_c = \sigma/s_u$, is as much as halved by outward shear stress, $0 \geq \tau \geq -s_u$. (Note the sign convention that denotes as negative the outward shear stress which reduces bearing capacity.)

Reinforcement placed at foundation level across the full width of an embankment, and which can support the lateral thrust from the fill, can relieve the foundation of the outward shear loading and thereby preserve the bearing capacity for vertical embankment loading.

The question of compatibility concerns the extension in the reinforcement which must be compatible with the lateral deflection at the surface of the foundation. An example of incompatibility would be a case where the axial extension in the reinforcement, due to the tensile load from the thrust in the fill, would imply a relative outward displacement of the reinforced embankment with respect to the surface of the foundation. Such relative displacement could not occur without outward shear stress being applied to the foundation surface. This implies that only part of the lateral thrust, P_{Fill}, could actually

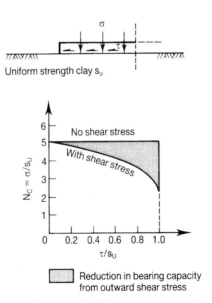

Figure 11.3 *The influence of outward shear stress on bearing capacity (replotted from Figure 5.22)*

be supported by the reinforcement, the remainder would be transmitted down through the reinforcement to act on the foundation as an outward shear stress. Compatibility demonstrates in this case that the reinforcement would carry less force and provide less improvement to the embankment stability than envisaged in the equilibrium analysis (Section 11.2).

In general, soil cannot support direct tensile stress and an unreinforced embankment cannot resist lateral displacement in the foundation (Figure 11.4a). A layer of reinforcement placed in the embankment may resist such lateral displacement, however, by exerting an inward shear stress on the foundation surface (Figure 11.4b). The cases of zero and maximum inward shear stress at the foundation surface are broadly equivalent to the loadings applied by conventional smooth and rough footings (Figure 11.5a). Inward shear stress, or lateral restraint at the foundation surface can increase the bearing capacity, as illustrated in Figure 11.5b for a foundation with strength increasing with depth.

11.1.1 Summary of mechanics

The mechanics described above may be summarised as follows.

The stability of an embankment on soft soil is influenced significantly by the foundation bearing capacity. An unreinforced embankment exerts a worse loading than from vertical self-weight only, because the lateral thrust in the fill exerts an outward shear stress on the foundation that reduces the bearing capacity (Figures 11.6a to c).

The primary role for reinforcement, therefore, is to hold the lateral thrust in equilibrium with a tensile force (Figure 11.6d). If this can be achieved with no relative outward displacement of the reinforced embankment with respect to the surface of the underlying soft soil, the foundation will be subjected only to the vertical loading from the embankment. This primary mechanism of reinforcement improves the stability for all foundation cases.

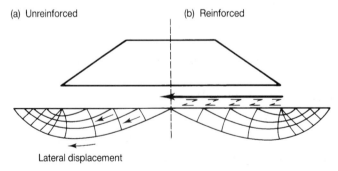

Figure 11.4 *Reinforcement providing lateral restraint on the foundation surface*

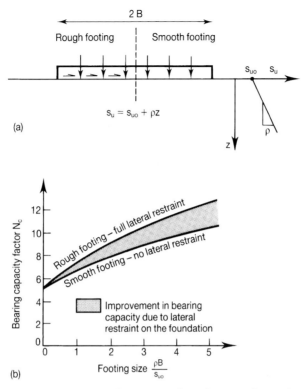

Figure 11.5 *Improvement in bearing capacity due to lateral restraint on the foundation surface (after Davis and Booker, 1973)*

A second role for the reinforcement is to resist lateral displacement in the foundation soil. Within the limits imposed by the shear contact with the foundation surface, and by the reinforcement extensibility, a reinforced embankment can provide restraint at the foundation surface in a manner analogous to a rough footing (Figures 11.6d and e). This improves the bearing capacity when (a) the strength in the foundation increases with depth, or (b) where the soft clay is of limited depth, above a hard stratum.

Finally, the reinforcement must first support the lateral thrust in the fill (the primary mechanism) before it can provide restraint at the foundation surface (the secondary mechanism). The reason is that when the reinforcement cannot support the full lateral thrust in the fill, the remainder acts on the foundation as an outward shear stress.

11.2 Slip mechanisms and deformation

The mechanisms by which reinforcement improves the stability of embankments on soft soil are described above. The limiting equilibrium in reinforced embankments is now considered in terms of the potential slip mechanisms. The 'pre-failure' deformation caused by the envisaged equilibrium is then investigated.

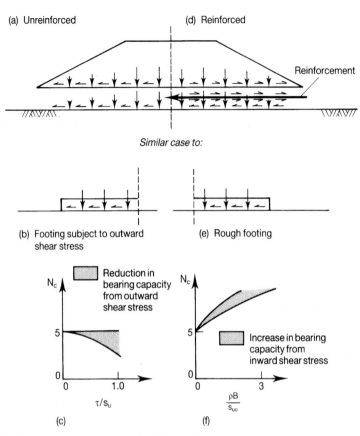

Figure 11.6 *Summary of mechanics in a reinforced embankment on soft soil*

11.2.1 Internal stability

Equilibrium entirely within the embankment fill is considered first, and preferential direct sliding across the surface of the reinforcement layer and shallow slips in the embankment side-slopes both have to be examined.

Direct sliding

A point emphasised throughout this book is that the inclusion of reinforcement in soil can allow preferential direct sliding to occur across the surface of a reinforcement layer. In an embankment on soft soil, such direct sliding would develop between the fill and the upper surface of the reinforcement. Gross slippage would result if the available resistance at the reinforcement interface were insufficient to support the lateral thrust from the fill (Figure 11.7a).

For a simple analysis, consider the horizontal active thrust beneath the edge of the embankment crest pushing the embankment side-slope horizontally (Figure 11.7b). Active stresses would develop in the fill so that, $P_{Fill} = K_{ad}(\gamma H^2/2 + qH)$, where design values for all the parameters should be used, namely the bulk unit weight, γ, and design

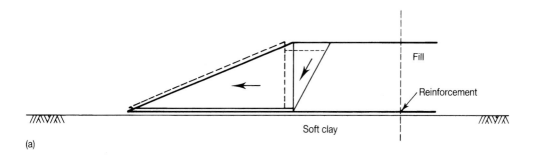

(a)

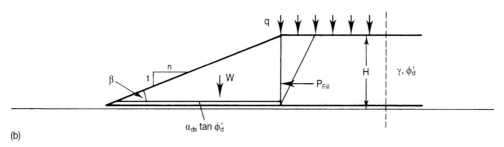

(b)

Figure 11.7 *Internal stability: direct sliding failure in the fill*

angle of friction, ϕ'_d, of the fill, from which the design active earth pressure coefficient, K_{ad}, may be calculated. Uniform vertical surcharge on the embankment crest is denoted as q.

The direct sliding resistance at the contact between the fill and the reinforcement layer is α_{ds} tan ϕ'_d (Section 4.5). This resistance is mobilised by the weight of the soil in the embankment side-slope, $\gamma n H^2/2$, which applies for a side-slope angle, tan $\beta = 1/n$ (Figure 11.7b). For satisfactory horizontal equilibrium,

$$n > \frac{K_{ad}}{\alpha_{ds} \tan \phi'_d} \left(1 + \frac{2q}{\gamma H}\right) \qquad \text{...(11.1)}$$

When the above equality is satisfied, the lateral thrust, P_{Fill}, may be transferred from the fill to the reinforcement layer. Depending on the reinforcement properties, the stability in the foundation, and the deformation in the embankment and foundation, this force may be either entirely supported by the reinforcement as a tensile force, or only partially supported by the reinforcement, the remainder being transmitted to the foundation surface as an outward shear load (Section 11.1).

The above analysis is for free-draining fill but it may be extended to allow for other factors such as a water-filled tension crack in the fill. More sophisticated wedge mechanisms may be used, as in steep slope design, for example, Figure 8.14. But as noted below, this would only be useful where sliding was a critical factor, which is seldom the case for embankments on soft soil.

Shallow slope failures
It is also necessary to demonstrate that shallow slips will not develop entirely within the embankment side-slopes. This may be checked with conventional methods of limit equilibrium analysis since no reinforcement layers are intersected by such slip surfaces.

Comment on internal stability
The internal stability of an embankment on soft soil is an important aspect of design. However, the side-slopes of granular fill embankments over soft clay are usually governed by the stability in the underlying soft clay, rather than by the internal stability of the embankment. But internal stability could be critical where less frictional fill materials are used.

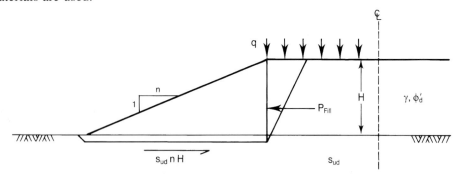

Figure 11.8 *Overall stability: slippage across the foundation surface*

11.2.2 Overall stability
Potential failure mechanisms passing through the foundation normally govern the stability of embankments on soft soil. The type of failure mechanism that is critical, and the pattern of deformation in the foundation before failure, are considered in the example of an embankment with a uniform side-slope, $1:n$, constructed over soft clay of limited depth, D, with a design value of undrained shearing resistance, s_{ud}.

Slippage across the foundation surface
Direct sliding across the surface of the soft clay could occur in an unreinforced embankment (Figure 11.8). If the soft clay resists the lateral thrust in the fill over the distance between the embankment toe and the edge of the crest, then for satisfactory equilibrium,

$$n > \frac{K_{ad}}{2} \frac{\gamma H}{s_{ud}} \left(1 + \frac{2q}{\gamma H}\right) \qquad ...(11.2)$$

where design values for the parameters should be used (Chapter 6 and Section 11.7).

The inclusion of reinforcement at the base of an embankment improves dramatically the resistance to this potential sliding mechanism. For example, if the reinforcement can support the lateral thrust in the fill, then it will eliminate entirely the driving force for this slip mechanism (Figure 11.2d).

Deeper-seated failure in the foundation is usually the more critical condition for both unreinforced and reinforced embankments.

Stability in the foundation

Vertical embankment loading causes an increase in the vertical stress in the foundation soil and a corresponding increase in the horizontal stress. Therefore, a lateral thrust develops in the foundation soil beneath the embankment crest which can eventually cause the foundation soil beneath the embankment side-slope to displace laterally. A simplified analysis illustrates this behaviour.

Consider a zone of the soft clay beneath the embankment side-slope, the soil block $oabc$ (Figure 11.9a). It may be assumed that the vertical stress applied by the embankment, $\sigma_v = \gamma H$, acts uniformly through the limited depth of soft clay, and that the principal axes of stress in the clay are vertical and horizontal on either side of the block $oabc$ (Figure 11.9a). The soil block then experiences a net horizontal stress,

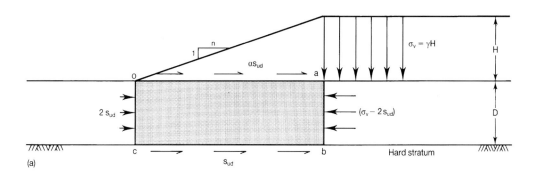

(a)

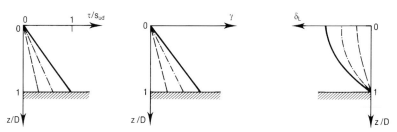

Figure 11.9 *Foundation stability: (a) applied stresses, (b) and (c) shear on horizontal planes, and (d) shear displacement, for the case $\alpha = 0$*

$\sigma_v - 2s_{ud}$, on the right-hand boundary ab, and a net resisting stress, $2s_{ud}$, on the left-hand boundary oc, the self-weight terms in the level foundation having a neutral effect.

Consider first the equilibrium where there is neither outward nor inward shear stress acting on the top of soil block, on the surface oa, $\alpha = 0$ (Figure 11.9a). The applied vertical loading on the foundation and the net lateral thrust on the soil in the foundation both increase as the embankment height is raised. Eventual lateral sliding of the soil block is resisted by the available shear strength on horizontal planes, nHs_{ud}. This strength is mobilised and the limiting equilibrium reached when the embankment height and side-slope satisfy the relation,

$$n = \frac{\gamma D}{s_{ud}} - \frac{4D}{H} \qquad \qquad ...(11.3)$$

for cases where, $\gamma H/s_{ud} > 5$. Equation (11.3) is for the case of zero shear stress applied to the foundation surface, $\alpha = 0$, which assumes that reinforcement supports the lateral thrust in the fill.

Deformation in the foundation

Consider now the shear stress on horizontal planes within the block $oabc$ (Figure 11.9b). The solid line represents the limiting condition of Equation (11.3), when the undrained strength is mobilised on the most highly stressed plane bc at the base of the block (Figure 11.9a). The dotted lines in Figure 11.9b indicate the shear stress at earlier stages of loading.

The corresponding shear strain on horizontal planes, for clay with a constant shear modulus, $\tau/\gamma = G$, are shown in Figure 11.9c, from which the lateral shear displacement in the foundation may be found by integration (Figure 11.9d). The maximum lateral displacement at the ground surface, at the limiting equilibrium, is,

$$\delta_h = \frac{\gamma_{max}D}{2} = \frac{\tau_{max}D}{2G} \qquad \qquad ...(11.4)$$

where τ_{max} and γ_{max} are the maximum shear stress and shear strain at the base of the sliding block. In the limit, $\tau_{max} = s_{ud}$, $\gamma_{max} = s_{ud}/G$, so that $(\delta_h)_{max} = s_{ud}D/2G$. Again, this result is for the case of zero shear stress on the foundation surface, $\alpha = 0$.

What eventually limits the embankment height is the maximum shearing resistance mobilised on critical planes through the foundation. Only once this maximum resistance is mobilised can gross displacements on a 'failure mechanism' occur through the foundation. In the present example, that would occur on the slip surface $dcbef$ (Figure 11.10).

The above analysis highlights the following features of behaviour:

1. The foundation soil experiences increasing shear load and shear deformation as the embankment is built.

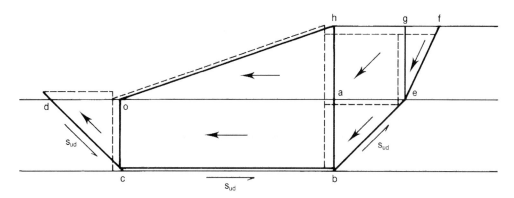

Figure 11.10 *Overall stability: envisaged rigid body failure mechanism*

2. The 'pre-failure' lateral deformation at the surface of the foundation governs the compatibility with the reinforcement.
3. Additional lateral displacements occur on the critical failure mechanism (Figure 11.10), but these would not normally be considered for compatibility because of the potential loss of strength in the soft clay resulting from intense shearing on localised slip surfaces.

Influence of reinforcement extensibility

The above analysis was for zero shear stress applied to the surface of the soft clay, $\alpha = 0$ (Figure 11.9a). For the analysis to apply, the net extension in the reinforcement, caused by the axial tension mobilised to support the thrust in the fill, must be compatible with the lateral deflection at the surface of the soft clay. Thus the lateral displacement at the clay surface and the net lateral displacement of the reinforcement (with respect to the embankment centre line) must be compared.

The initial assumption of zero shear stress at the ground surface would be unreasonable if it implied a greater extension in the reinforcement than the lateral deflection in the soft clay. The reinforced embankment could not displace outward with respect to the foundation without inducing outward shear stress on the clay surface, and some of the fill thrust would thus be supported by the foundation, reducing the force carried by the reinforcement.

The opposite would be the case if the reinforcement extended less than the lateral deflection in the clay, which would also be unreasonable. The reinforced embankment could not displace inward relative to the foundation surface without applying inward shear stress to the clay surface ($\alpha > 0$, Figure 11.9a), in which case there would be greater axial tension in the reinforcement than due to the fill thrust alone.

Where geotextile reinforcement is in contact with the clay surface, the permissible range for the coefficient, α, is limited by the applicable interaction coefficient for the reinforcement product (Section 4.4).

The equilibrium with (a) full outward shear stress, $\alpha = -1$, (b) zero shear stress $\alpha = 0$, and (c) full inward shear stress, $\alpha = +1$, on the surface of the clay is illustrated in Figure 11.11. The relative heights of the embankments may be found from the general expression summarised in Table 11.1.

Note that the outward shear stress in an unreinforced embankment depends on the thrust in the fill and on the side-slope, as indicated by Equation (2) in Table 11.1.

The lateral deflection in the foundation is illustrated to show how the 'pre-failure' deflections in the foundation reduce in more highly reinforced embankments (Figure 11.11). A situation of diminishing returns can be seen to apply to reinforced embankments. To be more effective, the reinforcement must carry greater tensile force, first supporting the thrust in the fill and then restraining the foundation surface. But in becoming more effective, the reinforcement reduces the magnitude of 'pre-failure'

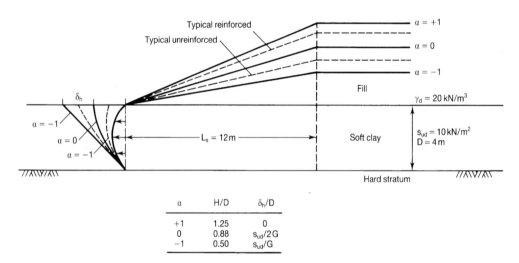

α	H/D	δ_h/D
+1	1.25	0
0	0.88	s_{ud}/2G
−1	0.50	s_{ud}/G

Figure 11.11 *Foundation stability: limiting embankment cross-sections and 'pre-failure' lateral deflections in the foundation for the cases, $\alpha = +1, 0, -1$*

Table 11.1 Equations from simplified analysis for an embankment on a foundation of uniform undrained strength, s_{ud}, and limited depth, D

Embankment height	$H = \dfrac{4D}{(\gamma D)/s_{ud} - (1 + \alpha)n}$	(1)
α for an unreinforced embankment	$\alpha = -\dfrac{K_{ad}\gamma H}{2ns_{ud}}$	(2)
Lateral deflection at the ground surface	$\delta_h = \dfrac{s_{ud}D}{2G}(1 - \alpha)$	(3)

Note: applicable range $\gamma H/s_{ud} > 5$.

deflection in the foundation. Thus, much greater stiffness is required for the reinforcement to support greater tensile force at lower tensile elongation.

This demonstrates why a 'fully reinforced' embankment ($\alpha = +1$) is unlikely to be achieved in practice. Not only do all geotextiles elongate under load, but the interaction coefficient between the reinforcement and the soft clay may limit the magnitude of inward shear stress that can be exerted on the foundation surface. The embankments indicated by the dotted lines in Figure 11.11 illustrate typical reinforced, $\alpha \approx +0.5$, and unreinforced, $\alpha \approx -0.5$, embankment cases.

11.3 Construction rate and drainage

The rate of filling and the rate of drainage in the soft clay are important factors in the design of reinforced embankments on soft soil.

11.3.1 Construction period

Reinforcement is generally required to maintain stability in an embankment on soft soil only until the excess porewater pressures caused by the embankment construction have dissipated (Figure 11.1). Thus, the same embankment cross-section could be built, without reinforcement, simply by filling slowly enough so that minimal excess porewater pressures develop.

This behaviour was illustrated in Figure 11.1, and may be represented in terms of the maximum required reinforcement force versus time (Figure 11.12). The highest force is required if the embankment were built 'instantaneously'. Lesser force is needed with

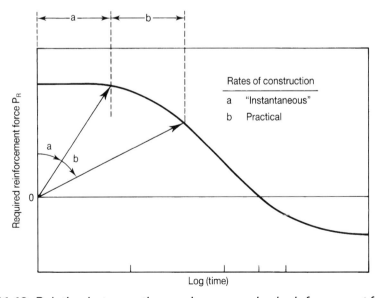

Figure 11.12 *Relation between the maximum required reinforcement force and the rate of construction*

more practical rates of filling which permit some drainage in the foundation during construction. Only very slow and gradual filling would allow the foundation strength to keep pace with the increased embankment loading so that reinforcement is not required.

Reinforcement is found to be attractive for many reasons:

1. On very soft ground, reinforcement doubles as a construction expedient that prevents local loss and intermixing of the fill and the soft soil, and improves the bearing capacity for construction equipment.
2. In comparing reinforced and unreinforced alternatives, the reinforced embankment will cost less if the fill saved, due to steeper side slopes, and the economies of more rapid construction, exceed the cost of the reinforcement. This is often the case, and the reinforcement can bring the additional benefit of more uniform embankment settlement and an ability to bridge over localised 'soft spots' in the foundation.
3. Major embankments on soft soil are often built in several stages. The use of reinforcement is attractive in this case because a greater embankment height can be built in any one stage. This leads to extra improvement in the foundation strength during consolidation, and reduces the number of stages required, and hence the construction time. Reinforcement is particularly effective when combined with vertical drains for stage construction.

11.3.2 Drained and undrained shear

A critical feature for the stability analysis of embankments on soft soil is the drainage conditions in the soft clay at failure (Ladd, 1991).

This is illustrated by an example of second-stage filling where the clay beneath the embankment berm is normally consolidated, and the porewater pressures are known (Figure 11.13). Consider the element of clay indicated in the figure.

When the shearing resistance for this element of clay is estimated from an effective stress analysis, based on the current porewater pressures, the maximum available resistance is anticipated to be at point (1) in Figure 11.13b, $\tau_f = \sigma'_{vc} \tan \phi'_{cv}$. Rapid shear in the clay, due to the second stage of filling, would cause an undrained response that is limited by the current undrained strength, $\tau_f = s_u$, point (2) in Figure 11.13b.

There is a dramatic difference in available resistance between these two cases which stems entirely from the excess porewater pressures induced by undrained shear. These were not allowed for the effective stress analysis. When the factors of safety from the two analyses are compared for typical embankment cases, they are found to differ by a factor about 1.5 to 2.5 (Ladd, 1991). In other words, an effective stress analysis which does not anticipate the excess porewater pressures which will be induced by rapid shear in the soft clay may overestimate the factor of safety by about a factor of 2.

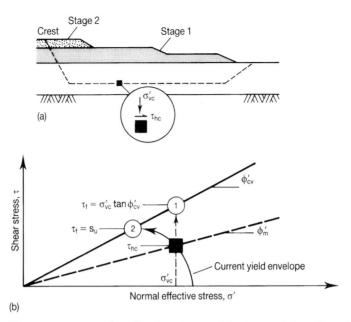

Figure 11.13 *The response of soft clay to rapid stage 2 loading beneath an embankment (after Ladd, 1991)*

The issue, then, is not one of total versus effective stress analysis, but rather one of an appropriate allowance for the porewater pressures induced by rapid, undrained shear. In the design of an embankment, a sudden, unexpected change in loading is a possibility which must be guarded against.

Ladd (1991) concludes that it is preferable to assess the stability of embankments on soft soil in terms of the current undrained shearing resistance in the soft clay, which may be estimated with relative confidence from the consolidation history and current *in-situ* effective stresses in the clay (Section 5.3). It is relatively difficult, in comparison, to evaluate the change in porewater pressure that will occur when the clay is sheared rapidly to failure.

It is helpful to consider standard laboratory tests as a reference for the loading cases that may apply for soft clay. A conventional undrained analysis may be compared with an *unconsolidated undrained* (UU) test in which no consolidation, with respect to the applied stresses, occurs before undrained shear to failure. A conventional drained analysis may be compared with a *consolidated drained* (CD) test in which there has been full consolidation, with respect to the applied stresses, and no excess porewater pressures are induced by shear. The undrained strength analysis, which is recommended for the design of embankments on soft soil, may be compared with a *consolidated undrained* (CU) test in which there has been partial or full consolidation, with respect to the applied stresses, and a corresponding increase in undrained strength, before undrained shear to failure.

11.3.3 Design strategies

Two main design strategies are used for reinforced embankments on soft soil which are built in one stage.

One approach starts with the final embankment cross-section after consolidation in the foundation is complete, and determines first the unreinforced cross-section that will provide the required long-term factor of safety. Reinforcement is then viewed simply as an expedient to boost the intermediate end-of-construction stability, and the stability during consolidation. The amount of reinforcement required depends on the rate of construction, the rate of filling and whether wick drains are used in the foundation.

An alternative approach starts with the stability at the end of construction. Various possible embankment cross-sections are examined, and the required quantity and type of reinforcement, and the volume of fill, compared for each. The long-term stability, after consolidation, is checked separately. It is desirable that embankments on soft soil should have an adequate long-term factor of safety without reinforcement. It is fortunate, therefore, that reinforced embankments which are stable in the short term, after rapid construction, are usually found to be stable in the long term without need for reinforcement (see Figures 11.1 and 11.12).

The measurement of porewater pressures is an important means of monitoring embankment performance. But the *in-situ* effective stresses determined from these measurements are best considered as consolidation stresses from which the current undrained shearing resistance in the clay may be estimated for use in stability analysis.

The properties of the fill material for embankment construction are generally not known prior to construction. The routine procedure is to design the embankment with assumed fill properties, and then to specify the fill and control the construction to ensure that the properties in the field either equal or exceed those assumed in design.

11.3.4 Significance of foundation stability

It has been emphasised that the bearing capacity of the soft clay foundation limits the improvement that can be achieved by reinforcing an embankment on soft soil. The important first step in design, therefore, is to check that the desired embankment cross-section will not cause bearing failure in the foundation.

In addition to the reinforcement force needed to maintain stability in the foundation, the reinforcement must also support the thrust in the fill. This latter loading can be very significant, and some reinforced embankments are designed assuming that the reinforcement only supports the lateral thrust in the fill.

11.4 Concepts from plasticity analysis

Conventional bearing capacity analysis was derived from plasticity theory (Terzaghi, 1943), and this same theory is relevant to embankments on soft soil. Rather than focus on the overall bearing capacity, as for a surface footing (Figure 11.5), it is more helpful for embankments to determine the variation of vertical stress that can be applied to the foundation surface with distance from the edge of the loading (Figure 11.14a).

As explained earlier, reinforcement enables a soft clay foundation to support greater vertical loading. This reduces the required distance, x_{req}, between the point of maximum loading beneath the crest of the embankment, and the toe (Figure 11.14b).

11.4.1 Plasticity solutions

Solutions have been derived for a foundation with shear strength, s_{uz}, that increases linearly with depth, z, according to the relation,

$$s_{uz} = s_{uo} + \rho z \qquad \qquad ...(11.5)$$

where, s_{uo}, is the shear strength at the ground surface, and the linear rate of increase in strength is ρ.

The results (Figure 11.15) for a fully restrained foundation, $\alpha = + 1$ (rough footing), and for no restraint at the foundation surface, $\alpha = 0$ (smooth footing), were derived by Davis and Booker (1973). The analysis was extended to the other loading cases by Houlsby and Jewell (1988).

The corresponding results for a foundation of uniform shear strength, s_u, and limited depth, D, were derived by Mandel and Salençon (1969 and 1972), for the same two loading cases, $\alpha = +1$ and $\alpha = 0$. These results can be matched by simpler limit

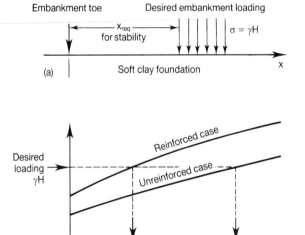

Figure 11.14 *Bearing capacity expressed in terms of the allowable vertical loading versus distance from the edge of loading, relevant to embankment design*

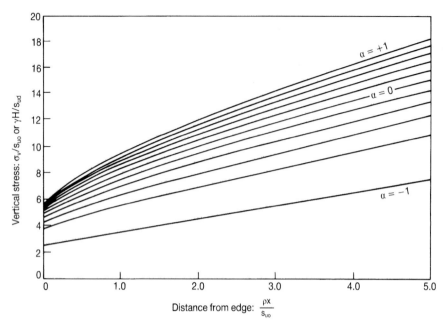

Figure 11.15 *Plasticity solutions for strength increasing with depth (after Davis and Booker, 1973, and Houlsby and Jewell, 1988)*

equilibrium analysis which has been used to derive the loading cases shown in Figure 11.16 (Jewell, 1988).

11.4.2 Application of plasticity theory

The application of the plasticity solutions for the design of embankments is illustrated in Figure 11.17. The simplest embankment shape that closely reproduces the results

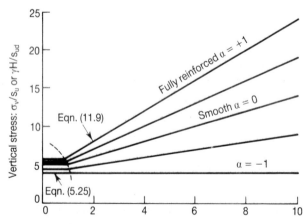

Figure 11.16 *Solutions for a foundation of uniform strength and limited depth above a rough stratum*

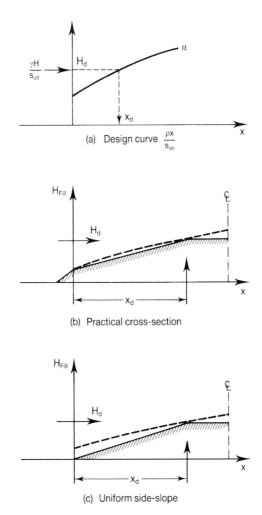

Figure 11.17 *Practical embankment cross-sections derived from plasticity solutions*

from plasticity theory is shown in Figure 11.17b. Studies using limit equilibrium analysis and finite element analysis have shown empirically that an embankment with a uniform side-slope, as defined in Figure 11.17c, preserves the same equilibrium and factor of safety (Russell, 1992). Thus the solutions in Figures 11.15 and 11.16 are a convenient tool for the preliminary sizing of embankments.

11.5 Limit equilibrium analysis

Limit equilibrium methods have proved effective for the design of reinforced embankments on soft soil. Rotational stability on circular mechanisms and translational stability on wedge mechanisms may both be used. There are some limitations to slip circle analysis which are discussed below.

11.5.1 General considerations

A more sophisticated approach is demanded for the limit equilibrium analysis of reinforced embankments than for unreinforced embankments.

While it is necessary to check the overall stability in both reinforced and unreinforced embankments, other stability checks are as important for reinforced embankments. For example, the stability in the foundation must be examined to ensure that there is sufficient bearing capacity to support the weight of the embankment.

In more detail, the main failure mode for an unreinforced embankment is large-scale movement on a failure mechanism passing through both the embankment fill and the foundation. Settlement and spreading of the embankment, and the period over which this occurs, influences the serviceability of unreinforced embankments.

The main failure modes in a reinforced embankment are as follows:

1. Where the reinforcement is relatively inextensible but has adequate strength, there may be foundation failure which causes lateral spreading and heave in the soft clay, resulting in excessive settlement of the embankment.
2. Where the reinforcement is relatively inextensible but has insufficient strength, the reinforcement may become overloaded and rupture, triggering a similar failure mode to that in an unreinforced embankment.
3. Where the reinforcement has adequate strength but is too extensible, it may only be able to mobilise the forces required for equilibrium at excessive elongation. The embankment would then settle and spread laterally to an unacceptable degree, with heave at the embankment toe and tension cracks in the crest.

Guidance on selecting reinforcement strength and extensibility parameters is given in Section 11.7.

11.5.2 Rotational stability: slip circle analysis

A conventional slip circle analysis for an unreinforced embankment is shown schematically in Figure 11.18. The portions of the slip circle in the fill and in the foundation may be considered separately to identify the two main disturbing forces, namely:

1. The lateral thrust in the fill, generated on the portion of the slip circle within the fill (Figure 11.18b), and
2. The vertical loading due to the self-weight of the embankment above the highly stressed zone in the foundation (Figure 11.18c).

Indeed a conventional slip circle analysis may be represented as shown in Figure 11.18d, when the lateral thrust, P_{Fill}, is calculated from the same circle. (The thrust has been assumed to act horizontally.)

The cross-section of a reinforced embankment is ultimately restricted by the capacity of the foundation to support the vertical embankment loading. The slip circle analysis for

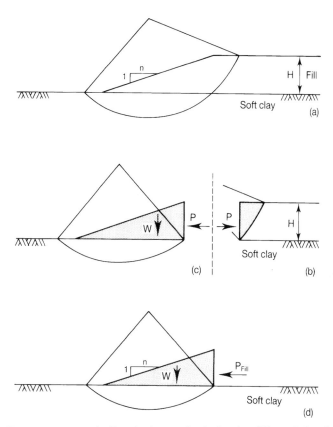

Figure 11.18 *Components of slip circle analysis in the fill and the foundation*

this case is shown in Figure 11.19a, where the disturbing lateral thrust in the fill (Figure 11.18d) is supported by the reinforcement (i.e. not supported by the foundation soil). The reinforcement can provide restraint on the foundation, an inward shear stress, which mobilises a net restoring force, $P_R = P_{Fndn}$, which can be used in the slip circle analysis (Figure 11.19a).

There are two ways of proceeding with limit equilibrium analysis of an embankment on soft soil. One way is to assume that the desired factor of safety applies on all potential slip surfaces, and then to calculate the reinforcement force required to achieve this for each. This gives a distribution of maximum required reinforcement force for stability (for example, Figures 11.19c and d). The reinforcement is then checked to ensure that the available force in the reinforcement (Figure 11.19b), limited by the reinforcement material and interaction parameters, everywhere exceeds the required force. This method is recommended and used throughout the book (Section 7.1).

An alternative approach starts with the variation of the maximum available force in the reinforcement (Figure 11.19b). The factor of safety on potential slip surfaces is then calculated using the maximum force corresponding to where the reinforcement is

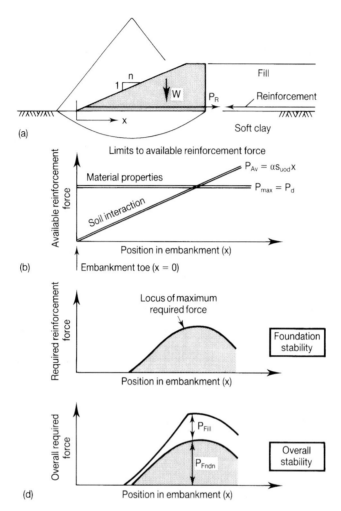

(a)

(b)

(d)

Figure 11.19 *Slip circle analysis for reinforced embankments: (a) foundation stability, with (b) available and (c) required forces; (d) overall stability, required forces*

intersected by the trial slip mechanism. The factor of safety is calculated for all potential slip mechanisms to check that in every case this exceeds the desired minimum value.

11.5.3 Foundation and overall stability

The required force to maintain stability in the foundation beneath an embankment may be found from limit equilibrium analysis. The distribution of the reinforcement force depends on the design loadings and resistances, and on the embankment cross-section. The maximum available reinforcement force is governed by the reinforcement material properties and by the limiting shear interaction with the surface of the soft clay (Figure 11.19b).

The soil interaction limits the maximum available force, P_{Av}, at a distance, x, from the toe of the embankment, that can develop to maintain foundation stability. In the general case.

$$P_{Av} = x\alpha s_{uod} \qquad \qquad ...(11.6)$$

where s_{uod} is the design shear strength of the clay at the ground surface, and α a coefficient of interaction. Where the reinforcement is in direct contact with the soft clay, $\alpha = \alpha_{ds}$, the coefficient of direct sliding (Section 4.5).

Limit equilibrium analysis proceeds by trial and error. Design values for the material parameters and a trial embankment geometry are selected, and the required reinforcement force evaluated using a range of trial slip surfaces. For example, many different combinations of slip circle centres and radii would be examined to intersect the reinforcement in various positions. The distribution of maximum required force along the reinforcement found from this analysis (Figure 11.19c) must be less than or equal to the available force (Figure 11.19b).

A reinforced embankment that satisfies the above design check may be supported in equilibrium without exceeding either the design shear strength of the foundation soil or the limiting interaction between the foundation and the reinforcement. It remains, then, to check that the reinforcement is able to carry the additional thrust from the fill and hence to provide satisfactory overall stability (Figure 11.19d).

11.5.4 Limitations of slip circle analysis

The limitation to slip circle analysis occurs where failure in the foundation is constrained to occur on shallow slip surfaces, due to a hard stratum beneath the soft soil, for example.

Slip circle analysis underestimates the thrust in the fill in such cases and therefore overestimates embankment stability (Gudehus, 1981, and Leroueil *et al.*, 1985). This error can be avoided by using a logarithmic spiral mechanism which both cuts steeply upward through the embankment fill (like an active wedge) while reducing to a slip circle in the foundation (Leshchinsky, 1987). Alternatively, the analysis for the thrust in the fill may be decoupled from the search for critical slip circles in the foundation, and a Coulomb wedge, or Rankine earth pressure theory, used instead to calculate the active thrust.

Even using the above techniques, slip circle analysis is still found to be inadequate for very shallow foundations. This is illustrated in Figure 11.20 by comparing the loads calculated from slip circle analysis and plasticity theory (for $\alpha = 0$ in this case). While slip circle analysis performs well for foundations with strength increasing with depth (Figure 11.20a), it overestimates considerably the stability in foundations of limited depth (Figure 11.20b). It is preferable to use a translational wedge analysis for this latter case (Section 11.5.5).

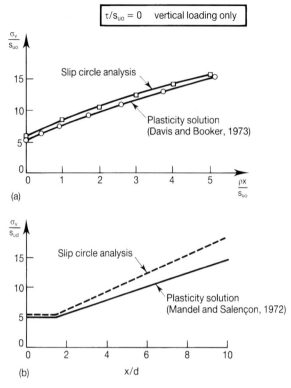

Figure 11.20 *Comparison of slip circle analysis with plasticity solutions: (a) strength increasing with depth, and (b) foundation of limited depth*

In general terms, the error in slip circle analysis could exceed 10% for reinforced embankments where $x/D > 2$, and for unreinforced embankments where $x/D > 3$. The critical distance is between the toe of the embankment and the edge of the crest, so that $x/D = nH/D$, for a side-slope $1:n$.

11.5.5 Translational stability: wedge analysis

In a wedge stability analysis, critical wedges and sliding blocks are examined to check horizontal equilibrium. In other respects the analysis and the steps that should be followed are the same as those described above for slip circle analysis.

A typical wedge mechanism for an embankment on soft soil is illustrated in Figure 11.10. The exploded view in Figure 11.21a emphasises once more the separate roles played by the reinforcement to support the thrust in the fill and to provide lateral restraint at the foundation surface.

Satisfactory foundation stability is achieved when the design shearing resistance in the soft clay, and the available force from the reinforcement, are sufficient to provide horizontal equilibrium in the foundation subject to the vertical loading from the embankment (Figure 11.21b).

212

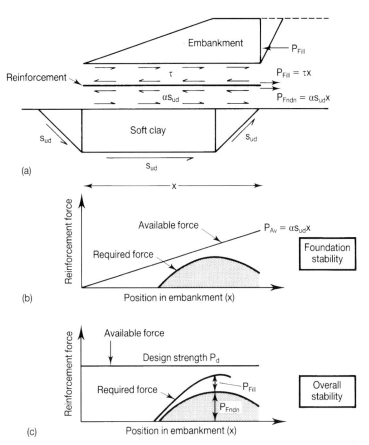

Figure 11.21 *Wedge analysis for reinforced embankments: (a) exploded view of limiting stresses, (b) check on foundation stability, and (c) check on overall stability*

To check overall stability, the design strength of the reinforcement must be greater than the maximum force required to support the lateral thrust in the fill, P_{Fill}, in addition to the maximum required force to maintain foundation stability (Figure 11.21c).

11.5.6 Method of slices

More general methods of limit equilibrium analysis may be applied to embankments on soft soil, such as the method of slices. Both force and moment equilibrium may be examined, and more detailed consideration given to the equilibrium on inter-slice boundaries. Whatever method is used, it is essential that both foundation stability and overall stability are examined for a reinforced embankment.

The simple slip circle analysis and translating wedge analysis described in this chapter are adequate for preliminary design purposes, and in many cases for final design. The methods give very similar results to more sophisticated analyses, and capture well the main mechanics in reinforced embankments. The uncertainty in evaluating the current soil shearing resistance, the interaction between the reinforcement and the foundation, and the design strength for the reinforcement, will often outweigh the gain in computational accuracy.

More complex slip mechanisms with multiple slices are useful, however, where many different strengths apply in soil zones within the embankment and foundation. An example would be the analysis for stage construction where the clay experiences different levels of applied stress and degree of consolidation, giving different undrained strengths depending on position beneath the embankment.

11.6 Analytical solutions

Analytical solutions are useful for preliminary design investigations, and for making rough checks on designs, as an adjunct to limit equilibrium methods. Their benefit is that they can be applied quickly and without computation. Analytical solutions have been derived for foundations of uniform strength and limited depth, and strength increasing with depth, and have been shown to give results comparable with more sophisticated methods, over the applicable range.

The derivation of the equations is not given here for reasons of length (see Jewell, 1988). Horizontal equilibrium of a rectangular block in the foundation is considered (Figure 11.22). The most critical loading is at the edge of the crest and this defines the

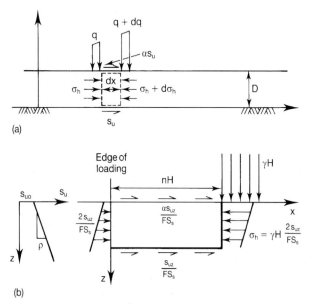

Figure 11.22 *Assumed equilibrium for analytical solutions: (a) foundation of limited depth, and (b) foundation with strength increasing with depth*

critical length, nH, for an embankment of height, H, and uniform side-slope, $1:n$. The equations below are for this most critical case. The more general use of the analysis to find the required reinforcement force at other positions in the embankment is illustrated in the design example (Section 11.8).

The equations are expressed in terms of the factor of safety and maximum required reinforcement force. This reflects the use of the equations to check stability and evaluate the maximum required force. As usual, the factor of safety, FS_s, defines the proportion of the representative soil shearing resistance, s_u, that is mobilised, s_{um}, to maintain stability (Section 6.3.4),

$$s_{um} = \frac{s_u}{FS_s} \qquad ...(11.7)$$

and design values are used for the other parameters in the analysis.

The solutions apply for embankments which exert significant loading on the foundation clay, consistent with the definition of 'soft clay' given earlier. In general,

$$\frac{FS_s \gamma H}{s_u} = \frac{\gamma H}{s_{um}} \geq 6 \qquad ...(11.8)$$

It is the coefficient, α, which defines the magnitude of inward shear stress applied to the foundation surface, αs_{um}, and is a critical parameter for design. The ultimate limit to this interaction is the maximum shear stress that can be developed between the soil and the underside of the reinforcement. But the compatibility between the extension in the reinforcement and the deformation in the foundation may influence the magnitude of the coefficient which can be mobilised. In an unreinforced embankment, there is a net outward shear stress acting on the foundation surface because of the thrust in the fill, $\alpha < 0$.

11.6.1 Foundation of uniform strength and limited depth

The analysis is for a foundation of uniform undrained shear strength, s_u, and limited depth, D, underlain by a rough stratum. The equations are found from integration of the incremental equilibrium shown in Figure 11.22a. The integration is over a distance, $x = nH$, between the toe and crest of the embankment where the maximum loading is $\sigma_v = \gamma H$.

The factor of safety in a reinforced embankment is:

$$FS_s = \frac{s_u}{\gamma H}\left(4 + (1 + \alpha)\frac{nH}{D}\right) \qquad ...(11.9)$$

and the maximum reinforcement force required to provide the above stability is:

$$P_R = \gamma H^2 \left(\frac{\alpha n D}{4D + (1 + \alpha)nH} + \frac{K_{ad}}{2} \right) \qquad \text{...(11.10)}$$

where the design value of the active earth pressure coefficient, K_{ad}, is for the design angle of friction, ϕ'_d, i.e.

$$K_{ad} = \frac{1 - \sin \phi'_d}{1 + \sin \phi'_d} \qquad \text{...(11.11)}$$

If the reinforcement were not included, the factor of safety in the unreinforced embankment would be:

$$FS_s = \frac{s_u}{\gamma H} \left(\frac{8D + 2nH}{2D + K_{ad}H} \right) \qquad \text{...(11.12)}$$

Please note the range for which the solutions apply (Equation 11.8).

11.6.2 Foundation with strength increasing with depth

Now consider a foundation with an undrained shear strength, s_{uz}, that increases linearly with depth, z, at a rate, ρ, from an initial shear strength at the ground surface, s_{uo} (Figure 11.22b). Again, the solution considers the horizontal equilibrium of a rectangular block of soil in the foundation, the critical depth of which is determined by calculus.

The factor of safety in a reinforced embankment is,

$$FS_s = \frac{s_{uo}}{\gamma H} \left(4 + \frac{\rho n H}{s_{uo}} + 2 \sqrt{\frac{2(1 + \alpha)\rho n H}{s_{uo}}} \right) \qquad \text{...(11.13)}$$

and the maximum required reinforcement force mobilised to maintain the above equilibrium is:

$$P_R = \gamma H^2 \left(\frac{\alpha n s_{uo}}{FS_s \gamma H} + \frac{K_{ad}}{2} \right) \qquad \text{...(11.14)}$$

where the factor of safety, FS_s, is defined by Equation (11.13), and the mobilised earth pressure coefficient, K_{ad}, found from Equation (11.11).

The critical depth of the sliding block is:

$$z_{crit} = \sqrt{\frac{(1 + \alpha)s_{uo}nH}{2\rho}} \qquad \text{...(11.15)}$$

The factor of safety for an unreinforced embankment is also found from Equation (11.13) but using the value for α corresponding to the outward shear stress exerted by the unreinforced fill:

$$\alpha = - \frac{K_{ad}}{2n} \frac{FS_s \gamma H}{s_{uo}} \qquad \text{...(11.16)}$$

An initial guess, $\alpha = -0.5$, in Equation (11.13) gives an initial factor of safety, FS_s, that may be substituted into Equation (11.16) to recalculate α. Convergence is rapid. The critical depth of the sliding block may be found from Equation (11.15).

As before, the range for which the solutions apply is defined by Equation 11.8.

11.6.3 Reinforcement stiffness

The analysis may be extended to assess the required reinforcement stiffness by equating the lateral deflection at the surface of the foundation with the extension of the reinforcement, caused by the force exerted by the fill and the shear stress mobilised between the foundation and the reinforcement.

An approximate (slightly conservative) expression for the extension in the reinforcement due to the thrust in the fill is,

$$\delta_r^{fill} = \frac{1}{J} \frac{K_{ad} \gamma H^2}{2} \left(\frac{L_s}{3} + \frac{L_c}{2} \right) \qquad \text{...(11.17)}$$

where $L_s = nH$ is the length of the embankment side-slope, $L_c/2$ is the half-width of the crest, and J is the stiffness of the reinforcement, the other parameters having been defined previously.

An approximate expression for the extension in the reinforcement caused by the shear stress ($\alpha \geq 0$) applied by the foundation surface is,

$$\delta_r^{fndn} = \frac{\alpha s_{ud}}{J} \frac{(L_s + D)^2}{2} \qquad \text{...(11.18)}$$

The corresponding lateral deflection at the surface of a foundation of uniform strength and limited depth is given in Table 11.1 (from the analysis in Section 11.2.2). The required reinforcement stiffness, J_{Req}, for the envisaged equilibrium may now be found by equating the soil deflection and the reinforcement extension to give,

$$J_{Req} = \frac{1}{(1 - \alpha) s_{ud}} \frac{G}{} \left(K_{ad} \gamma H^2 \left(\frac{nH}{3D} + \frac{L_c}{2D} \right) + \alpha s_{ud} D \left(1 + \frac{nH}{D} \right)^2 \right) \qquad \text{...(11.19)}$$

The following should be noted. Equation (11.19) is valid for cases, $\alpha \geq 0$, and applies to embankments on foundations of uniform strength and limited depth (Section 11.6.1). The embankment should be proportioned using Equations (11.9), with a selected design value, α, to determine the factor of safety, FS_s. Only these values should be used in Equation (11.19). The design shearing resistance in the foundation is defined as, $s_{ud} = s_u/FS_s$, and the design earth pressure coefficient is defined in Equation (11.11).

The adequacy of the reinforcement stiffness is a question of serviceability rather than stability, as is discussed further in Section 11.7. If it were assumed, for example, that 90% of the representative values of the foundation and fill shearing resistance were mobilised in the working equilibrium, then the value of α in Equation (11.9) would be reduced by trial and error to find the equilibrium with $FS_s \approx 1.1$, corresponding with $s_{ud} \approx 0.90s_u$. Reducing α reduces the reinforcement force in the analysis, and hence the factor of safety. The lesser value of α corresponding to the new equilibrium with $FS_s \approx 1.1$ would then be used in Equation (11.19) together with the serviceability values of s_{ud} and K_{ad} to define the required reinforcement stiffness for serviceability.

In effect the analysis provides an expression of compatibility which links the elongation in the reinforcement to the assumed maximum (allowable) shear strain in the soft clay. The link is through the parameter, G/s_{ud}, which is evaluated by selecting the magnitude of shear strain, γ_{max}, required to mobilise the design shearing resistance, s_{ud}. The secant shear modulus for the clay, $G = \tau/\gamma$, then has a value, $G/s_{ud} = 1/\gamma_{max}$, when the design shearing resistance is mobilised.

The analysis above is for a foundation with uniform strength and limited depth. The more general analysis of serviceability is described in Section 11.7.3.

11.7 Parameters for design

The selection of design values for the ultimate and serviceability limit state analysis of reinforced embankments on soft soil is described in the following sections. The application of the limit state concepts is considered first.

11.7.1 Limit states

The separate limit states of ultimate collapse and serviceability should be considered in the design of a reinforced embankment. At least the conditions at the end of construction and at the end of foundation consolidation have to be examined. Stability at the end of the service life of the embankment would also need to be considered where the reinforcement was intended to play a long-term role, but this is not the usual case for embankments on soft soil and is not discussed further below.

For ultimate limit state analysis, design values are selected for the ultimate resistances of the soil and the reinforcement, for their interaction parameters, and for the embankment self-weight and any externally applied loads. The design values must apply to the design situations being considered (Section 6.1). Analysis is used to demonstrate that the internal stability, the foundation stability and the overall stability in the embankment are sufficient to guard against the envisaged ultimate limit states. These must cover critical stages of embankment construction, loading, and foundation consolidation.

The consequence of an ultimate limit state is either collapse of the embankment involving rupture of the reinforcement or gross sliding of the foundation or fill relative to the reinforcement.

Expected values of the parameters are adopted in the analysis of serviceability (Sections 6.2 to 6.5) in which the lateral deformation and the settlement of the embankment are the major concerns. In contrast to the ultimate limit state, where the design strength of the reinforcement is governed by the risk of rupture, the serviceability strength is governed by an allowable tensile elongation in the reinforcement (Section 6.4.1).

The limit equilibrium methods of analysis for serviceability described below have proved adequate for routine design purposes. It is emphasised, however, that only a numerical analysis (such as the finite element method) can predict in detail the embankment and foundation deformations, and their development with time.

11.7.2 Ultimate limit states

The design values and safety margins recommended below follow the guidance in Sections 6.2 to 6.4.

Loadings and water pressures

The maximum expected unit weight of the fill, γ_{max}, should be selected, together with the most critical embankment cross-section in the chainage covered by the analysis.

Usually no allowance is made for porewater pressures or water-filled tension cracks in free-draining fills. However, possible construction-induced porewater pressures and tension cracks in clayey or fine-grained fills should be considered. A water-filled tension crack can significantly affect embankment stability.

The worst expected live loadings should be used, allowing for equipment and stockpiled materials during construction. A minimum vertical surcharge on the crest, $q = 5$ kN/m^2, is recommended in all cases as a prescriptive measure to allow for unexpected over-filling or surcharge loading.

Soil properties

Relatively large deformations may occur in embankments on soft soil and the critical state angle of friction for the soil fill, ϕ_{cv}, is recommended for design. This applies to all fills, so that $c'_d = 0$ and $\phi'_d = \phi'_{cv}$.

A representative value of the current undrained shearing resistance at large strain in the soft clay is the relevant strength for the analysis of ultimate limit states. Methods to measure and predict this strength are discussed in Section 5.3.4. Any consolidation in the foundation with respect to the applied stresses from the embankment loading should always be taken into account (Section 11.3.2).

When the representative undrained strength is selected conservatively, as recommended above, only a relatively small additional partial factor of safety need be applied to define the design strength, $s_{ud} = s_u/FS_s$. The partial factor, FS_s, would typically be in the range 1.1 to 1.5, with the value reflecting the confidence in the knowledge of the foundation soil properties, the consequences of the envisaged limit state, and the duration of the envisaged design situation.

A higher partial factor of safety on the undrained shearing resistance of the soft clay would normally be used for the long-term stability following consolidation (Section 11.3.2).

The most appropriate analysis for the long-term stability of an embankment on soft soil remains under discussion, however (Section 11.3.2). Thus it is necessary to think carefully of the uncertainties being guarded against and the risk that these could lead to a sudden change in loading and failure. The reserve of strength in soft clay to resist rapid (undrained) shear is significantly less than to resist slow (drained) shear (Figure 11.13). It is pragmatic to use both undrained strength analysis (as recommended in this chapter) and effective stress analysis when investigating the long-term stability of embankments on soft soil. But the factor of safety required in the effective stress analysis should reflect the potential shortcomings of the analysis for this application (Section 11.3.2).

The recommended soil properties for ultimate limit state analysis are summarised in Table 11.2.

Reinforcement material properties

The case where the reinforcement only maintains the short-term stability of an embankment is considered here. The strength of geotextile materials gradually reduce with time (Section 2.4), and to ensure that an adequate allowance for time has been made, the design strength should be selected assuming that the reinforcement has to support the design load continuously until consolidation in the foundation is complete. The recommended design loading period, t_d, is the sum of the time required for embankment construction and the time to achieve 90% consolidation in the foundation.

Table 11.2 Recommended soil properties for ultimate limit state analysis

Foundation soil	Criterion for design	Design
Foundation shearing resistance	Large-strain value	s_{uz}
Safety margin	Construction $(FS)_s \approx$ 1.1 to 1.3 Long-term $(FS)_s \approx$ 1.3 to 1.5	$s_{ud} = \dfrac{s_{uz}}{FS_s}$
Granular fill Unit weight Shearing resistance	Maximum expected Large-strain value	$\gamma_d = \gamma_{max}$ $\phi'_d = \phi'_{cv}$

The design strength for the geotextile reinforcement must allow for the conditions in the ground which requires an allowance for the reduction in strength due to mechanical damage, f_d, and due to the soil environment, f_{env} (Section 6.4).

The material factor, f_m, provides a margin of safety between the design strength and the expected rupture strength of the reinforcement at the end of the design loading period, and would normally have a value in the range 1.3 to 1.5 (Table 6.1). Because of the relatively short period under load in embankments on soft soil, the lower partial factor is usually adequate.

The main reinforcement properties for ultimate limit state analysis are summarised in Table 11.3.

Interaction properties

There are two main interactions between the reinforcement and the soil which need to be considered, between the reinforcement and the fill above it, and between the reinforcement and the soft clay below it.

The bond coefficient and the direct sliding coefficient are equal for continuous reinforcement materials that separate the soil on either side, such as woven geotextiles, (Section 4.4). For these materials in free-draining fill, the appropriate interaction coefficient is typically in the range, $0.90 \geq \alpha_{ds} \geq 0.60$, depending on the surface roughness of the geotextile material. There are fewer data on the interaction between geotextiles and soft clay under rapid shear, where additional factors such as the drainage conditions at the interface need to be considered. The direct shear tests by Garbulewski (1990), however, indicate that a relatively high proportion of the strength of clay can be mobilised at a clay-to-geotextile interface.

Table 11.3 Recommended reinforcement properties for ultimate limit state analysis

Strength	Criterion for design	Design
Design life	Time for 90% consolidation	$t_d = t_{90}$
Design temperature	Maximum buried temperature	T_d
Reference strength	Reference strength at (t_d, T_d)	$(P_{Ref})_{t,T}$
Mechanical damage	Fill type and construction procedure	f_d
Influence of soil environment	Soil and water exposure for (t_d, T_d)	f_{env}
Expected field strength		$(P_{Field})_{t,T} = \dfrac{(P_{Ref})_{t,T}}{f_d f_{env}}$
Material factor	Margin between design and expected field strength, typically $f_m \approx 1.3$	f_m
Design strength		$(P_d)_{t,T} = \dfrac{(P_{Field})_{t,T}}{f_m}$

The interaction between a geotextile and the top surface of a soft clay foundation can be influenced by several factors.

1. The undrained shear strength at the surface of the clay may be greater than at some depth, 200 mm or 500 mm say, below the ground surface (Section 5.3.3).
2. The surface of the soft clay, at the interface with the geotextile, is a drainage boundary at which the excess porewater pressures caused by construction would dissipate quickly.
3. When the geotextile is placed on existing (unprepared) ground, the interface may be affected by plant materials, roots and other surface detritus.

No general recommendation can be made for such variable conditions. Rather, it is suggested that at least three modes of relative slippage between the foundation clay and the reinforced embankment be considered.

1. Undrained slip at the clay-to-geotextile interface for which an 'undrained' direct sliding coefficient, α_{ds}^u, of the order 0.3 to 0.5, might be assumed (i.e. 30 to 50% of the undrained strength at the clay surface may be mobilised).
2. Partially or fully drained slip at the same interface, analysed in terms of effective stress, the effective angle of friction for the soft clay and a frictional direct sliding coefficient, α_{ds} (Section 4.5).
3. Slip entirely within the clay, away from the reinforcement, just below a strong surface crust.

Sometimes the reinforcement is placed above the clay on a working platform of granular fill. In this case the direct sliding at the reinforcement level would be within the granular fill. Consideration would then need to be given to the fill-to-soft-clay interface.

What is being sought are the possible mechanisms that could limit the load transfer between the base of the reinforced embankment and the soft clay. In the limit, a pessimistic assumption of no load transfer at this interface, $\alpha = 0$, could be examined.

The case for geogrids (as opposed to woven geotextiles) is complicated by the different interaction coefficients for direct sliding and bond mechanisms of interaction (Section 4.4), and by the possible penetration of soil through the grid apertures. The distinguishing feature between the bond and direct sliding modes of interaction is whether the soil on one side of the geogrid is moving laterally with respect to the geogrid only, or with respect to both the geogrid and the soil on the other side (Figure 4.6). For example, foundation failure in the soft clay beneath a stable reinforced embankment (Figure 11.10), or internal failure by direct sliding of the embankment fill over the reinforcement layer (Figure 11.7), are both failure modes for which the coefficient of direct sliding would be the relevant interaction parameter.

The coefficient of direct sliding between geogrids and free-drainage soil is typically in the range, $0.90 \geq \alpha_{ds} \geq 0.70$, depending on the geogrid material and geometry, and the soil properties (Section 4.5). Again, there are few data on the direct sliding resistance of soft clay over geogrids.

A different value of the interaction coefficient is normal on the upper and lower sides of reinforcement that separates dissimilar soils.

11.7.3 Analysis for serviceability

The finite element method has been used to carry out theoretical investigations into the influence of reinforcement stiffness on embankment performance and are summarised by Rowe and Mylleville (1989) and Hird and Kwok (1900). In general, the shearing strength in the foundation and the fill are found to be mobilised relatively rapidly compared to the development of tensile force in the geotextile reinforcement at the embankment base. Unfortunately it is not possible to develop a compatibility curve for embankments on soft soil similar to that for steep slopes and walls. But the same pattern of behaviour applies, namely rapid mobilisation of soil strength compared to reinforcement force so that at the working equilibrium much of the safety resides in unused capacity of the reinforcement.

The reinforcement stiffness defines the relation between load and elongation, and depends on the time under load and the ambient temperature (Section 2.3.2).

$$J_{t,T} = \frac{P_R}{\varepsilon_r} \qquad ...(11.20)$$

The influence of the reinforcement stiffness on the equilibrium at the end of construction, for an embankment that is just stable when unreinforced, is illustrated by the numerical results in Figure 11.23. (The unreinforced case is with 'zero' reinforcement stiffness.) The maximum lateral displacement in the unreinforced embankment, 750mm (Figure 11.23a), and the maximum (immediate) vertical settlement, 250mm (Figure 11.23b), are both markedly reduced by the reinforcement. The improvement due to the reinforcement depends critically on the reinforcement stiffness, but with diminishing returns (as discussed in Section 11.2.2). A balance must be found between the improvement and the cost of the reinforcement.

Limit equilibrium analysis can be used to investigate serviceability. Expected values for the soil strength and the loadings are used in the analysis to calculate the distribution of maximum required force for the expected, serviceability equilibrium (Figures 11.19d and 11.21c). The elongation of the reinforcement is then determined from the reinforcement stiffness properties.

It is the reinforcement deformation that is used to assess embankment serviceability. The maximum reinforcement elongation, and the total extension in the reinforcement between the centreline and the toe of the embankment, are both considered (Figures 11.23a and b). The reinforcement extension indicates the likely lateral deflection at the toe of the embankment.

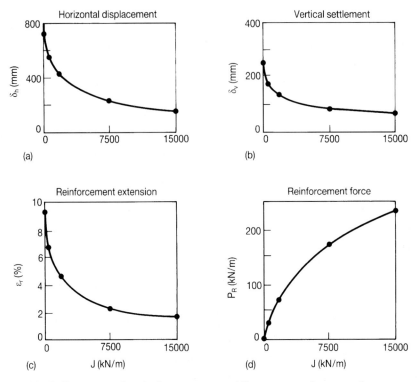

Figure 11.23 *Influence of reinforcement stiffness on the maximum values of embankment displacement and reinforcement elongation (after Hird and Kwok, 1990)*

The acceptable magnitude of reinforcement elongation and lateral deflection depend on the amount of deformation that may be tolerated in the embankment. In current practice, a limit to the maximum reinforcement elongation is often set in the range 2 to 5%, with the higher values being appropriate to relatively low embankments on very soft soils.

Discussion on parameters for serviceability

Guidance on the choice of expected values for the design parameters is given in Sections 6.2 to 6.4. The assumed shearing resistance in the fill and the foundation dominate the results of the analysis, however, and these are considered further below.

The concern for embankment serviceability is the behaviour at modest deformation, before any significant zones of localised shear deformation have developed in the fill or the foundation soil.

When the deformation is limited, it may be reasonable to assume that the representative peak angle of friction is developed in the fill, since this is already a cautious estimate of the peak strength (Section 6.3.1). Otherwise the guidance in Section 6.3.3 should be followed, and a partial factor of the order 1.25 applied to the representative peak shearing resistance to derive a mobilised strength for the analysis of serviceability, $\phi'_m = \tan \phi'_p/1.25$. The critical state shearing resistance, ϕ'_{cv}, should be used if this is greater.

Where significant deformation may be tolerated, the representative undrained shearing resistance in the soft clay might be used for the analysis of serviceability with only a small partial factor of the order, $s_{um} = s_u/1.1$. However, where the deformation in the embankment must be more strictly controlled, a partial factor of the order 1.25 may be applied to derive a mobilised strength for analysis, $s_{um} = s_u/1.25$ (Section 6.3.4.). But note that finite element analysis should be used in cases where embankment deformation is critical.

More rapid drainage in the soft clay than allowed for in design is often observed to occur. Thin bands of more permeable soil, and the naturally greater horizontal permeability of soft clay are two reasons for this behaviour. Enhanced drainage may increase the shearing resistance in the soft clay more than is allowed for in design. This will reduce the immediate displacements in the embankment and the force in the reinforcement.

The expected reinforcement stiffness, $J_{t,T}$, is normally used directly in serviceability analysis. Note also that because the loadings are smaller, and the assumed soil shearing resistances greater, than in the ultimate limit state analysis, the reinforcement interaction parameters do not normally enter into the analysis of serviceability.

Embankment settlement

The main source of settlement beneath an embankment on soft soil is due to consolidation in the foundation, and so unreinforced and reinforced embankments settle to a similar degree. However, by restraining the foundation against lateral displacements, the immediate settlements caused by undrained shear will be reduced by reinforcing an embankment (Figure 11.23b). More uniform settlement in reinforced embankments is also frequently observed, and this can improve serviceability, for example where a road pavement is to be constructed before the end of consolidation.

Some lateral displacement often occurs during consolidation, and this can further extend the reinforcement. The phenomenon is simply mentioned, since it has not been observed to cause any problems to date in the performance of reinforced embankments designed as described above.

11.7.4 Reinforcement mattress design

Cellular reinforcement mattresses formed from polymer grids have been used successfully for construction on soft sites (see Figure 3.3). The cellular mattress provides a relatively stiff working platform, which can bridge over weak spots, as described by Paul (1988).

It was thought that new stabilising mechanisms might stem from the bending stiffness when the mattress is filled with compact granular soil. However, the evidence suggests that it is the tensile properties which govern behaviour, and the tensile force in the mattress that improves stability (Bonaparte and Christopher, 1987). This has been demonstrated in numerical analyses by Symes (1984), Low and Duncan (1985) and Hird and Kwok (1990). Trial embankments built to compare the performance of mattress and horizontal reinforcement arrangements showed no marked difference (Busbridge *et al.*, 1985).

With the present knowledge, therefore, it is recommended that the tensile properties of a reinforcement mattress should meet the same design criteria as if the reinforcement were simply placed horizontally. In other words, the net tensile force in the mattress is what improves the embankment stability.

11.8 Design example

The design example illustrates the analysis for an embankment on soft soil under conditions at the end of rapid construction, including analysis for the reinforcement stiffness.

11.8.1 Embankment details

A 200m length of a 4m high road embankment, with a crest width 15m, will cross an area of up to 4m depth of soft clay, which is underlain by stronger alluvial deposits. The representative undrained strength of the clay is found from a field vane and laboratory triaxial compression tests to be $s_u = 15$ kN/m^2, almost constant with depth.

Possible unreinforced and reinforced alternatives for the embankment are to be considered in a preliminary design review, assuming the embankment is built rapidly in one stage. Thus the end-of-construction stability is the focus in the calculations below.

Granular fill is available in the area and it is assumed that this will be used for construction. The fill has a maximum unit weight 21 kN/m^3, but the expected unit weight, after field compaction, is 20 kN/m^3. The representative peak angle of friction for the compacted fill measured in direct shear tests is $\phi_p' = 40°$, and the strength at large strain is $\phi_{cv}' = 33°$ (Section 5.2.2).

Woven geotextiles made from polyester are to be considered for the reinforcement, and these are available with a range of index strengths between 100 kN/m and 400 kN/m.

It is assumed for the preliminary design investigation that 90% of foundation consolidation will be achieved within two years of the end of filling, and that the embankment will then be stable, without need for reinforcement (Section 11.3.1). The analysis for foundation consolidation and settlement, the potential application of wick drains, and the long-term stability in the embankment, are important aspects of the embankment design which are not included below for reasons of length.

From the above, a maximum design loading period for the reinforcement is selected, $t_d = 2.5$ years, together with a representative temperature for conditions in the ground,

226

T_d = 20°C. Under these conditions, the manufacturer's data show that the reference strength at the end of the design life is 60% of the index strength (Table 11.3).

An allowance for damage to the reinforcement from construction and compaction of the granular fill, f_d = 1.2, is selected (Table 2.2). A relatively small allowance for environmental degradation, f_{env} = 1.1, is assumed because of the chemically neutral conditions at the site and the relatively short design life. The minimum recommended partial factor of safety between the expected reinforcement strength in the ground and the design strength, f_m = 1.3, is chosen (Table 11.3).

The properties for two of the available woven polyester geotextiles are summarised in Table 11.4.

For the design conditions, the load-elongation properties of the polyester reinforcement may be approximated to be linear, with a cumulative elongation at rupture of 10%. Thus the secant stiffness of the reinforcement, $J_{t,T}$ = $P_{Ref}/0.1$, may be determined and the values are given in Table 11.4.

The coefficient of direct sliding between granular fill and the woven geotextile is assumed to be, α_{ds} = 0.70. The actual coefficient is likely to be higher, and this will be checked for the actual combination of fill and reinforcement selected for the project. A limiting value for the interaction between the reinforcement and the surface of the soft clay, α = 0.5, is selected for design. As part of the design study, an alternative design is considered in which the reinforcement is assumed only to support the lateral thrust in the fill, α = 0.

11.8.2 Ultimate limit state

The greatest expected unit weight of the fill and the critical state angle of friction are appropriate for the analysis of ultimate limit states, γ_d = 21 kN/m³ and ϕ'_d = 33°. It may be noted that this assumed design strength in the fill is equivalent to a partial factor, $\tan \phi'_d$ = $\tan \phi'_p/1.3$. An embankment height, H_d = 4.5m, is assumed to make some allowance at this design stage for immediate and consolidation settlement of the embankment (i.e. overfilling), and any unexpected temporary surcharges (see Figure 11.24).

Two different levels of safety (or strength mobilisation) in the soft clay are to be investigated, with a partial factor of safety on the foundation strength, FS_s = 1.30 and 1.10. Although the second design is less safe, it can be an attractive option where greater

Table 11.4 Two available woven polyester geotextiles

Index strength (kN/m)	P_{index}	200	400
Reference strength (kN/m)	$(P_{Ref})_{t,T}$	120	240
Field strength (kN/m)	$(P_{Field})_{t,T}$	91	182
Design strength (kN/m)	$(P_d)_{t,T}$	70	140
Secant stiffness (kN/m)	$(J_{Ref})_{t,T}$	1200	2400

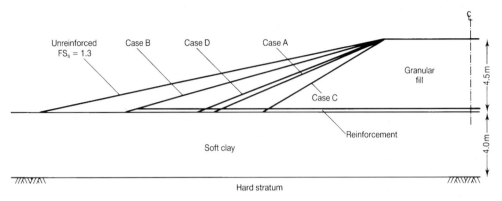

Figure 11.24 *Possible embankment cross-sections for the design example*

embankment deformation is acceptable and observational control of the construction can be adopted. The latter requires provision in the contract for a halt to filling for a suitable rest period where excessive deformation or porewater pressures are observed.

The design analysis below uses the equations presented in this chapter, and can be followed through numerically (Tables 11.5 and 11.6 for the cases shown in Figure 11.24). In practice this would only be a first stage that would be followed by more

Table 11.5 Ultimate limit state results to achieve FS_s = 1.3 on the clay strength

			Case A	Case B	Unreinforced
Reinforced FS	FS_s		1.30	1.30	—
Shear on foundation	α		0.50	0.00	−0.24
Unreinforced FS	FS_s	Eqn. (11.12)	0.93	1.11	1.30
Side slope	n	Eqn. (11.9)	1:2.5	1:3.7	1:4.9
Side-slope angle	β		22°	15°	12°
Required force (kN/m)	P_R	Eqn. (11.10)	127	62	0

Notes: $P_{Fill} = K_{ad}\gamma_d H^2/2$ = 63kN/m

Table 11.6 Ultimate limit state results to achieve FS_s = 1.1 on the clay strength

			Case C	Case D	Unreinforced
Reinforced FS	FS_s		1.10	1.10	—
Shear on foundation	α		0.50	0.00	−0.24
Unreinforced FS	FS_s	Eqn. (11.12)	0.81	0.94	1.10
Side slope	n	Eqn. (11.9)	1:1.75	1:2.6	1:3.6
Side-slope angle	β		30°	21°	16°
Required force (kN/m)	P_R	Eqn. (11.10)	116	63	0

Notes: $P_{Fill} = K_{ad}\gamma_d H^2/2$ = 63kN/m

detailed investigation using limit equilibrium analysis. In cases where the deformation is critical, the design cross-section would also be checked using finite element analysis.

The two standard products in the range of woven polyester geotextiles that would satisfy the embankment design strength requirements are those with an index strength 400kN/m and 200kN/m, respectively. The design strengths for these materials are given in Table 11.4, and in both cases the standard products are slightly stronger than strictly required. In a later stage of refinement, the design would normally be adjusted to make full use of the available strength of the reinforcement.

A point to be noted is that the geometry of each of these six embankments is as close to collapse as permitted in design. The collapse limit would be reached should the peak soil strength turn out to be lower than anticipated and equal to the design value (possibly because of poorer fill material or compaction in the embankment, and weaker foundation soil than anticipated from site investigation), and should the reinforcement strength be less than anticipated and equal to the design strength (perhaps due to more damage and degradation than expected, or through a quality control error). Such a combination of factors would cause collapse involving both rupture of the reinforcement (in the reinforced embankments) and overall slip failure.

Foundation failure is also imminent in the two 'fully' reinforced embankments (Cases A and C). If in addition to the conditions in the foundation described above the maximum sliding resistance between the underside of the reinforcement layer and the surface of the soft clay turned out to be worse than expected, and equal to the assumed design value, $\alpha = 0.5$, then failure with lateral sliding of the foundation relative to the reinforced embankment would also occur. In these two embankments, whether the collapse involved the reinforcement rupturing or lateral sliding in the foundation would depend on the particular combination of factors leading to the limit state (i.e. in some cases the reinforcement strength might be adequate and sliding occur first, and in other cases the opposite might apply with collapse being triggered by rupture of the reinforcement).

Internal stability

The internal stability mechanism of sliding across the surface of the reinforcement layer must be considered. Using a coefficient of direct sliding $\alpha_{ds} = 0.70$, in the analysis presented in Section 11.2.1, gives a limiting maximum embankment slope, 1:0.65 or $\beta = 57°$ (Equation 11.1). That such a relatively steep side-slope could be built before internal direct sliding became critical supports the observation in Section 11.2.1 that collapse by internal direct sliding is seldom critical for an embankment on soft soil.

A more critical internal stability limit to the embankment side slope is the stability on shallow slip surfaces in the slope face. For granular fill, a limit to the side-slope angle,

$\beta \leq \phi'_{cv}$, would normally suffice. This gives a limiting slope, $\beta = 33°$ or $1:1.6$, which is satisfied by all four reinforced embankment designs.

The possibility of direct sliding over the surface of the foundation in the unreinforced embankments may also be checked to complete the designs (Section 11.2.1). The worst case is with the largest factor of safety on the foundation clay, $FS_s = 1.3$, for which the steepest slope angle that prevents direct sliding is, $\beta = 40°$, or $1:1.2$ (Equation 11.2). The slope angle is much steeper than overall stability would permit, which supports the observation that such a mechanism is unlikely to be critical in embankments on soft soil (Section 11.2.2).

The conclusion from the ultimate limit state analysis is that readily available woven polyester geotextiles would allow significant steepening of the side slopes for the proposed road embankment (Figure 11.24). It is necessary now to check whether the reinforcement products can meet the serviceability requirements in the embankments.

11.8.3 Serviceability limit state

The expected conditions should be assumed in the serviceability analysis. The expected unit weight of the fill, $\gamma_d = 20\text{kN/m}^3$, would be used together with the representative peak strength in the fill, $\phi'_d = 40°$. (The latter choice may appear bold but it reflects two facts: (a) that the peak angle of friction in compact granular soil under relatively low confining stress is usually underestimated by standard laboratory testing, and (b) that the peak strength is mobilised rapidly in an active mode of deformation, as discussed in Section 5.2.2.)

The expected shearing resistance that would be mobilised in the soft clay foundation under working conditions is assumed to be, $s_{um} = s_u/1.1$, or 90% of the representative peak strength (Section 11.7.3). This gives a serviceability strength, $s_{um} = 13.5\text{kN/m}^2$. Again, this reflects the knowledge of geotextile reinforced embankment behaviour in which the soil strength is mobilised relatively rapidly with respect to the development of force in the reinforcement (Section 11.7.3).

The embankment geometry in each case was determined from the ultimate limit state analysis (Tables 11.5 and 11.6). The analysis is now repeated for each embankment to find the maximum required force for equilibrium with the combination of parameters for serviceability. The procedure when using the design equations is to reduce the parameter, α, to increase the magnitude of outward shear on the foundation, until the envisaged serviceability equilibrium is found, $FS_s = 1.1$.

The results of the serviceability analysis are summarised in Table 11.7.

Several points arise from the results in Table 11.7. First, note the increase in the unreinforced factor of safety when the expected values of the parameters are used in the analysis rather than the worst expected values assumed for the ultimate limit state. For embankment Case B, the unreinforced factor of safety for serviceability is actually

Table 11.7 Serviceability limit state to achieve $FS_s = 1.1$

			Case A	Case B	Case C	Case D
Side-slope angle	β		22°	15°	30°	21°
Unreinforced FS	FS_s	Eqn. (11.12)	1.01	1.21	0.89	1.03
Shear on foundation	α	Eqn. (11.9)	−0.08	−0.21	0.31	−0.12
Required force (kN/m)	P_R	Eqn. (11.10)	32	0	77	25
Allowable strain †	ε_{all}		3%	3%	3%	3%
Req. stiffness (kN/m)	J_{Req}	$P_{Req}/\varepsilon_{all}$	1058	0	2580	830
Toe deflection (mm)	δ_h	Tab. (11.1)	215	242	138	225
Req. stiffness (kN/m) ‡	J_{Req}	Eqn. (11.19)	(1700)	0	5400	(1340)

Notes: $P_{Fill} = K_{ad}\gamma_d H^2/2 = 44$ kN/m.
  † Assumed maximum allowable strain in reinforcement in range 2 to 5% (Section 11.7.3).
  ‡ Assumed maximum shear strain in clay $\gamma_{max} = 10\%$, giving $G/s_{ud} = 10$ (Section 11.6.3).

greater than the required value, $1.21 > 1.10$, and so no additional reinforcement force is needed for this case (Table 11.7).

It is interesting to compare the difference between the maximum required force in the ultimate and serviceability limit states by comparing the results in Tables 11.5, 11.6 and 11.7. Design based simply on an ultimate limit state analysis and a relatively high factor of safety will lead to reinforced embankment cross-sections in which little or no reinforcement force is mobilised under normal serviceability conditions. Contrast embankment design Cases A and B with Cases C and D, for example.

In the limit, if the representative shear strength in the foundation was fully mobilised, $FS_s = 1.0$, but all the other parameters and loadings were at their expected values, only embankment Case C would actually need assistance from the reinforcement to maintain equilibrium (see Table 11.7, where $FS_s = 0.89 < 1.0$ for embankment Case C).

Reinforcement stiffness

The conventional approach to checking serviceability has been to set a limit to the maximum allowable elongation in the reinforcement, and a value, $\varepsilon_{all} = 3\%$, is typical in design (Table 11.7). Thus the required stiffness of the reinforcement may be determined to enable the required force for serviceability to be mobilised at this limiting tensile elongation, as shown in Table 11.7. The expected stiffness of the woven geotextiles, $J_{Ref} = 2400$kN/m for embankment Cases A and C, and $J_{Ref} = 1200$kN/m for embankment Cases B and D (Table 11.4), meet this check on serviceability, and there is only a marginal discrepancy for embankment Case C. The criterion would be met in the latter case if the reinforcement were allowed to extend by $\varepsilon = 3.2\%$, which would probably be considered acceptable.

The simple analysis for lateral deflection at the embankment toe has been applied to the embankments under serviceability conditions, assuming a limiting maximum shear strain in the clay, $\gamma_{max} = 10\%$. This corresponds to a secant shear modulus, $G/S_{ud} = 10$ (Section 11.6.3). The expected lateral deflections are of the order 220mm, which is not unreasonable.

A second estimate for the required reinforcement stiffness comes from comparing the total extension in the reinforcement with the lateral displacement at the toe of the embankment. This comparison can be made using the analytical solution presented in Section 11.6.3 to give the results recorded in Table 11.7. (Note the results given in brackets are where $\alpha < 0$ for which the analysis will be slightly in error, Section 11.6.3.) This suggests that the selected geotextile reinforcement for embankment Cases A and B are adequate, and would also be so for embankment Case D if a slightly greater maximum shear strain in the clay were allowed, $\gamma_{max} = 11\%$. However, the analysis indicates a problem with the serviceability in embankment Case C, where much higher reinforcement stiffness, or much more shear strain in the foundation, would be needed to develop the serviceability equilibrium. This illustrates the aspect of 'diminishing returns' that applies to reinforced embankments on soft soil (Sections 11.2.2 and 11.7.3) whereby markedly increased reinforcement stiffness is needed if the embankment is to be strengthened beyond an optimum point (Figure 11.23).

11.8.4 Conclusions for the design example

The conclusion from the design study would be that embankment Cases A or D provide the most suitable reinforced design (Figure 11.24) to give a side slope 1 : 2.5. Compared to the unreinforced design with a side slope 1 : 5, this would provide an approximate fill saving, $50m^3/m$, and a saving in land-take, $22m^2/m$, for the additional cost of the reinforcement, $37.5m^2/m$ (all values are expressed per unit length of the embankment).

The cost of the reinforcement depends significantly on the decision made concerning the foundation equilibrium. The use of a lower factor of safety on the clay strength brings great benefit, but at increased risk. For the design cases above, the difference is between reinforcement with an index strength, 400kN/m and 200kN/m.

There is an argument to justify a lower factor of safety for a reinforced embankment which considers the additional reserve of strength in the reinforcement. The increased risk of foundation instability may be counterbalanced to an extent by assuming an artificially low value for the interaction between the reinforcement and the foundation clay, α. This provides a reserve of stabilising inward shear stress that would be mobilised if the foundation became distressed. Should this happen, increasing lateral deflection would be seen at the toe of the embankment, or through inclinometers, and a temporary halt to filling would be called to permit some consolidation and increase in foundation strength.

Where the risk of a temporary halt to filling is acceptable, the choice of a low factor of safety on the end of construction strength in the foundation clay, used together with a low design value for the interaction between the reinforcement and the foundation, $\alpha \approx 0$, is likely to yield the most cost-effective reinforced embankment design (Embankment Case D, above). A similar low factor of safety on the foundation could not be justified for a comparative unreinforced design because there is no extra reserve of safety from reinforcement.

11.9 Case histories

There are many published case histories of reinforced embankments, and a review of project details for 37 case histories was published by Humphrey and Holtz (1986). A discussion on the field experience may be found in Bonaparte and Christopher (1987), and an early review on reinforced embankments by Milligan and La Rochelle (1985) is recommended.

There is much published information on the analysis of reinforced embankments, particularly using the finite element method. Papers describing predictions for the behaviour of trial reinforced embankments were presented at two conferences (Bassett and Yeo, 1988, and Koerner, 1987).

More general investigations of reinforced embankment behaviour have been made using the finite element method in order to quantify the influence of the reinforcement stiffness. Notable work has been carried out by Rowe and co-workers (see Rowe, 1982, to Rowe and Mylleville, 1990), and by Hird (see Hird and Kwok, 1990). Duncan *et al.* (1987) describe a major reinforced embankment project that was designed using limit equilibrium methods, checked by finite element analysis, and compared with data from the instrumentation in the field.

Published case histories using mattress reinforcement are given by Edgar (1984), Busbridge *et al.* (1985) and Paul (1988).

11.10 Synopsis of Chapter 11

(1) The main disturbing forces for an embankment on soft soil are the vertical self-weight loading of the embankment and the outward lateral thrust in the fill.

(2) Reinforcement acts to support the outward thrust from the embankment fill and to restrain the surface of the foundation soil against lateral displacement.

(3) Three main limits for a reinforced embankment are:
   • with reinforcement of adequate strength and stiffness; failure in the foundation causing excessive settlement of the embankment and lateral spreading and heave in the foundation.
   • with reinforcement of inadequate strength; the reinforcement may rupture and cause the same type of failure as in an unreinforced embankment.

- with reinforcement of inadequate stiffness; the required forces may not be mobilised to prevent the embankment settling and spreading laterally, causing tension cracks in the fill.

(4) Limit equilibrium methods of analysis can be applied to reinforced embankments on soft soil. A modified slip circle analysis and a translating wedge analysis are described.

(5) Two approximate analytical solutions for the stability in unreinforced and reinforced embankments are presented as a tool for making preliminary design estimates.

(6) Guidance is given on the selection of design values and safety margins for design. Procedures are described to allow limit equilibrium analysis to be used to check embankment serviceability.

Key references

Davis, E.H. and Booker, J.R. (1973). The effect of increasing strength with depth on the bearing capacity of clays. *Géotechnique*, Vol. 23, No. 4, 551–563.

Humphrey, D.N. and Holtz, R.D. (1986). Reinforced embankments – a review of case histories, *Geotextiles and Geomembranes*, Vol. 4, 129–144.

Jewell, R.A. (1988). The mechanics of reinforced embankments on soft soils, *Geotextiles and Geomembranes*, Vol. 7, No. 4, 237–273.

Leroueil, S., Magnan, J.P. and Tavenas, F. (1985). *Remblais sur Argiles Molles.* Lavoisier, Paris.

12 Working platforms and unpaved roads

The working platforms and unpaved roads considered in this chapter comprise a layer of granular fill overlying a soft clay subgrade (Figure 12.1). Geotextile or polymer grid reinforcement may be placed between the fill and the subgrade to improve the load-carrying capacity. While additional reinforcement can be placed toward the surface of the granular fill, to boost the bearing capacity of the fill itself, this is not common and is not considered here.

The design of working platforms and unpaved roads has traditionally been based on semi-empirical methods (Hammitt, 1970; Giroud and Noiray, 1981). Spurred by the successful application of geotextiles to reinforce these structures, a more fundamental understanding of behaviour has been developed, so that the benefit from the reinforcement, and the required reinforcement properties, may be determined more precisely.

There are strong similarities between the action of reinforcement in a working platform or unpaved road and in an embankment on soft soil (Chapter 11). The critical factor is the deterimental effect of outward shear stress on the bearing capacity of the clay subgrade (Section 12.1).

The analysis for a working platform subjected to a temporary, or slowly moving, live load is considered first (Section 12.2). Practical examples include working platforms to install wick drains ahead of embankment construction or for the construction of a bridge abutment to be piled through soft clay. A two-dimensional loading is assumed to be applied by the tracked vehicles in these cases.

The analysis must be extended to account for the three-dimensional effects of a wheel loading on an unpaved road (Section 12.5). The static analysis applies only for a few load

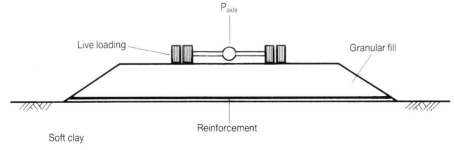

Figure 12.1 *Typical arrangement for an unpaved road*

repetitions, and empirical relations must be introduced to allow for the fatigue caused by repeated loading from traffic (Section 12.7).

The existing empirical guidance for unreinforced unpaved road design is reviewed and compared with the results from the new analysis (Section 12.9.1). The design procedure for reinforced unpaved roads developed by Giroud and Noiray (1981) is also compared with the new analysis to show the similarities, and where the improvements have been made (Section 12.9.2).

The knowledge of the response of soil to repeated loading, particularly under the conditions in an unpaved road, is at the limit of the understanding of soil mechanics. Thus a reliance on empiricism still remains in unpaved road design (Section 12.10).

12.1 Mechanics of reinforcement action

The parameters used to define the two-dimensional loading on a working platform are shown in Figure 12.2. The pressure at the ground surface, p, is applied over a width, $2B$, and is assumed to spread outward at an angle, β, through a thickness of granular fill, D. The underlying soft clay has a uniform undrained shear strength with a design value, s_{ud}, and is loaded over the larger area, $2B'$, as a result of load-spreading. The granular fill has unit weight, γ, and a design value of the angle of friction, ϕ'_d.

The application of vertical load at the ground surface causes increased vertical and horizontal stresses to develop in the granular fill which displaces laterally from beneath the loaded area. The principal stresses are vertical and horizontal beneath the centreline, and the minimum horizontal stress, $\sigma_h = K_{ad}\sigma_v$, is governed by the active earth pressure coefficient, $K_{ad} = (1 - \sin \phi'_d)/(1 + \sin \phi'_d)$.

A horizontal thrust, P_{Fill}, develops in the granular fill, and normally this is only partially supported by the lateral, passive resistance in the adjacent (unloaded) soil, P_L, (Figure 12.3). Only limited lateral resistance is available because of the low self-weight

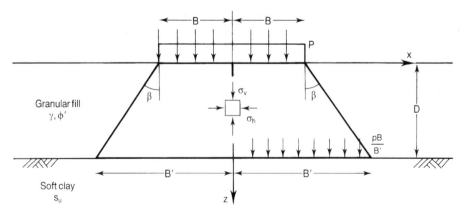

Figure 12.2 *General definitions for the two-dimensional loading on a working platform*

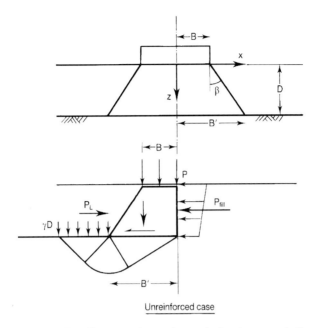

Figure 12.3 *Combined loading on the subgrade in the unreinforced case*

stresses in the unloaded fill, and the balance of the horizontal thrust is transmitted to the underlying soft clay as an outward shear stress (Figure 12.3). As described previously, the consequence of outward shear stress is to reduce the bearing capacity by as much as 50% (Section 5.5 and Equation 5.25).

Reinforcement placed just above the clay can support the outward shear stress, and the full bearing capacity of the clay can be maintained if the reinforcement is able to support all the lateral thrust (Figure 12.4). This is the main mechanism of reinforcement.

A second, minor mechanism of reinforcement stems from inward shear stress that can be exerted by the reinforcement on the surface of the clay beyond the loaded area, B', as indicated in Figure 12.4. At best, full inward shear stress at this location, $\tau = s_{ud}$, would improve the bearing capacity of the clay by an additional 11%. Analysis shows, however, that it is prudent to disregard this source of improvement for routine design. Only a small confining stress, γD, acts at the interface between the clay and the geotextile, limiting the shear stress that can be mobilised. Further, when good shear contact is assumed in analysis, a much greater reinforcement stiffness is needed if this mechanism of improvement is to be mobilised within the serviceable range of surface displacement.

The action of reinforcement described above (Figures 12.3 and 12.4) explains why vertical load-carrying capacity in a working platform or unpaved road can be improved with little or no rutting (Houlsby *et al.*, 1989). The reinforcement need not deform into

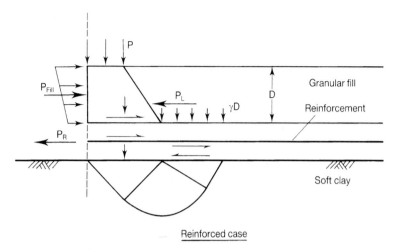

Reinforced case

Figure 12.4 *Action of the reinforcement to relieve subgrade of outward shear stress*

a curved tension-membrane before it can act, and thus it can be effective against load applied anywhere on the ground surface.

Studies suggest that the benefit from typical geotextiles acting as a tension-membrane is only significant after rutting of the order, $\delta_v/2B > 0.20$. Giroud *et al.* (1985) found for the typical wheels of heavy vehicles that the benefit from a tension-membrane was negligible up to a rut depth, $\delta_v \approx 75$mm, and contributed only a 10% improvement at a rut depth $\delta_v \approx 150$mm. The plastic deformation in the clay at such displacement would make the road susceptible to repeated loading. Indeed failure is usually observed to occur rapidly under repeated loading once rutting exceeds $\delta_v \approx 75$mm (Webster and Watkins, 1977). For these reasons, it is considered prudent in routine design to ignore the potential benefit from the reinforcement acting as a tension-membrane.

The exception to the above is where carefully channelled traffic is maintained over a significantly rutted reinforcement layer, with the fill being regraded to allow for the rutting. This special case is not considered here.

Anchorage of the reinforcement beyond the loaded area, B', is seen to be less critical than previously thought (Figure 12.2). The main tension in the reinforcement is due to the outward shear stress transmitted from the fill to the reinforcement surface within the area of vertical load-spreading (Figure 12.4). Relatively high vertical stress acts on this critical interface between the fill and the reinforcement, and an average ratio of shear to normal stress, $\tau_r/\sigma_r < 0.40$, is typical under two-dimensional loading. It is the modulus of the reinforcement that is of greater significance since it governs the force that can be mobilised with acceptable deformation in the soil.

The design method presented below is based on the above concepts which have been supported by the evidence from laboratory-scale tests and from field data (Milligan *et al.*, 1990). The basic mechanisms have been confirmed by detailed finite element studies (Burd and Brocklehurst, 1990). But most importantly, the new understanding explains the central empirical assumptions made in the previous design methods for reinforced unpaved roads (Section 12.9). In other words, analysis is catching up with the empirical knowledge.

12.2 Analysis for working platforms

Stability is governed by the bearing capacity of the soft clay, and the analysis is expressed directly in terms of the loading that must be supported by the clay (the required stresses) and the limiting resistance of the clay (the available stresses).

12.2.1 Subgrade bearing capacity

The analysis for the bearing capacity of a clay foundation under combined vertical and shear loading is described in Section 5.5. The combinations of (available) shear stress, τ_a, and normal stress, σ_a, that can be supported by the clay are defined in Equations (5.25), which for the case of a working platform are:

$$\frac{(\sigma_a - \gamma D)}{s_{ud}} = N_{ca} = 1 + \frac{\pi}{2} + \cos^{-1}\left(\frac{\tau_a}{s_{ud}}\right) + \sqrt{1 - \left(\frac{\tau_a}{s_{ud}}\right)^2} \qquad ...(12.1)$$

where, N_{ca}, is the available bearing-capacity factor, and the granular fill provides a surcharge on the clay, γD. Outward shear stress is defined as positive, $\tau_a \geq 0$, to give simpler equations.

The limiting resistance of the clay is represented by the envelope *ABCE* in Figure 12.5. The full bearing capacity, $N_{ca} = (2 + \pi)$ is only mobilised when there is no outward

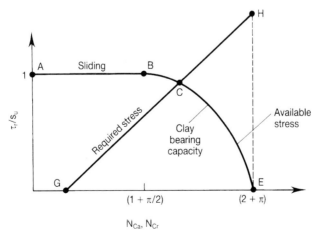

Figure 12.5 *Envelope of available subgrade resistance (ABCE) and the stress applied by surface load (GCH)*

shear stress, $\tau_a = 0$ (point E in Figure 12.5). The bearing capacity is reduced by half, $N_{ca} = (1 + \pi/2)$, when the outward shear stress reaches the limiting value, $\tau_a = s_{ud}$, (point B in Figure 12.5). Lateral sliding on the surface of the clay can then occur, under a bearing stress in the range, $0 \leq N_{ca} \leq (1 + \pi/2)$.

12.2.2 Stresses within the fill

The vertical stress within the fill is found by assuming a uniform load-spread angle, β, to give an average vertical stress at depth, z,

$$\sigma_v = \gamma z + \frac{pB}{B + z \tan \beta} \qquad ...(12.2)$$

which applies within the loaded region $ABED$ (Figure 12.6), and where p is the average pressure applied at the ground surface. Elsewhere in the granular fill,

$$\sigma_v = \gamma z \qquad ...(12.3)$$

The fill tends to displace outward from beneath the surface load and, in the limit, the horizontal stress on the centreline reduces to $\sigma_h = K_{ad}\sigma_v$. The minimum horizontal thrust, P_{Fill}, acting on the surface AD, is then:

$$P_{Fill} = \frac{K_{ad}pB}{\tan \beta} \ln \left(\frac{B'}{B} \right) + \frac{K_{ad}\gamma D^2}{2} \qquad ...(12.4)$$

where $B' = B + D \tan \beta$ is the half-width of the loaded area of clay (Figure 12.6).

Lateral, passive pressure is mobilised in the surrounding soil to resist the outward movement of fill, and a lateral resistance, P_L, develops on the surface CE (Figure 12.6),

$$P_L = \frac{K_{pm}\gamma D^2}{2} \qquad ...(12.5)$$

The mobilised passive resistance will be in the range, $K_{pd} \geq K_{pm} \geq K_o$, where the passive earth pressure coefficient $K_{pd} = 1/K_{ad}$. Because significant lateral displacement is needed to mobilise passive resistance, a smaller earth pressure coefficient may be

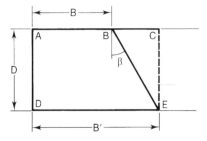

Figure 12.6 *Elemental block of fill beneath the surface pressure*

assumed, $K_{pm} = 2K_{pd}/3$, or, $K_{pd}/2$. The coefficient of earth pressure at rest, K_o, sets the lower limit for no lateral displacement in the soil at the surface CE (Section 5.1). The full passive resistance is usually assumed for the analysis of ultimate collapse, with a reduced resistance for the analysis of serviceability.

Shear load at the surface of the granular fill, such as caused by a cornering force, can be defined in proportion to the vertical load. An inclination, tan δ, defines a lateral loading, pB tan δ, (Figure 12.7). (Note that an outward acting surface load is defined by a negative inclination, tan $\delta < 0$.)

The shear stress at the surface of the clay, τ_r, depends on the applied pressure, p, and can be found by considering the horizontal equilibrium of the rectangular block of soil $ABCED$ (Figure 12.7),

$$\tau_r = p\frac{B}{B'}\left(\frac{K_{ad}}{\tan \beta}\ln\left(\frac{B'}{B}\right) - \tan \delta\right) + (K_{ad} - K_{pm})\frac{\gamma D^2}{2B'} \qquad ...(12.6)$$

12.2.3 Unreinforced design

The shear stress, τ_r, and the net vertical stress on the clay, pB/B', are linked through Equation (12.6) which defines a straight line (GCH) in Figure 12.5. The limiting equilibrium in the unreinforced case is reached when the required bearing capacity to support the applied load, N_{cr}, equals the available bearing capacity, N_{ca}. This is the point of intersection, C, of the line representing the applied loading, GCH, with the envelope representing the limiting resistance of the clay, $ABCE$ (Figure 12.5).

Equation (12.6) may be rewritten in a non-dimensional form to relate the shear stress on the clay, τ_r/s_{ud}, directly to the required bearing capacity factor, $N_{cr} = (\sigma_r - \gamma D)/s_{ud}$. Note that the vertical stress on the clay surface is $\sigma_r = pB/B' + \gamma D$, so that the required bearing capacity factor is $N_{cr} = pB/s_{ud}B'$. Equation (12.6) becomes:

$$\frac{\tau_r}{s_{ud}} = N_{cr}\left(\frac{K_{ad}}{\tan \beta}\ln\left(\frac{B'}{B}\right) - \tan \delta\right) + (K_{ad} - K_{pm})\frac{\gamma D^2}{2s_{ud}B'} \qquad ...(12.7)$$

The limiting equilibrium is sometimes reached with sliding at the clay surface, $\tau_r = s_{ud}$, when the line GCH intersects the resistance envelope in the segment AB (Figure

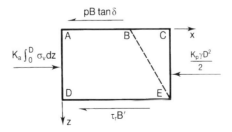

Figure 12.7 *Horizontal forces considered in the equilibrium analysis*

12.5). In other cases, bearing failure can occur, $N_{cr} = N_{ca} = (2 + \pi)$, before any outward shear stress acts on the clay (point E in Figure 12.5). This happens when the lateral resistance in the fill entirely balances the thrust in the fill.

The intersection at point C (Figure 12.5) defines the limiting equilibrium for an unreinforced working platform. The solution may be found by numerical or graphical means, since it cannot be expressed conveniently in a single formula. The limiting pressure that may be applied to an unreinforced working platform, p^u, depends directly on the unreinforced bearing capacity factor, N_c^u, which is defined by the equilibrium, $N_c^u = N_{cr} = N_{ca}$,

$$p^u = N_c^u s_{ud} \frac{B'}{B} = N_c^u s_{ud} \left(1 + \frac{D \tan \beta}{B}\right) \qquad ...(12.8)$$

12.2.4 Reinforced design

The reinforced case follows simply from the above. If the reinforcement can support the outward shear stress at the base of the fill (Figure 12.8), the full bearing capacity in the clay can be mobilised, $N_c^r = N_{ca} = (2 + \pi)$, to give a limiting resistance to surface loading, p' (Equation 12.8):

$$p' = (2 + \pi)s_{ud} \left(1 + \frac{D \tan \beta}{B}\right) \qquad ...(12.9)$$

The corresponding maximum tension in the reinforcement, P_R, due to the surface pressure, p', is then (Equation 12.9 and Figure 12.8):

$$P_R = \tau'_r B' = p'B \left(\frac{K_{ad}}{\tan \beta} \ln \left(\frac{B'}{B}\right) - \tan \delta\right) + (K_{ad} - K_{pm}) \frac{\gamma D^2}{2} \qquad ...(12.10)$$

The equilibrium for the unreinforced and reinforced working platforms, and the outward shear stress that must be supported by the reinforcement, τ'_r, are illustrated in Figure 12.9.

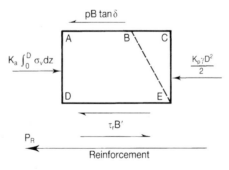

Figure 12.8 *Outward shear stress supported by the reinforcement*

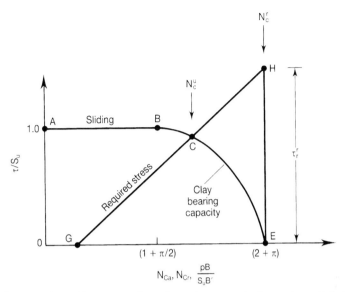

Figure 12.9 *Interaction diagram showing the unreinforced and fully reinforced equilibrium*

12.2.5 Fill bearing capacity

The above analysis may lead to values of allowable surface load that are greater than the available bearing capacity of the fill. This can be checked using conventional bearing capacity theory (Vesic, 1975). The limiting surface load that the fill can support, p_γ,

$$p_\gamma = N_{\gamma d}B\gamma \qquad \qquad ...(12.11)$$

where $N_{\gamma d}$, is the bearing capacity factor corresponding to the design angle of friction, ϕ'_d. (Note that the apparently missing factor 1/2 in Equation (12.11) is due to the width of the loaded area, $2B$.)

The bearing capacity of the fill may act as a cut-off to the envelope of available resistance as shown by the line *FDH* in Figure 12.10. In many practical cases, however, the point F falls to the right of point E, $p_{\gamma d}B/s_{ud}B' > (2 + \pi)$, and the fill bearing capacity is not a critical factor (Figure 12.10).

The analysis for bearing capacity is summarised in Section 5.4 where values for the bearing capacity factor, N_γ, are listed (Table 5.3).

Direct sliding

The possibility of direct sliding of the fill over the reinforcement must be considered. A good stress transfer between the fill and the reinforcement is highly desirable, and a substantial coefficient of direct sliding resistance is a beneficial property of reinforcement material. The interlock afforded by geogrids can be a positive advantage in this respect.

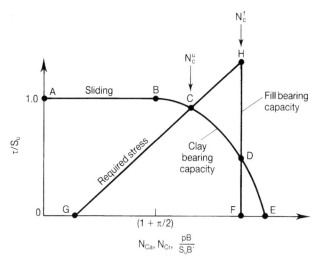

Figure 12.10 *Limit imposed by the bearing capacity of the fill* ($N_c^f = p\gamma B/s_u B'$)

The average ratio of shear to normal stress applied to the reinforcement, $\tau_r/\sigma_r < 0.4$, is rather low under two-dimensional loading. However, the main shear interaction between the fill and the reinforcement occurs over the outer half of the contact length, $B'/2$, and it is recommended to check for potential direct sliding in the ultimate limit state as follows, $2(\tau_r/\sigma_r) < \alpha_{ds}$ (Section 4.5).

Load-spread angle
An assumed load-spread angle in granular materials of $2:1$ or $\beta = 26.6°$, has been conventional in foundation engineering. However, substantially more load spreading can occur in relatively strong soils over soft ground, when the load-spread angle may even exceed $\beta = 45°$, in certain cases.

It is suggested that a load-spread angle, $\beta = 27°$, is likely always to be conservative, and even an angle $\beta = 31°$, as assumed by Giroud and Noiray (1981), is likely to be representative of the lower values in the range. Greater load-spreading in the range $\beta = 35°$ to $45°$ can occur in well compacted granular fill over soft clay, and this is demonstrated later.

12.2.6 Serviceability for known reinforcement properties
An important part of limit state design is to check serviceability using expected values for the loadings and the soil resistances (Chapter 6). The geotextile or geogrid reinforcement must be shown to support the required force under the working equilibrium at a deformation that is compatible with a serviceable structure. In common with the other applications of reinforced soil, acceptable serviceability is defined most simply in terms of a maximum allowable elongation in the reinforcement.

Thus ultimate and serviceability limit states are investigated in design (Section 12.3), and the maximum reinforcement force is limited by the design strength in the ultimate limit state analysis, and by the allowable force in the serviceability limit state and analysis.

The allowable force depends on the maximum allowable elongation, ε_{all}, and a value in the range 2 to 5% is often chosen, depending on the degree of deformation that is acceptable. The allowable force then depends on the reinforcement stiffness (modulus), for the relevant loading period and design temperature, $P_{all} = J_{t,T}\varepsilon_{all}$ (Section 6.4).

The case examined here is where the load-carrying capacity is governed by serviceability (i.e. the reinforcement has sufficient strength but insufficient stiffness). This occurs when the allowable reinforcement force is less than the maximum required force for the fully reinforced equilibrium, $P_{all} < P_R$, under working loads. The required force, P_R, is found from Equation (12.10), and in this case the working platform can only support a reduced load, $p_{all} < p'$.

The equilibrium described above is one in which the reinforcement supports only part of the outward shear stress, τ_r, up to the limit $\tau_{all} = P_{all}/B'$, with the remainder of the shear stress being supported by the clay, τ_a, as shown in Figure 12.11,

$$\tau_r - \tau_a = \tau_{all} = \frac{P_{all}}{B'} \qquad \text{...(12.12)}$$

The equilibrium is found by graphical or numerical methods. For example, a trial load is selected, $\sigma_a = pB/B'$, to determine the required outward shear stress τ_r (Equation 12.6), and the shear stress that can be suported by the clay, τ_a, (Equation 12.1). Possible

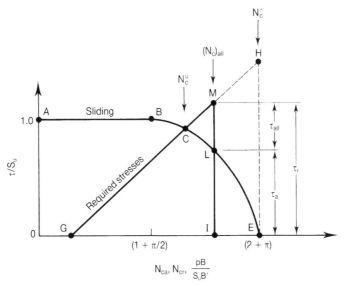

Figure 12.11 *Limit imposed by the allowable reinforcement force (*$P_{all} = \tau_{all}B'$*)*

equilibrium is checked using Equation (12.12) to see whether the allowable reinforcement force is sufficient to support the balance of outward shear stress, and the surface load is adjusted until the equilibrium is satisfied.

A simpler, approximate solution is available for preliminary analysis. If a linear approximation is made to the curved envelope of available stress (i.e. the dotted line versus the curve CE in Figure 12.11), the allowable equilibrium depends simply on the proportion of the full outward shear stress that can be supported by the reinforcement,

$$p_{all} = p^u + \frac{P_{all}}{P_R}(p^r - p^u) \qquad \qquad ...(12.13)$$

12.2.7 Serviceability for a known applied loading

The analysis above found the maximum pressure that could be applied to a working platform when the equilibrium is governed by the known stiffness of the reinforcement. Where a range of potential reinforcement materials is to be investigated, an ultimate limit state analysis is used first to define the required strength of the reinforcement. The maximum required force is then determined for serviceability under the expected surface load. Following this, the required reinforcement stiffness is determined to enable this force to be mobilised within the range of allowable tensile strain in the working platform.

The above is illustrated by a worked example (Section 12.4.2). Briefly, the interaction diagram is derived from the serviceability loadings, dimensions and resistances (i.e. Figure 12.11) and the required bearing capacity is derived, $(N_c)_{Req} = p_d B / s_{ud} B'$. One of three cases may be found (Figure 12.11):

1. If the required bearing capacity is less than the unreinforced capacity of the clay, $(N_c)_{Req} < N_c^u$, no reinforcement force is needed to maintain serviceability.
2. If the required bearing capacity is greater than the fully reinforced value, $(N_c)_{Req} < N_c^r$, then equilibrium cannot be achieved under serviceability conditions. (However, this should never be the case since the design resistances should be higher and the design loadings lower for serviceability than for ultimate conditions.)
3. The serviceability equilibrium usually falls between the above limits, and the maximum required reinforcement force corresponding to the bearing capacity, $(N_c)_{Req}$, is found from the difference between the outward shear stress caused by the loading, and the shear stress supported by the clay, $P_{Req} = (\tau_r - \tau_a)B'$.

12.3 Procedure for working platform design

The design steps and the choice of design values should follow the general guidance set out in Chapters 6 and 7. The commentary below offers specific guidance for the application of the general methods to working platforms.

A designer would normally consider stability first (the ultimate limit state), allowing for the worst expected loadings and the lowest likely resistances. The required reinforcement tension to maintain the equilibrium under the expected loadings would be investigated subsequently. A suitable reinforcement material would have sufficient strength to maintain stability at the ultimate limit state, and sufficient stiffness to enable the required force to be mobilised for the expected equilibrium without exceeding a specified maximum elongation in the reinforcement.

Usually, the fill thickness is the unknown and is required to support a known loading with a specified margin of safety. Given the properties of the subgrade soil and the granular fill, it is usually convenient to consider a range of possible fill thickness to derive a plot of the unreinforced and reinforced load-carrying capacity, and the maximum required force, versus the fill thickness. This provides a 'design chart' of fill thickness against load-carrying capacity.

12.3.1 Ultimate limit state analysis

The guidance in Chapter 6 should be followed, and stability assessed for the worst expected loading. The unsatisfactory limits include rupture of the reinforcement (Section 12.2.4), bearing capacity failure in the fill (Section 12.2.5), and direct sliding across the surface of the reinforcement (Section 12.2.5).

The worst expected load should be assumed (the most heavily loaded equipment) acting on a slightly thinner than expected thickness of granular fill (to allow for variability across the site). A partial factor of safety, $FS_s = 1.25$, is recommended to derive the design shearing resistance for the fill, $\tan \phi'_d = \tan \phi'_p/1.25$, and foundation soil, $s_{ud} = s_u/1.25$ (Section 6.3).

It is helpful to consider the link between the peak angle of friction, the relative density, and the confining stress in granular fill when interpreting laboratory test data to select a representative peak strength for design (Section 5.2.2). The choice of a representative strength for the clay subgrade should account for the relatively shallow depth involved in any slip failure (Figures 12.3 and 4). The average strength over a depth, $\sqrt{2}B'$, would normally be appropriate, but a greater depth might be considered where a relatively strong but thin crust overlies much weaker clay.

The worst expected (i.e. longest) period that the equipment may remain stationary determines the time that the reinforcement must support sustained load, t_d, and this loading should be assumed to coincide with the highest expected ambient temperature of the reinforcement in the ground, T_d (Section 6.4). The reference strength of the reinforcement is chosen to reflect these conditions. Allowance for mechanical damage, f_d, and the effects of the soil environment, f_{env}, should then be made to derive the field strength. A partial factor of safety, $f_m = 1.3$, would normally suffice as the margin of safety between the expected field strength, and the assumed design strength of the reinforcement.

The coefficient of direct sliding, α_{ds}, is the relevant interaction parameter for granular fill sliding over woven or non-woven geotextiles (Section 4.5). Allowance could be made in a detailed investigation of this property for the possible migration of water and fine soil particles through the geotextile if this could reduce the direct sliding resistance. The sliding resistance offered by geogrid reinforcement depends on whether the reinforcement is placed over a geotextile separator layer, or direct on to the clay subgrade, or just within the granular fill. Care is needed in a test programme to examine the relevant direct sliding interface. This may involve: granular fill over (a) geogrid placed on a textile separator, (b) geogrid placed on the clay subgrade, (c) geogrid underlain by granular fill, or (d) some other combination.

12.3.2 Serviceability limit state analysis

The expected values for the design parameters are used in the analysis of serviceability. A high proportion of the representative soil shearing resistances can be assumed to be mobilised, and a partial factor of safety of the order, $FS_s = 1.15$, would be appropriate. This reflects the knowledge of the working equilibrium in which the soil resistance tends to be mobilised before that of the reinforcement. It also reflects some conservative aspects in the analysis of working platforms, such as the assumed two-dimensional loading when, in practice, a tracked vehicle has only a limited length. A reduced lateral resistance in the fill should be assumed for the analysis of serviceability, perhaps only one half or one third of the full passive earth pressure, to account for the smaller lateral deformations.

The analysis with the expected loadings and resistances gives a maximum required reinforcement force for serviceability (the expected working condition). The required stiffness of the reinforcement then depends on the maximum allowable elongation, normally in the range, $\varepsilon_{all} = 2$ to 5%.

12.4 Design example: working platform

A rig weighing 350kN has to be brought on site for the construction of a piled bridge abutment. The rig has two 400mm wide tracks, spaced 2m apart, each 2.5m long and applying an essentially two-dimensional loading, $p = 175\text{kN/m}^2$. The rig will be used in various positions on the working platform, but stored off it.

The representative strength in the top 1m of the soft clay is found to be, $s_u = 25\text{kN/m}^2$, and direct shear tests on the granular fill indicate a representative peak angle of friction, $\phi'_p = 42°$, for the expected relative density in the field. The unit weight of the fill, $\gamma = 20\text{kN/m}^3$.

A range of likely fill thickness, $D = 0.3\text{m}$, 0.4m and 0.5m, is to be investigated.

12.4.1 Stability

The following parameters are selected for the ultimate limit state analysis. The half-width of the track defines the size of the loaded area, $B = 0.2\text{m}$. A slightly greater than expected loading from the rig is allowed, 400kN, giving a design loading, $p_d = 200\text{kN/m}^2$, over a total area of contact, 2m^2. The rig is assumed to apply vertical load only, $\delta = 0°$.

The design strengths of the fill, $\phi'_d = 35°$, and of the foundation, $s_{ud} = 20\text{kN/m}^2$, are found by applying a partial factor of safety, $FS_s = 1.25$. The full passive resistance in the fill is assumed to be mobilised at collapse, and the relevant earth pressure coefficients are, $K_{ad} = 0.0271$, and, $K_{pm} = K_{pd} = 3.69$. Conventional load-spreading at $2:1$ is assumed, an angle $\beta = 26.6°$.

Substituting these design values into Equation (12.7) gives the required stresses, which for $D = 0.4\text{m}$ are:

$$\frac{\tau_r}{s_{ud}} = 0.376 N_{cr} - 0.684 = 0.376\,\frac{pB}{s_{ud}B'} - 0.684 \qquad \text{...(12.14)}$$

where, $N_{cr} = pB/s_{ud}B'$.

The required stresses are plotted in Figure 12.12, the line $GCJH$, together with the limiting available resistance of the clay (Equation 12.1). The point of intersection, C, gives the unreinforced design, $N_c^u = 3.89$, when, $\tau_r/s_{ud} = 0.78$ (Section 12.2.3). The unreinforced limit occurs for a surface load (Equation 12.8),

$$p^u = N_c^u s_{ud}\,\frac{B'}{B} = 156\text{kN/m}^2 \qquad \text{...(12.15)}$$

which is less than the required design load, $p_d = 200\text{kN/m}^2$.

If the fill is reinforced, and assuming the reinforcement can support the necessary outward shear stress, $N_c^r = 5.14$, (point H in Figure 12.12), corresponding to a surface load, $p^r = 206\text{kN/m}^2$ (Equation 12.9). This is just greater than the required value, and the reinforcement has provided a 32% increase in load-carrying capacity.

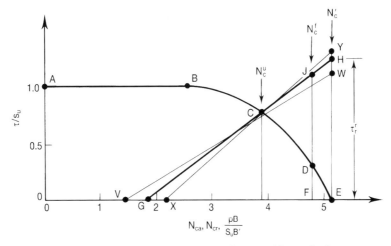

Figure 12.12 *Required and available stresses for working platform example*

The maximum required reinforcement force is then (Equation 12.10),

$$P_R = p'B \left(\frac{K_{ad}}{\tan \beta} \ln \left(\frac{B'}{B} \right) - \tan \delta \right) + (K_{ad} - K_m) \frac{\gamma D^2}{2} = 10\text{kN/m} \quad ...(12.16)$$

The shear stress exerted at the base of the fill in the reinforced case is $\tau_r/s_{ud} = 1.25$, (Equation 12.14, and point H in Figure 12.12), which represents an average shear stress ratio at the reinforcement interface, $\tau_r/\sigma_r = 1.25/(5.14 + 0.4) = 0.23$, allowing for the weight of the fill. It is recommended that the direct sliding resistance should exceed twice this value (Section 12.2.5), so that the minimum required coefficient of direct sliding resistance for the reinforcement $\alpha_{ds} > 0.46$.

The bearing capacity of the fill must be checked. The design angle of friction gives a bearing capacity factor, $N_{\gamma d} = 48$ (Table 5.3), or a bearing capacity, $p_\gamma = 192\text{kN/m}^2$ (Equation 12.11). This is slightly less than needed to support the design load, $P_d = 200\text{kN/m}^2$. The fill bearing capacity would then control the maximum load, as indicated by the vertical line FDJ in Figure 12.12, at an equivalent bearing capacity factor, $N_c^f = 4.79$.

However, the sensitivity of the bearing capacity to the assumed angle of friction should be considered. If the design angle of friction were one degree higher, $\phi' = 36°$, there would be satisfactory bearing capacity, $p_\gamma = 225\text{kN/m}^2$. The assumption, $\phi_d' = 36°$, is likely to be acceptable since it corresponds to a partial factor of safety on the fill strength, $FS_s = 1.24$, or a lumped factor of safety on the fill bearing capacity, $FS = 2.76$, (where, $N_\gamma = 156$, for $\phi_p' = 42°$, Table 5.3).

The results for the three trial depths of fill are shown on the 'design chart' of Figure 12.13. This indicates the savings in fill thickness that can be obtained by reinforcing the

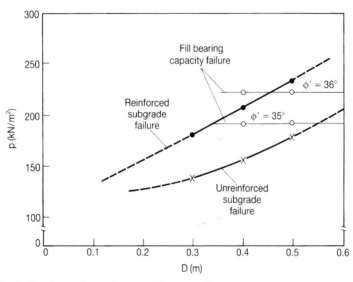

Figure 12.13 *Design chart for working platform example*

working platform, and the maximum required reinforcement force in each case. The limit set by the fill bearing capacity is also clearly represented. (The lines *VW* and *XY* dotted on Figure 12.12 are the required stresses for $D = 0.3$ and 0.5m, respectively.)

12.4.2 Serviceability

The expected geometry and the expected surface loading, $p_a = 175 \text{kN/m}^2$, would be used to check serviceability (Section 12.2.7). The mobilised resistance in the soil is found by assuming $FS_s = 1.15$, to give mobilised soil resistances, $\phi'_d = 38°$ and $s_{ud} = 21.7 \text{kN/m}^2$. Less lateral resistance in the fill is assumed, $K_{pm} = K_{pd}/2$, to reflect the smaller displacements under working conditions (Section 12.2.2). These parameters define the required stresses for equilibrium (Equation 12.7), and for $D = 0.4 \text{m}$

$$\frac{\tau_r}{s_{ud}} = 0.33 N_{cr} - 0.34 \qquad \qquad ...(12.17)$$

and the unreinforced equilibrium occurs with, $\tau_r/s_{ud} = 0.854$, and $N_c^u = 3.63$ (Equations 12.1 and 12.7).

Since more than the unreinforced bearing capacity is needed to support the serviceability load, $(N_c)_{Req} = 4.03 > 3.63$, reinforcement will be needed to maintain the serviceability equilibrium (Section 12.2.7). The outward shear stress, $\tau_r/s_{ud} = 0.986$, and the available resistance from the clay, $\tau_a/s_{ud} = 0.720$, under the serviceability loading, are found from Equations (12.17) and (12.1), respectively. These define the maximum required reinforcement force, $P_{Req} = (\tau_r - \tau_a)B'$ or $P_{Req} = 2.3 \text{kN/m}$. (This equilibrium was illustrated by the line *ILM* in Figure 12.11, showing a total outward shear stress, *IM*, an available resistance from the clay, *IL*, and the portion of shear stress carried by the reinforcement, *LM*.)

If the maximum allowable elongation is $\varepsilon_{all} = 3\%$, the minimum required reinforcement stiffness would be $J_{t,T} \geq 2.3/0.03 = 77 \text{kN/m}$.

12.4.3 Reinforcement properties

A reinforced fill of thickness, $D = 0.4 \text{m}$, would be sufficient to support the assumed design loading. A satisfactory geotextile reinforcement for this application would need a design strength $(P_d)_{t,T} \geq 10 \text{kN/m}$, a secant stiffness, $J_{t,T} \geq 77 \text{kN/m}$, and a coefficient of direct sliding resistance, $\alpha_{ds} \geq 0.46$.

The selection of a suitable reinforcement might proceed as follows. A worst expected design loading period, $t_d = 1$ week, could be assumed and a highest expected ground temperature, $T_d = 20°C$. A range of polyester grid products could be considered for which the manufacturer's data show a reference strength for the required design loading conditions of not less than 65% of the index strength (Section 6.4). Allowing for mechanical damage, $f_d = 1.2$ (Table 2.2), but assuming no environmental degradation in the temporary structure, $f_{env} = 1.0$, while allowing for a margin of safety between the expected strength in the ground and the design strength, f_m = 1.3 (Table 6.1), would define the minimum required index strength for the grid material, P_{index} = 24kN/m.

The reference strength of the grid that just satisfies the above would be $(P_{Ref})_{t,T}$ = 15.6kN/m. If the data show that this load causes a cumulative elongation, ε = 10%, for the design conditions of one week loading at 20°C under the design load, the relevant secant stiffness is $J_{t,T}$ = 156kN/m.

When placed within the granular fill, the polyester grid has a measured coefficient of direct sliding resistance, α_{ds} > 0.8.

The material properties for the above product would satisfy the three main design criteria.

12.4.4 Comparative designs

The maximum increase in load-carrying capacity in the above example was of the order of 30% (Figure 12.12). A comparatively greater reduction in fill thickness is found to support the same design load, a saving of up to 50%. For example, an unreinforced fill, D = 0.4m, would support an applied stress, p = 150kN/m², which could be supported on a reinforced fill thickness, D = 0.2m (Figure 12.12).

A wider comparison has been made for the typical parameters, B = 0.2m, tan β = 0.5, and γ = 20kN/m³ (Table 12.1). This illustrates that reinforcement is beneficial only when there is an appropriate combination of fill and foundation material properties.

The analysis shows that the capacity of a 'weak' fill over a 'strong' subgrade is always governed by bearing failure in the fill. Placing reinforcement at subgrade level will not help. Similarly, a 'strong' fill is wasted over 'weak' subgrades because the available

Table 12.1 Ratio of load-carrying capacity for reinforced and unreinforced designs (two-dimensional loading case)

Subgrade	Fill depth	ϕ'_d	ϕ'_d	ϕ'_d
S_{ud} (kN/m²)	D (m)	30°	38°	45°
10	0.20	1.29	1.10	1.00
10	0.40	1.30	1.02	1.00
		(1.14)		
30	0.20	†	1.22	1.11
30	0.40	†	1.31	1.09
			(1.06)	
80	0.20	†	†	1.16
80	0.40	†	†	1.25

( ) value in bracket where fill failure intervenes
† fill failure governs in both unreinforced and reinforced cases

lateral resistance in the fill can always counterbalance the fill thrust, and the subgrade is subjected only to vertical loading whether or not reinforcement is included.

12.5 Static analysis for unpaved roads

A two-dimensional analysis was used for working platforms (Section 12.2), where a load of much greater length than width was idealised as being infinitely long (i.e. plane strain conditions were assumed). Typical wheel loads on unpaved roads have a similar width and length, and this requires a three-dimensional analysis which may be idealised by assuming a circular load (i.e. axi-symmetric conditions are assumed).

The basic mechanics described in Section 12.1 still apply and the analysis follows the same basic steps (Section 12.2). The main difference between the two cases is the enhanced bearing capacity of clay under circular (as opposed to strip) loading, the greater benefit from load-spreading in three dimensions, and the effect of the radial shear stress loading on the reinforcement.

A slice through an unpaved road is shown in Figure 12.14. A circular load of radius, R, is assumed to act on the surface of a fill thickness, D. Load-spreading at an angle, β, increases the area over which the load acts in the ratio, $(R'/R)^2$.

12.5.1 Subgrade bearing capacity

The combination of outward shear stress, τ_a, and normal stress, σ_a, that can be resisted by clay under axi-symmetric loading conditions cannot be expressed analytically. Numerical values for the bearing capacity factor may be calculated by the method of characteristics, and these are summarised in Table 12.2, and may be compared with the values for plane strain loading (Section 12.2.1).

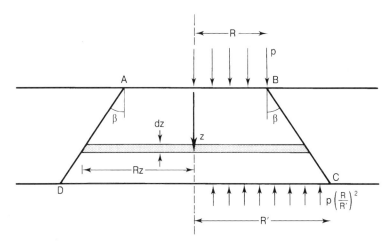

Figure 12.14 *General definitions for the three-dimensional loading on an unpaved road*

Table 12.2 Variation of bearing capacity factor with outward shear stress for plane strain (2D) and axi-symmetric (3D) loading

Shear	2D loading	3D loading	Shear	2D loading	3D loading
$\alpha = \tau/s_u$	$(N_c)_{2D}$†	$(N_c)_{3D}$‡	$\alpha = \tau/s_u$	$(N_c)2_D$†	$(N_c)2_D$‡
0.0	5.14	5.69	0.6	4.30	4.86
0.1	5.04	5.59	0.7	4.08	4.64
0.2	4.92	5.48	0.8	3.81	4.37
0.3	4.79	5.35	0.9	3.46	4.00
0.4	4.65	5.21	1.0	≤ 2.57	≤ 3.07
0.5	4.48	5.05		≥ 0.00	≥ 0.00

† Equation (12.1)
‡ Houlsby and Jewell (1990)

As before, the data in Table 12.2 define the maximum resistance of the clay in terms of the available combinations of shear stress, $\tau_a = \alpha s_{ud}$, and normal stress, $\sigma_a = \gamma D + N_c s_{ud}$, that can be supported.

12.5.2 Stresses within the fill

The surface load, p, acts over a circular area of radius, R. A vertical slice through this axi-symmetric loading reveals a block of soil that looks similar to the previous two-dimensional case (compare Figures 12.2 and 12.14). However, the active pressures beneath the loaded area act on the radial sections shown, the surface $ABCD$, and the lateral (passive) resistance of the surrounding fill acts around the circumference.

Vertical stress, σ_v, reduces with depth beneath the surface load, p, and at a depth, z, the load acts over an area of radius, $R_z = R + z \tan \beta$. The vertical stress is then $\sigma_{vz} = \gamma z + p(R/R_z)^2$. Active stresses are assumed to develop in the fill beneath the load, and the horizontal stress, $\sigma_{hz} = K_{ad}\sigma_{vz}$, acts over an incremental area, $2R_z dz$, (Figure 12.14). The total lateral thrust in the fill may be found by integration,

$$P_{Fill} = 2\int_0^D \sigma_{hz}R_z dz = \frac{2K_{ad}\,pR^2}{\tan\beta}\ln\left(\frac{R'}{R}\right) + \frac{K_{ad}\gamma D^2}{2}\left(2R + \frac{4D\tan\beta}{3}\right) \quad ...(12.18)$$

Lateral, passive pressure is mobilised in the surrounding soil to resist the radial displacement of the fill, and a net lateral resistance, P_L, opposes the lateral thrust, P_{Fill},

$$P_L = \frac{K_{pm}\gamma D^2}{2}\left(2R + \frac{4D\tan\beta}{3}\right) \quad ...(12.19)$$

(See Section 12.2.2 for a discussion on the mobilised passive earth pressure coefficient, K_{pm}.)

Now consider a plan view at the level of the clay (Figure 12.15a). The net lateral thrust on any diameter, $(P_{Fill} - P_L)$, must be supported in shear, but because of axial-symmetry the required shear stress acts radially outward at every point, so that the magnitude of the shear stress, τ_r,

$$\tau_r = \frac{(P_{Fill} - P_L)}{R'^2} = p \left(\frac{R}{R'}\right)^2 \frac{2K_{ad}}{\tan \beta} \log_e \left(\frac{R'}{R}\right)$$

$$+ (K_{ad} - K_{pm})\gamma D^2 \left(\frac{R + 2R'}{3R'^2}\right) \qquad ...(12.20)$$

Note that the effect of radial shear on the surface of the fill has been omitted for simplicity (see Section 12.2.2).

12.5.3 Unreinforced design

The shear stress, τ_r, and the net vertical stress, $p(R/R')^2$, acting on the clay are linked through Equation (12.20). As before, the required stresses plot as a straight line on the non-dimensional interaction diagram of required and available bearing capacity (see Section 12.2.3 and Figure 12.5).

The limiting capacity of the unreinforced unpaved road is reached at the intersection of the line of the required stresses (found from Equation 12.20) with the envelope of limiting resistance for the clay (found from Table 12.2). The point of intersection gives the solution, $N_c^u = N_{cr} = N_{ca}$, which may be found graphically or by numerical methods, and which defines the capacity of the unreinforced unpaved road, p^u,

$$p^u = N_c^u s_{ud} \left(\frac{R'}{R}\right)^2 \qquad ...(12.21)$$

12.5.4 Reinforced design

The reinforced case follows simply from the above (Section 12.2.4). The full bearing capacity in the clay can be mobilised when the reinforcement supports the outward shear stress at the base of the fill. Recalling that a greater bearing capacity factor applies for axial symmetry, $N_c^r = 5.69$ (Table 12.2), the fully reinforced capacity is then,

$$p^r = 5.69 s_{ud} \left(\frac{R'}{R}\right)^2 \qquad ...(12.22)$$

Now consider a plan view of the reinforcement (Figure 12.15b). When the reinforcement supports all the applied shear stress, τ_r, an equilibrium analysis shows that the reinforcement tension (force per unit width) varies across the diameter from zero at the edges to a maximum value, $\tau_r R'$, at the centre. The average tension is $\tau_r R'/2$.

It is suggested that the average tension is most relevant for design since it would correspond to the average loading in a biaxial test (Figure 12.15c). Biaxial testing is

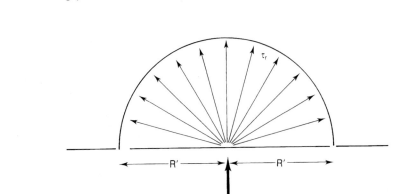

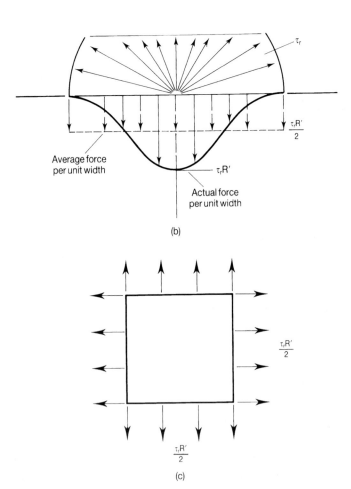

Figure 12.15 *Shear loading under axi-symmetric conditions: (a) shear stresses, (b) force in the reinforcement, and (c) average biaxial conditions*

likely to be the most practical way to measure the strength and stiffness parameters for geotextiles under loading conditions relevant to unpaved road design, and it is emphasised that the strength and stiffness properties of a given geotextile will differ depending on whether the product is subjected to uniaxial or biaxial load.

In the remaining text, the required reinforcement tension refers to the average tension defined above. Note that this average tension corresponds to a force per unit width, $(P_{Fill} - P_L)/2R'$, (Figure 12.15a).

The required tension in the fully reinforced unpaved road, p^r, may now be found, (Equations 12.20 and 12.22),

$$P_R = \frac{\tau_r^r R'}{2} = 5.69 \frac{s_{ud} R^2}{R'} \frac{K_{ad}}{\tan \beta} \log_e \left(\frac{R'}{R}\right)$$
$$+ (K_{ad} - K_{pm}) \frac{\gamma D^2}{2} \left(\frac{R + 2R'}{3R'}\right) \qquad ...(12.23)$$

When a lesser surface load is applied, but one that exceeds the unreinforced capacity, $p'' < p < p'$, the intermediate loading case that was discussed in Section 12.2.7 will apply. The required shear stress, τ_r, would be partially supported by the reinforcement and partially by the clay, τ_a, so that the required tension in the reinforcement is:

$$P_{Req} = (\tau_r - \tau_a)\frac{R'}{2} \qquad ...(12.24)$$

12.5.5 Fill bearing capacity

It is recommended that the surface bearing capacity of the granular fill should be assessed as described in Section 12.2.5. Previously there has been a reliance on semi-empirical measures, such as the California Bearing Ratio (CBR) test, or compliance with a grading and compaction specification. This is likely to be because of the critical nature of the bearing capacity, due to the relatively high contact pressure exerted over a small surface area. A high mobilised angle of friction is needed to maintain the equilibrium in this case, which demands a thorough assessment of the frictional properties of the fill under the field loading conditions, if an adequate margin of safety is to be demonstrated (Section 5.2.2).

Two other features of the analysis are important. First, the bearing capacity of a circular load on frictional fill increases rapidly with settlement, δ_y, so that small settlements have a significant impact. Second, for small contact areas, $R < 0.2m$, particle size effects may become important where the average particle size, D_{50}, is significant relative to the size of the surface load, $D_{50}/2R > 0.1$. Some allowance should probably be made for the beneficial influence of particle size on the bearing capacity factors in such cases, perhaps along the lines introduced for the bond capacity of grids (Section 4.6 and Figure 4.11).

The analysis for plane strain bearing capacity (Equation 12.11) may be adapted for a circular load by using a shape factor, 0.6 (Vesic, 1975). Allowing for the surcharge due to settlement in the fill, $\gamma\delta_v$, the bearing capacity for a circular load is

$$p_\gamma = 0.6N_{\gamma d}R\gamma + (1 + \tan \phi)N_{qd}\delta_v\gamma \qquad ...(12.25)$$

where the bearing capacity factors, $N_{\gamma d}$ and N_{qd}, correspond to the design angle of friction, ϕ'_d (Table 5.3).

Other influences

The comments made in Section 12.2.5 on potential direct sliding in working platforms apply equally to unpaved roads. The shear stress at the level of the reinforcement, τ_r/σ_r, should be checked to ensure that the reinforcement has sufficient direct sliding resistance. The comments on load-spread angles also apply, namely that relatively high load-spread angles can develop in well-compacted frictional soils, as illustrated in Section 12.9.

12.5.6 Serviceability

The approach to the analysis of serviceability described in Sections 12.2.6 and 12.2.7 may be applied to unpaved roads. Briefly, the limiting allowable load in the reinforcement would be found from the reinforcement stiffness, $J_{t,T}$, measured in a biaxial test, and from a specified maximum allowable elongation.

Alternatively, the maximum required tension may be defined by the analysis of serviceability. In this case, a minimum required reinforcement stiffness would be determined from the maximum required tensile force and the maximum allowable elongation (Section 12.2.7).

12.5.7 Design charts

The calculations above for unreinforced unpaved roads are too complex to be expressed in a single formula or a single diagram, although they are readily carried out by computer. The results of such analysis, covering a range of cases, may be summarised in design charts. Two types of design chart are presented.

The first allows the required thickness of fill to be determined for a specified loading, for both reinforced and unreinforced unpaved roads (Figure 12.16a). The fill thickness is defined in terms of the radius of the loaded area, D/R, and the surface load is defined in terms of the strength of the soft clay, p/s_u.

The second design chart gives the maximum required reinforcement force for the reinforced equilibrium (Figure 12.16b) expressed as a non-dimensional quantity, P_R/s_uR.

The design charts are for vertical loading only. Subject to this restriction, the relation between the surface load, p/s_u, and the required fill thickness, D/R, for a given angle of

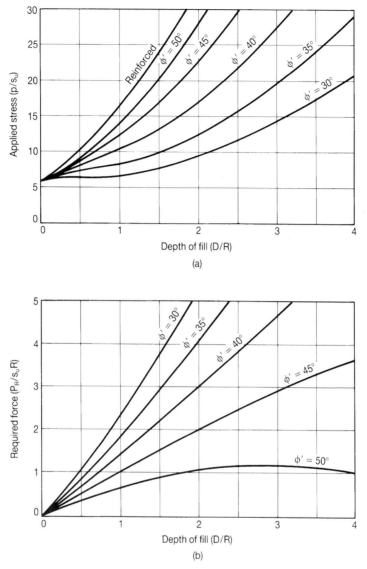

Figure 12.16 *Design chart for unreinforced and reinforced stability under axi-symmetric loading: (a) required fill thickness, and (b) required reinforcement force*

friction, ϕ'_d, depend only on the assumed load-spread angle, β, and the value of the non-dimensional quantity, $s_u/\gamma R$. The latter quantity has a lower value for weak subgrades and the large loaded areas.

A set of design charts was published by Houlsby and Jewell (1990) for the cases, $\beta = 45°$, $35°$, and, $25°$, and for, $s_u/\gamma R = 20$, 10 and 5. The chart for the central case, $\beta = 35°$ and $s_u/\gamma R = 10$, is given in Figure 12.16. Compared to this central case, the charts in Figure 12.17 illustrate the influence of load-spread angle ($\beta = 45°$ and $25°$), while the charts in Figure 12.18 illustrate the influence of the parameter, $s_u/\gamma R$, for the case, $\beta = 35°$.

Interpolation between design charts is possible without too much loss of accuracy, but extrapolation should be treated with caution. The design charts are suitable for preliminary investigations, and for checking designs, but the design equations should be used for detailed studies.

12.6 Design example: static wheel loading

The static analysis for a wheel loading is the first part of the analysis for an unpaved road subject to traffic loading. An example of the static analysis is given here simply to illustrate the use of design charts. The loading capacity defined by static analysis applies only to a very few load repetitions.

Consider again the working platform discussed in Section 12.4. Some materials must be delivered to this site and the possibility of driving the delivery vehicle directly on to the working platform is to be investigated. An ultimate limit state analysis is to be used.

The delivery vehicle has a rear axle load, $P_{axle} = 80$kN, and dual wheels on either side (a total four wheels on the axle), inflated to a pressure, $p_{tyre} = 620$kN/m². Following the method proposed by Giroud and Noiray (1981), the average contact pressure between the tyres and the area of the ground surface loaded is assumed to be $p = p_{tyre}/\sqrt{2}$, (Section 12.7.5). Assuming a circular area of contact for each pair of wheels, the applied pressure is $p = p_{tyre}/\sqrt{2} = 438$kN/m², and the radius of the loaded area, $R^2 = (P_{axle}/\sqrt{2}\pi p_{tyre})$ or $R = 0.17$m.

The geometry for the loading on the working platform is $D/R = 0.4/0.17 = 2.35$, and the applicable design chart would be for $s_u/\gamma R = 5.9$. Recall that the design strength of the subgrade, $s_{ud} = 20$kN/m², and the design angle of friction in the fill, $\phi'_d = 35°$.

The design chart selected for a conservative preliminary investigation is for a load-spread angle, $\beta = 25°$ and for $s_u/\gamma R = 10$ (Figure 12.17a and b). The results corresponding to $D/R = 2.35$ are: a reinforced capacity $p'/s_u = 25$, a required reinforcement force $P_R/s_u R = 4.3$, and an unreinforced capacity $p''/s_u = 9$, which have been marked by points A, B, and C, respectively. These correspond to a reinforced capacity, $p' = 500$kN/m², which is sufficient to support the wheel loading, $p_d = 438$kN/m². The capacity without reinforcement would be $p'' = 180$kN/m².

The required reinforcement force is $P_R = 14.6$kN/m, whereas the design strength for reinforcement in the working platform was $(P_d)_{t,T} \geq 10$kN/m. However, the above is for the limiting load, $p' = 500$kN/m², whereas only $p = 438$kN/m² is applied allowing the clay to support some outward shear stress. The design load mobilises a bearing capacity, $N_{cr} = 5$, and the clay can support an outward shear, $\tau_d/s_u = 0.5$ (Table 12.2). Also, the

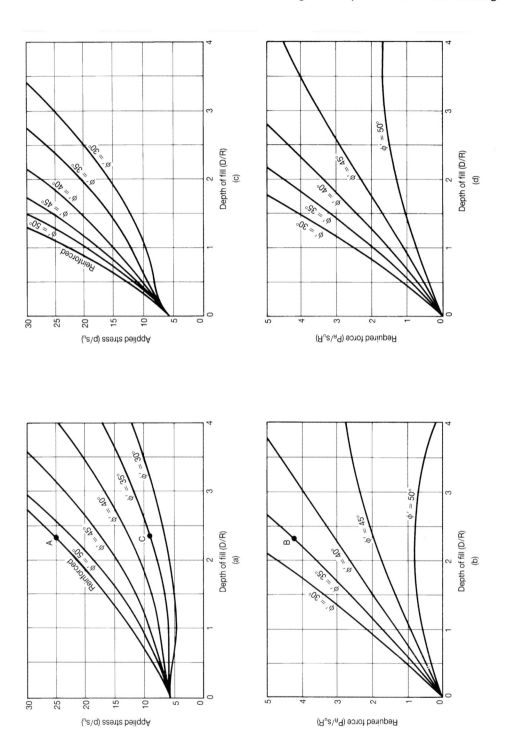

Figure 12.17 *Design charts for* $(s_u/\gamma R = 10)$ *illustrating the influence of load-spread angle: (a) and (b) with* $\beta = 25°$, *(c) and (d) with* $\beta = 45°$

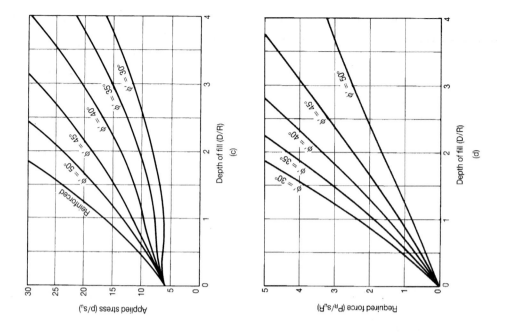

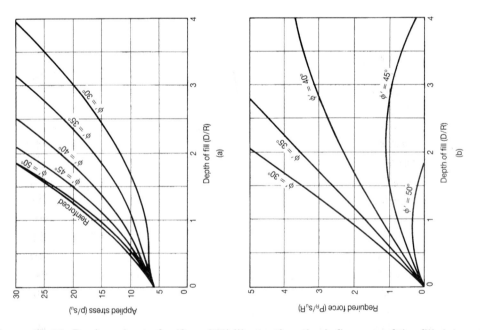

Figure 12.18 *Design charts for (β = 35°) illustrating the influence of the fill: (a) and (b) with s_u/γR = 5, (c) and (d) with s_u/γR = 20*

total shear stress is reduced, $\tau_r/s_u = 3$, because of the smaller applied load, i.e. Equation (12.20), so that the net force to be supported by the reinforcement is $P_{Req} = 9\text{kN/m}$ (Equation 12.24).

The surface bearing capacity must be checked. The results in Table 12.3, calculated from Equation (12.25) and the bearing capacity factors in Table 5.3, report the bearing capacity for three assumed angles of friction, $\phi'_d = 35°$, $40°$ and $45°$, and for three settlements, $\delta_v = 0, 75$ and 150mm.

The results indicate that the design loading, $p = 438\text{kN/m}^2$, is at the limit of the bearing capacity for the fill strength assumed in the working platform design, $\phi'_p = 42°$. Indeed, a settlement, $\delta_v = 37\text{mm}$, would be needed to maintain the equilibrium. However, the sensitivity of surface bearing capacity to the mobilised angle of friction and to the amount of settlement is apparent from these results.

In summary, the working platform is likely to have sufficient capacity to support the wheel loading without causing an overall failure. However, some difficulties with surface bearing capacity are expected, with the possibility of severe rutting. The judgement on whether a separate surfacing should be used, such as runner boards or a wearing layer, or whether the fill offers sufficient bearing capacity, will depend on the exact nature of the fill material, including the particle size, the angularity and the degree of compaction (i.e. the assumed angle of friction for the working platform design might be unduly conservative). A compact, crushed limestone fill with a representative peak angle of friction, $\phi'_p = 47°$, for example, would almost certainly be considered adequate to resist the wheel loading.

12.7 Allowance for traffic

So far the analysis has been for an idealised strip or circular load applied statistically to the surface of a granular layer overlying a soft clay subgrade. This approximation is satisfactory for design where the loading is due to stationary or slowly moving vehicles acting only once or twice over any given location. Specific allowance for the effects of traffic is required where there is significant repeated loading, more than about five to ten load repetitions.

Table 12.3 Limiting bearing stress for a circular load, $R = 0.17\text{m}$

Settlement (δ_r) (mm)	ϕ'_d 35°	ϕ'_d 40°	ϕ'_d 45°
0	98	223	554
75	183	400	959
150	268	577	1364

Notes: Bearing stresses from Equation (12.25), in kN/m²

Static and repeated load tests of model unpaved roads have shown that the failure mechanisms under repeated loading are the same as those for static loading, and that it is reasonable to link the former to the latter (Fannin, 1987). The behaviour in the repeated load tests is essentially one with deformations accumulating gradually with each load-unload cycle but at an accelerating rate to a failure defined by a limiting acceptable settlement.

A large study on fatigue in unreinforced unpaved roads was carried out by Hammitt (1970), who used the data to derive an empirical relation between the pavement thickness, the size of the loaded area, the subgrade strength, the number of wheel passes and the applied load to cause a 75mm rut. This empirical correlation for unreinforced unpaved roads is replotted in Figure 12.19. This shows a trend of failure load against pavement thickness that is similar to that found from static tests, which appear to be roughly equivalent to five wheel passes.

Tests at a relatively large scale on reinforced pavements have also indicated a pattern of reducing capacity with repeated loading, but at a lesser rate (Delmas *et al.*, 1986; De

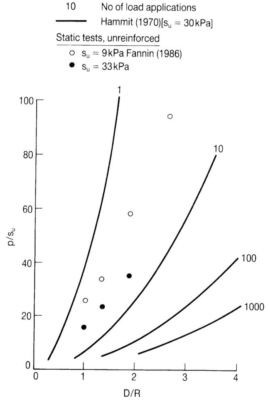

Figure 12.19 *Comparison between static and repeated-load tests on unreinforced unpaved roads (after Milligan et al., 1990)*

Special Publication 123 © CIRIA

Groot *et al.*, 1986). More full-scale trials are needed, however, to provide data on fatigue.

A method to allow for traffic loading is described below, and provides a complete design procedure for unreinforced and reinforced unpaved roads (Section 12.8). The design method builds on the previous work, but incorporates the new knowledge on the mechanisms governing stability in unpaved roads. The analysis provides a more sophisticated interpretation of Hammitt's (1970) data for unreinforced unpaved roads, and extends the relations for reinforced unpaved roads suggested by Giroud and Noiray (1981). Agreement with the field data is demonstrated by the back analysis in Section 12.9.

12.7.1 Definition of failure

A simple definition of failure in an unpaved road is used, as illustrated in Figure 12.19 for the typical behaviour observed in static and repeated load tests on unpaved roads. In each case a relatively well-defined 'yielding' occurs after which displacements accumulate rapidly leading quickly to failure by excessive deformation. A simple bi-linear interpolation is used to define the failure load in a static test, and the failure number of cycles in a repeated load test (Figure 12.20).

The onset of large displacement typically occurs at settlement in the range, $0.2 \le (\delta_v/R) \le 0.5$, where R is the radius of the loaded area. Hammitt (1970) adopted a limiting rut depth, $\delta_{rut} = 75$mm, as a failure criterion, observing that rutting developed rapidly thereafter. This criterion falls in the range, $\delta_v/R \approx 0.25$ to 0.45, for the wheel sizes in the tests.

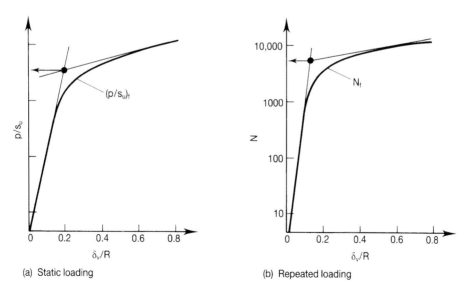

(a) Static loading   (b) Repeated loading

Figure 12.20 *Definition of failure in an unpaved road under static and repeated loading*

The results from trafficking trials on an unreinforced and two reinforced unpaved roads, all with the same thickness D = 0.36m, but with two markedly different reinforcement materials, are shown in Figure 12.21 (Webster and Watkins, 1977). The failure criterion defines a number of load cycles to failure in the range causing a rut depth δ_v = 75 to 150mm. When applied to similar data in Webster and Alford (1978), the failure criterion defines a number of load repetitions to failure corresponding closely with a rut depth, δ_v = 75mm.

12.7.2 Rate effects

A factor that contributes to the enhanced capacity of an unpaved road under traffic, compared to static loading is the influence of strain rate on the undrained shear strength of clay. Chandler (1988) has used the available data to derive a general expression for

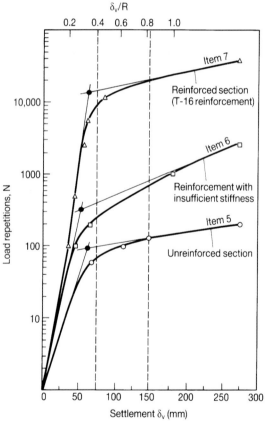

Figure 12.21 *Failure in unreinforced and reinforced unpaved roads subject to traffic (after Webster and Watkins, 1977)*

the vane correction factor, μ_r, to allow for the influence of strain rate. The strain rate is expressed in terms of the time to failure in minutes, t_f,

$$\mu_r = 1.05 - (0.015 + 0.0075 \log t_f)\sqrt{I_p} \qquad \qquad ...(12.26)$$

where the plasticity index, I_p, is in units of percent, and the equation applies to clays with $I_p > 5\%$. Equation (12.26) was derived from data in the range, $10 \text{ min} \leq t_f \leq 10,000 \text{min}$. The values of the vane correction factor are plotted in Figure 12.22.

Bjerrum's (1973) vane correction factor is recovered for $t_f = 10,000$ min which is relevant to field embankment failures. In contrast, a loading that would cause failure with $t_f = 1$ min, would require no correction at all, $\mu_r = 1$, of a standard vane test brought to failure in 1 minute (Chandler, 1988).

The effect of strain rate in an unpaved road subject to a traffic loading that caused a medium plasticity clay to shear rapidly to failure could account for a 25% increase, or more, in the available shearing resistance, relative to the strength deduced using Bjerrum's correction factor.

As shown below, rate effects are taken into account in the design of unpaved roads through the fatigue relation which equates a number of repeated loadings, N_s, as being equivalent to a static loading (as implied by the data in Figure 12.19).

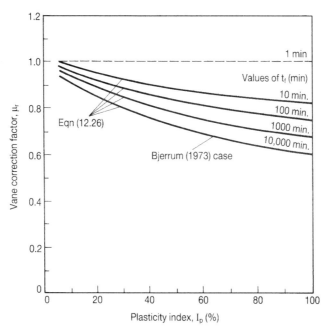

Figure 12.22 *Vane correction factors to allow for the influence of strain rate on undrained shear strength (after Chandler, 1988)*

12.7.3 Fatigue relation

The field laboratory test data on unpaved roads show a progressive reduction in load-carrying capacity with repeated loading. The loss of strength occurs relatively rapidly at first but to a lesser extent under large numbers of load repetitions. The data also show a lesser rate of degradation in reinforced unpaved roads.

A function that captures the measured pattern of degradation in unpaved roads is:

$$\frac{P_n}{P_s} = \frac{(p/s_u)_n}{(p/s_u)_s} = \left(\frac{N_s}{N}\right)^{\exp} = f_n \qquad \ldots(12.27)$$

where a load equal to the static capacity, P_s, causes failure when applied a number of times, N_s, usually in the range 3 to 10. The capacity of the road to sustain N load repetitions is P_a, and the ratio between the static and trafficked capacity is defined by the coefficient of fatigue, f_n.

An exponential factor, $\exp = 0.30$, fits the average degradation rate measured in unreinforced unpaved roads by Hammitt (1970), while De Groot et al. (1986) measured an average value, $\exp = 0.16$, from trafficking trials on reinforced unpaved roads. A similar rate of degradation in reinforced unpaved roads was observed in the trafficking trials by Delmas et al. (1986), and in the laboratory tests by Fannin (1987).

Unless there are other data on which to make a choice, it is suggested that the values $N_s = 5$ and $\exp = 0.30$ are appropriate for the general analysis of unreinforced unpaved roads. The same relation to static loading, $N_s = 5$, would apply to the reinforced case, but the rate of degradation, somewhere in the range, $0.30 \geq \exp \geq 0.16$, will depend on the properties of the reinforcement.

In an extreme case, a fine tissue of reinforcement with little or no strength could not be expected to retard the degradation caused by traffic. While it is difficult to make a general recommendation, a safe design value, $\exp = 0.20$, might be adopted for the design of reinforced unpaved roads in which the reinforcement material fully meets the strength, stiffness and direct sliding criteria defined by the analysis. However, the expected rate of degradation in such cases would be $\exp = 0.16$, and this is a more appropriate value for use in the back-analysis of field trials.

12.7.4 Permanent road thickness

For a given road geometry and soil properties, there should be a critical load below which an unpaved road can sustain an infinite number of load repetitions. Laboratory data from cyclic loading tests of surface footings on sand suggest that this may be a rather small proportion of the static capacity.

Hammitt's (1970) empirical relation for unreinforced unpaved roads built on an earlier expression by Ahlvin (1959) which relates the required fill thickness, D, to the applied surface pressure, p. The equation can be expressed in terms of a circular loaded area, $A = \pi R^2$, and using the standard correlation, $CBR = s_u/30$, gives the non-dimensional form,

$$\frac{D}{R} = f' \sqrt{\left(1.687 \frac{p}{s_u} - 1\right)} \qquad ...(12.28)$$

The factor, $f' < 1$, depends simply on the number of load repetitions, and equals unity when $N = 100,000$. (See Section 12.9.1 for further discussion.)

It is suggested that Equation (12.28), with $f' = 1$, might be used to estimate the limiting unreinforced road geometry, D/R, that would be able to sustain any number of load repetitions, p/s_u. The shortcoming of this approach, however, is that it does not account directly for the properties of the fill.

An alternative approach is to define the permanent load-carrying capacity of the road as a percentage of the static capacity. The percentage is likely to depend on the fill and foundation properties, but a residual strength of the order 10% of the full static capacity accords with Hammitt's empirical relation. (But note the considerable uncertainty in defining such a limiting capacity because of the scarcity of data on unpaved roads trafficked to this extent.)

To allow for a residual capacity in the fatigue relation, Equation (12.27) would be modified as follows,

$$\frac{P_n}{P_s} = \left(\frac{N_s + CN}{N + CN_s}\right)^{\exp} \qquad ...(12.29)$$

where the constant, $C = (Residual)^{1/\exp}$. The residual capacity has a value in the range zero to unity, so that a residual capacity 10% of the static capacity would define a constant, $C = (0.10)^{1/\exp}$.

The extended form of the fatigue relation need only be used if a very large number of load repetitions is involved. The simpler form of Equation (12.27) suffices for most practical purposes.

12.7.5 Practical wheel loading

The area of contact between a single wheel and the ground surface is simply a function of the load applied by the wheel, $P_{wheel} = P_{axle}/n$, and the average contact pressure, p, with the soil, where n, is the number of wheels on the axle (two or four).

Hammitt (1970) measured both the tyre pressure, p_{tyre}, and the average contact pressure, p, for various sizes and types of single wheel and found them to fall within the range, $1 \geq p/p_{tyre} \geq 0.8$. The conservative choice for design would be to assume that a single wheel exerts a pressure on the soil, $p = p_{tyre}$. However, the assumption, $p = 0.9p_{tyre}$, would on average provide a more realistic assessment of the average contact pressure. Thus for a single axle with two single wheels, the equivalent radius, R, of the area of soil loaded by each wheel is:

$$R = \sqrt{\frac{P_{wheel}}{\pi p}} = \sqrt{\frac{P_{axle}}{2\pi p}} \qquad \text{...(12.30)}$$

where the contact pressure, p, is the range, $p_{tyre} \geq p \geq 0.8p_{tyre}$.

A dual wheel configuration is widely used for heavy vehicles (two closely spaced wheels on either end of an axle), and each pair of wheels may be considered as providing a single load on the unpaved road. Giroud and Noiray (1981) suggested that the equivalent contact pressure exerted by a dual wheel configuration is $p = p_{tyre}/\sqrt{2}$, allowing for the thin area of soil between the two wheels. The equivalent radius, R, of the area loaded by each pair of wheels on a dual wheel axle (total of four wheels) is then:

$$R = \sqrt{\frac{P_{axle}}{2\pi p}} = \sqrt{\frac{P_{axle}}{\sqrt{2}\pi p_{tyre}}} \qquad \text{...(12.31)}$$

12.7.6 Allowance for mixed traffic

When an unpaved road is trafficked by different vehicles, or by the same vehicle carrying different loads, it is necessary to derive an equivalent loading, (P_{eq}, N_{eq}), for analysis. As suggested by Giroud and Noiray (1981), the equivalent loading may be defined either in terms of the greatest applied load or the greatest number of load repetitions. This is logical because the road may be damaged by excessive loading or by excessive load repetitions. It is recommended that both approaches are used, and the more critical result selected.

Traffic is represented in terms of the axle load, P_i, and the number of load repetitions over the design location, N_i. The subscript, i, represents a set of different loadings, (P_i, N_i). The relation between different load combinations is given by Equation (12.27), which can be written in terms of the applied axle load,

$$\left(\frac{P_i}{P_{eq}}\right)^{1/\exp} = \left(\frac{N_{eq}}{N_i}\right) \qquad \text{...(12.32)}$$

where (P_{eq}, N_{eq}) is an equivalent loading combination to (P_i, N_i). This is the form of equation used by Giroud and Noiray (1981) who suggested a value, $1/\exp = 3.95$. As shown earlier, the data for unreinforced unpaved roads suggest, $1/\exp = 1/0.3 = 3.33$, and for typical reinforced unpaved roads, $1/\exp = 1/0.2 = 5$ (Section 12.7.3).

When the equivalent load is set equal to the greatest load exerted on the road, $P_{eq} = (P_i)_{max}$, the total traffic is then expressed in terms of an equivalent number of passes, N_{eq}, of this maximum loading, and from Equation (12.32):

$$N_{eq} = \Sigma N_i \left(\frac{P_i}{(P_i)_{max}}\right)^{1/\exp} \qquad \text{...(12.33)}$$

Alternatively, the equivalent number of load repetitions may be set equal to the largest number, $N'_{eq} = (N_i)_{max}$, in which case the total traffic is expressed in terms of an equivalent load,

$$(P'_{eq})^{1/exp} = \Sigma(P_i)^{1/exp} \left(\frac{N_i}{(N_i)_{max}} \right) \qquad \qquad ...(12.34)$$

Design should be carried out for both equivalent traffic loadings, (P_{eq}, N_{eq}) and (P'_{eq}, N'_{eq}), and the more conservative result selected.

It is worth noting that the loading applied by the front axle of a truck is usually found from the analysis to have an insignificant effect on the net traffic. Also, one pass of a truck with two equally loaded rear axles causes two load repetitions.

12.8 Procedure for unpaved road design

The elements for the design of unpaved roads have been introduced in the previous sections. The application of these to the design of unpaved roads is described below, where the method is correlated against the existing data (Hammitt, 1970; Webster and Watkins 1977; Giroud and Noiray, 1981).

The response of soil to traffic loading is complex. The fatigue relation may be interpreted in two ways, and the method used affects the unreinforced analysis, although the difference is often insignificant. While a firm recommendation is made for design, a more detailed knowledge of the physical mechanisms governing fatigue in unpaved roads will only be developed through the back-analysis of a more extensive database of trafficking trials than is currently available.

The analysis for unpaved roads is concerned with the failure of the road under repeated loading. In previous studies, no factors of safety are introduced on the design parameters and this approach is adopted here. Thus the representative values of the peak strength of the soil are used directly in the analysis. An element of conservatism may be introduced in design through the cautious choice of the soil properties, the design loading (both the magnitude and the number of repetitions), and the parameters which govern fatigue.

The analysis below is expressed in terms of an applied load, P, repeated a number of times, N. This is the same as an equivalent loading, (P_{eq}, N_{eq}), in a design for mixed traffic (Section 12.7.6). The subscript has been omitted for clarity.

12.8.1 Unreinforced design

There are two parts to the calculation, namely a static analysis and an allowance for fatigue. Design analysis may be carried out to find the required fill thickness to sustain a specified loading, or to derive a design chart relating the required fill thickness to the applied loading (Figure 12.19).

The axle load and wheel configuration of the vehicle define the applied load intensity, p, and the size of the loaded area, R (Section 12.7.5). The maximum number of load repetitions, N, that may be applied to any position on the unpaved road is normally defined. A representative undrained shear strength, s_u, for the near surface of the subgrade (extending to a depth of the order $\sqrt{2}R'$) should be chosen based on the site investigation data and testing. Similarly, the representative properties of the compacted fill, ϕ'_p, and, γ, should be measured in laboratory tests for the range of relative density and mean stress expected in the field.

The above parameters define the intensity of the repeated loading, $(p/s_u)_n$, that must be resisted. The required fill thickness to sustain this loading may be found from a static analysis using a greater (equivalent) loading intensity, $(p/s_u)_s$, to allow for fatigue (Figure 12.23). The equivalent loading was defined in Equation (12.27), and depends on the coefficient of fatigue, $f_n = (N_s/N)^{\exp}$,

$$(p/s_u)_s = \frac{(p/s_u)_n}{f_n} = \frac{(p/s_u)_n}{(N_s/N)^{\exp}} \qquad \text{...(12.35)}$$

The values, $N_s = 5$ and $\exp = 0.30$, are typical for unpaved roads (Section 12.7.3).

Static analysis is used to find the required fill thickness, $(D/R)_n$, to support the equivalent loading (Figure 12.23). As before, the solution must be found by trial and error using either numerical or graphical means (Section 12.5.3). The load-spread angle in the fill, β, must be chosen and reference to values found from back-analysis can be used for guidance (Section 12.9.1). The full passive resistance in the fill is usually assumed to be mobilised, $K_{pm} = K_p$.

The derivation of design charts follows naturally from the above. A design chart applies for a specific combination of parameters, $(s_u/\gamma R)$ and β. It is always conservative to use the design chart for the initial value of $(s_u/\gamma R)$. In this case, the static analysis gives

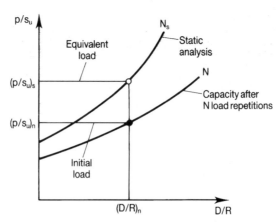

Figure 12.23 *Derivation of road capacity after N load repetitions in terms of an equivalent static load*

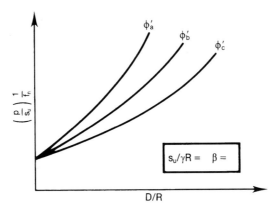

Figure 12.24 *Design chart for unreinforced unpaved roads; applicable to specific values, $s_u/\gamma R$, and, β*

the baseline result (Figure 12.24). The current capacity of the road is defined by the equivalent load, $(p/s_u)_n \times 1/f_n$, which allows for the appropriate number of load repetitions, where $N > N_s$. Using this approach, the results for a range of angles of friction can be plotted on one chart (Figure 12.14).

This technique applies equally to the design charts given earlier when the equivalent load, $(p/s_u)_n \times 1/f_n$, rather than the initial load, $(p/s_u)_n$, is used (Figures 12.16 to 12.18).

The conservatism in using a single design chart is that degradation in the strength of the subgrade reduces the quantity, $s_u/\gamma R$. The fill then plays an enhanced role that is not accounted for by a single design chart corresponding to the initial value of this parameter.

12.8.2 Reinforced design

The required design thickness for a reinforced unpaved road is found as described above, but the analysis is simpler as it can be expressed in a single equation (Equation (12.22)). The required thickness of reinforced unpaved road, $(D/R)_n$, required to support a design loading, $(p/s_u)_n$, repeated N times may also be expressed analytically (Equations (12.22) and (12.27)),

$$\left(\frac{D}{R}\right)_n = \frac{1}{\tan \beta}\left(\sqrt{\left(\frac{(p/s_u)_n}{5.69 f_n}\right)} - 1\right) \qquad \text{...(12.36)}$$

where the fatigue coefficient, $f_n = (N_s/N)^{\exp}$.

It is possible to plot Equation (12.36) to derive a master design chart for the required thickness of reinforced unpaved roads that applies for all loading cases (Figure 12.25).

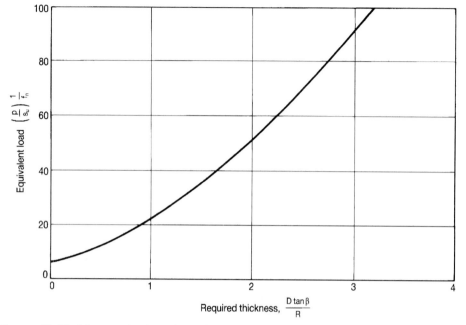

Figure 12.25 *Master design chart for reinforced unpaved roads*

(The parameter, $s_u/\gamma R$, does not enter into the analysis for the reinforced unpaved road thickness.)

Required reinforcement force

There are few or no data available on the magnitude of the reinforcement forces that are mobilised in reinforced unpaved roads under traffic loading. Ideally, measurements should be made of the development of tensile strain in the reinforcement through the life of the reinforced unpaved road. Without data on reinforcement forces, it is not possible to correlate the analysis directly against measurements.

It is recommended that the actual road geometry, $(D/R)_n$, and the actual applied loading, p, should be used in the analysis for the required reinforcement force. The increased load intensity, $(p/s_u)_s$, is then attributed to a reduction in the undrained shear strength of the clay subgrade due to fatigue, $(s_u)_n = f_n s_u$. The analysis then gives a required reinforcement force for equilibrium at point A in Figure 12.26. (Note that the applicable strength when calculating, P_R, is $(s_u)_n$, and the applicable design chart is that for $(s_u)_n/\gamma R$.)

It might be argued that at the end of the design life, as the road starts to fail after N load repetitions, the fill will have sheared sufficiently to reduce the mobilised angle of friction to the critical state value, ϕ'_{cv}. This lower angle of friction in the fill would cause greater force to be mobilised in the reinforcement, as illustrated by point, B, in Figure 12.26.

274

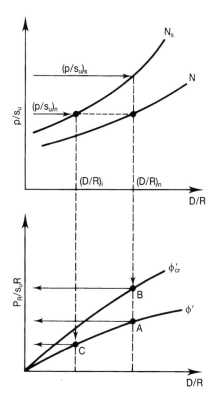

Figure 12.26 *Determination of the required reinforcement force allowing for traffic*

The approach adopted by Giroud and Noiray (1981) is to use static analysis to find the required force to resist the actual loading, $(p/s_u)_n$, applied to the minimum required thickness for equilibrium, $(D/R)_i$ (rather than the actual thickness of the road, $(D/R)_n$). In other words, the actual load, p, and the initial properties of the subgrade, s_u, and the fill, ϕ', are used in a static analysis to find the minimum required fill thickness, $(D/R)_i$, and the corresponding required reinforcement force. This force is assumed to act in the thicker unpaved road subjected to traffic loading. The procedure is shown schematically in Figure 12.26 by the point C. (Note that the applicable strength is s_u, so that the design chart for the initial conditions applies, $(s_u)_n/\gamma R$.)

12.9 Comparisons and back-analysis

The design method that has been presented builds on the previous design guidance. The earlier design methods are summarised below in sufficient detail to be applied in design, but the main purpose is to contrast the methods in terms of the data upon which they were based.

12.9.1 Unreinforced unpaved road design (Hammitt, 1970)

The empirical relation for unreinforced unpaved roads derived by Hammitt (1970) is widely used in practice, and is built into the analysis for reinforced unpaved roads by Giroud and Noiray (1981). The basic equation used by Hammitt was introduced in Section 12.7.4, Equation (12.28), and is repeated below,

$$\frac{D}{R} = f' \sqrt{\left(1.687\frac{p}{s_u} - 1\right)} \qquad ...(12.28\ bis)$$

where the fatigue coefficient, f', is:

$$f' = 0.176\log(N) + 0.120 \qquad ...(12.37)$$

The capacity of the road depends on the square of the thickness, $p/s_u \propto (D/R)^2$, which is the same as in the new analysis (see Equation 12.36, for example). Equation 12.28 is plotted in Figure 12.27 as a design chart for unreinforced unpaved roads based on Hammitt's work.

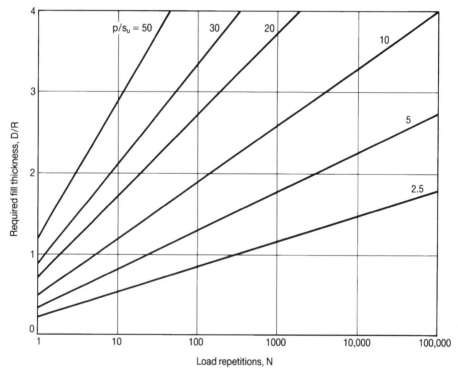

Figure 12.27 *Correlation for unreinforced unpaved roads proposed by Hammitt (1970)*

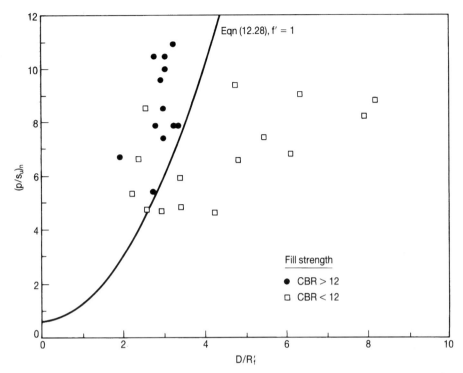

Figure 12.28 *Fit to the data achieved by the equation proposed by Hammitt (1970)*

Hammitt (1970) used a fatigue coefficient, f' (Equation 12.37), to fit the measured performance of unpaved roads to Ahlvin's (1959) basic equation (the remainder of Equation 12.28). The fit to the data is shown in Figure 12.28, where each data point represents a measured unpaved road failure after N_f load repetitions. The initial loading $(p/s_u)_n$ (i.e. applied load divided by initial subgrade strength) has been plotted against the transformed depth, $(D/R) \times 1/f'$, for the data where $N_f > 10$.

There is a significant scatter, but a likely cause of this is the range of fill materials used in the trials. The strength of the compacted fill was reported in terms of CBR values, and tests on the stronger fills, $CBR > 12$, have been plotted with a different symbol. This indeed confirms that the road behaviour depends on the fill properties. The limitation in Hammitt's approach is that no account is taken of the strength or the load-spreading ability of the fill. These parameters are an integral part of the new analysis.

Using the fatigue relation introduced in Section 12.7.3, Hammitt's data have been replotted in terms of the equivalent static capacity of each road tested. In other words, the fatigue coefficient, f_n (Equation 12.27), has been used to define the equivalent static loading, $(p/s_u)_n \times 1/f_n$, for each test result, i.e.

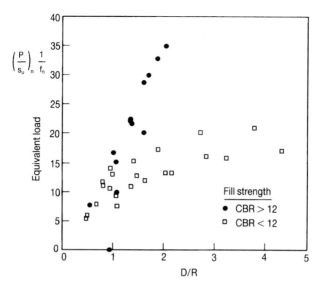

Figure 12.29 *The data of Hammitt (1970) plotted as an equivalent static load (allowing for fatigue, Equation 12.38)*

$$(p/s_u)_s = \frac{(p/s_u)_n}{f_n} = \frac{(p/s_u)_n}{(N_s/N_f)^{exp}} \qquad \qquad ...(12.38)$$

The results in Figure 12.29 are for the fatigue parameters recommended for unreinforced unpaved roads, $N_s = 5$ and exp $= 0.30$. All the data have been plotted and they are well organised by the transformation, and again reveal the difference in behaviour between stronger and weaker fills.

The new static analysis (Section 12.5.3) may now be superimposed on the data (Figure 12.30). The theoretical analysis is for the average case in the range of wheel sizes, tyre contact pressures and applied loads that were tested. The average values are a wheel width, 25in, a contact pressure, 100psi, and an applied wheel load, 30,000lb, (quoted in the original units for clarity). The number of load repetitions to failure was in the range, $N_f = 3$ to 700, and the depth of fill, $D = 6$in to 24in. The average radius of contact, $R = 0.25$m, may be found from the average applied load and contact pressure (Section 12.7.5).

The range of undrained shear strength in the subgrade for the two groups of fills has been used (the stronger fills were tested over slightly weaker subgrades). Since the non-dimensional quantity, s_u/γ_R, is not constant (i.e. various s_u, but constant γR), each subgrade strength plots as a separate line (Section 12.8.1). The assumed unit weight of the fill was $\gamma = 20$kN/m^3.

Two distinct combinations of angle of friction and load-spread angle in the fill fit the data. The values plotted in Figure 12.30 are ($\phi' = 40°$, $\beta = 35°$) for the weaker fills, $CBR < 12$, and ($\beta' = 45°$, $\beta = 45°$) for the stronger fills, $CBR > 12$.

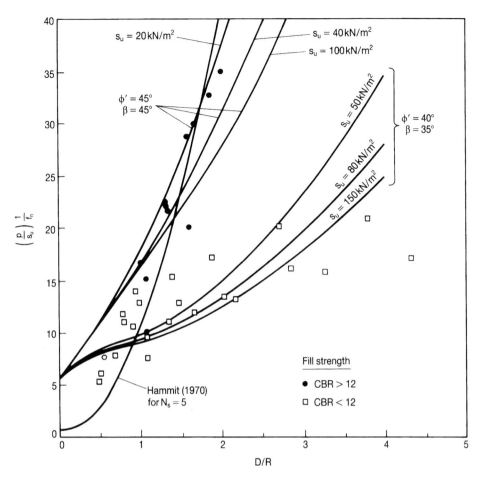

Figure 12.30 *Comparison between the new analysis, the relation proposed by Hammitt (1970) and the data for unreinforced unpaved roads*

However, the results for $\phi' = 35°$, $\beta = 40°$ also fit well with the data for the weaker fills, $CBR < 12$, as do the results with $\phi' = 45°$, $\beta = 40°$ for the data on the stronger fills, $CBR > 12$, but to a lesser extent.

What has been omitted in the above comparison is the potential limit imposed by the bearing capacity of the fill, which would be more likely to intervene in the weaker fills, and could explain the relatively low failure pressures measured on the thicker of the unreinforced fills with $CBR < 12$ (Figure 12.30).

Shown for comparison is the equivalent static capacity from Hammitt (1970) with $N_s = 5$ (Figure 12.30).

The conclusion to be drawn is that the new analysis is consistent with the earlier work but provides a more versatile capability for the analysis of unreinforced unpaved roads by allowing the influence of the fill properties to be taken into account through the choice of the angle of friction, ϕ', and the load-spread angle, β. The range of values found from the back-analysis in this section may be used as a guide in the selection of appropriate values for design. The new analysis provides a better correlation with the data of Hammitt (1970) than the previous analysis.

12.9.2 Reinforced unpaved road design (Giroud and Noiray, 1981)

Static analysis

Giroud and Noiray (1981) proposed the use of two separate bearing capacity factors for all unreinforced and reinforced unpaved roads, $N_c^u = \pi$ and $N_c^r = 2 + \pi$.

The new analysis has identified the outward shear stress on the clay subgrade as the mechanism that causes the change in bearing capacity. The fill properties and the unpaved road geometry critically influence the magnitude of the outward shear stress that acts on the clay, and hence the bearing capacity factor that is mobilised in the subgrade. It is a simplification to use a fixed value, $N_c^u = \pi$, since the mobilised bearing capacity factor in an unreinforced unpaved road may greatly exceed, or be less than, this value, depending on the soil properties and the road geometry.

The relation between the surface load, p/s_u, and the fill thickness, D/R, for the static analysis by Giroud and Noiray (1981) may be expressed in terms of a circular loaded area,

$$\frac{p}{s_u} = N_c \left(1 + 2.29\, \frac{D \tan \beta}{R} + 1.27 \left(\frac{D \tan \beta}{R} \right)^2 \right) \qquad \text{...(12.39)}$$

where the bearing capacity factor, $N_c^u = \pi$ in the unreinforced case and $N_c^r = (2 + \pi)$ in the reinforced case. The above applies at low rut depth, without membrane action.

The results from Equation (12.39) for unreinforced roads typically corresponds to a mobilised angle of friction in the fill of the order, $45° > \phi' > 35°$, when compared with the new analysis, as illustrated in Figure 12.31 (using the design chart of Figure 12.16a). The results for reinforced unpaved roads correspond very closely with those from the new analysis.

The conclusion to be drawn for the static analysis is that the new design method is consistent with the equations proposed by Giroud and Noiray (1981), and that practically identical results are found for reinforced unpaved roads. The new analysis offers the advantage, however, of allowing the influence of the fill properties to be taken into account, which is particularly significant for unreinforced unpaved roads. This is illustrated by the comparison in Figure 12.31, where the required fill thickness in an unreinforced road can vary by up to a factor of two, depending on the angle of friction in the fill. The analysis by Giroud and Noiray (1981) only gives an average thickness within the likely range.

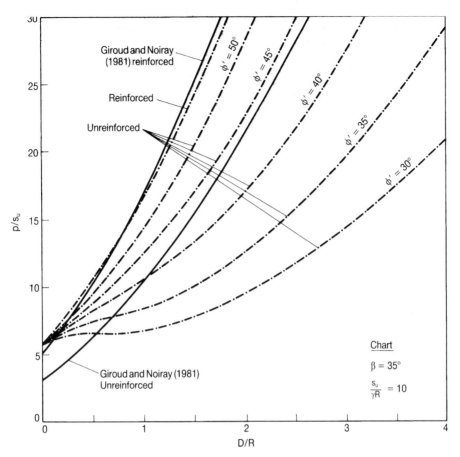

Figure 12.31 *Comparison of the new analysis with Giroud and Noiray (1981). (For the case, β = 35°, and, sᵤ/γR = 10, Figure 12.16)*

Allowance for traffic

In a later paper, Giroud *et al.* (1985) conclude that the effect of reinforcement acting as a tension-membrane in an unpaved road is negligible up to a rut depth of the order of δ_v = 75mm. This corresponds with the rutting after which settlement develops leading rapidly to failure in reinforced unpaved roads, as illustrated in Figure 12.21 (Section 12.7.1).

Giroud and Noiray (1981) proposed that the design thickness for a reinforced unpaved road to resist traffic loading, $((p/s_u)_n, N)$, was equal to the required fill thickness for the unreinforced road subject to traffic, as defined by Hammitt (1970), less the saving in fill thickness due to the reinforcement found from the static analysis of the initial loading conditions.

To complete the above analysis, the results for Hammitt (1970) are defined by Equations 12.28 and 12.37, and have been plotted in Figure 12.27. When the potential benefit of the reinforcement acting as a tension membrane is disregarded (for design against unchannelled traffic, or for limited rutting, $\delta_v < 75\text{mm}$), then the fill saving may be found directly from Equation (12.39), which is shown plotted in Figure 12.31.

What is missed in the above procedure is the reduced rate of degradation that has been observed in trials on reinforced unpaved roads (Section 12.7.3). Tests have demonstrated the two main sources of improvement from reinforcement in unpaved roads. First, the increase in strength due to the mechanical action of the reinforcement supporting outward shear stress. Second, the reduction in the rate of degradation, or fatigue, in reinforced unpaved roads compared to unreinforced unpaved roads. The latter source of improvement can be at least as significant as the former. Both aspects of behaviour are included in the new analysis, the latter being allowed for by means of the coefficient of fatigue, f_n (Section 12.7.3). This is illustrated by the back-analysis below.

12.9.3 Back-analysis of reinforced trafficking trials

The influence of the different rates of fatigue in reinforced and unreinforced unpaved roads can be illustrated by the test sections reported by Webster and Watkins (1977), (Figure 12.21), and Webster and Alford (1978). Three test sections used the same reinforcement and fill, but two different fill thicknesses were tested in the reinforced case (Table 12.4).

The test data are for a single axle load, $P_{axle} = 80\text{kN}$, acting on dual wheels (two pairs of tyres) inflated to a pressure, $p_{tyre} = 480\text{kN/m}^2$. The contact pressure, $p = p_{tyre}/\sqrt{2} = 340\text{kN/m}^2$, defines a radius of contact, $R = \sqrt{P_{axle}/\sqrt{2}\pi p_{tyre}} = 0.194\text{m}$, as described in Section 12.7.5. The strength of the subgrade and the thickness of the fill are known, and the number of load repetitions to failure are found from the measured performance (Section 12.7.1 and Figure 12.21). The test on the thinner, reinforced road section reported by Webster and Alford (1978) did not fail after 15,000 load repetitions (Table 12.4).

Table 12.4 Trafficking trials on a crushed stone fill over a clay subgrade, reinforced by a strong woven nylon membrane T-16

	Fill depth D (m)	Subgrade s_u (kN/m²)	Loading $(p/s_u)_n$	Failure $N_f^{[3]}$	Fatigue $f_n^{[5]}$
Unreinforced[1]	0.35	27	12.59	90	0.42
Reinforced A[1]	0.36	30	11.33	12000	0.29
Reinforced B[2]	0.15	102	3.33	(15000)[4]	0.28

Notes: 1. Webster and Watkins (1977) items 5 and 7
        2. Webster and Alford (1978) item 6
        3. See Figure 12.21
        4. Did not fail, 50mm rut depth after 15,000 load repetitions
        5. Equation (12.27) with $N_s = 5$; exp = 0.30 for unreinforced roads, and exp = 0.16, used for the back-analysis of reinforced roads.

Reinforced test sections
The reinforced case is the simpler to analyse. Equation (12.36) and Figures 12.25 summarise the results for reinforced unpaved roads, for any applied loading and number of load repetitions.

For the reinforced road A at failure, the equivalent load is $(p/s_u)_n \times 1/f_n = 11.33/0.29 = 39.1$, and from Figure 12.25 (or Equation 12.36), the road thickness that would lead to failure after $N = 12{,}000$ load repetitions is $D \tan \beta/R = 1.62$. The size of the loaded area $R = 0.194$m, so that the theoretical fill thickness for failure is $D = 0.31, 0.37$ and 0.45m, for assumed load-spread angles, $\beta = 45°, 40°$ and $35°$, respectively.

The actual fill thickness causing failure was $D = 0.36$m (Table 12.4), suggesting that a load-spread angle of the order of $\beta = 40°$ is appropriate for the crushed stone fill in the reinforced case. (The measured result is predicted to within an accuracy 10% by a load-spread angle in the range $44° \geq \beta \geq 37°$, for all ϕ'.)

The same fill, reinforcement and traffic loading was used in road B, but with less than half the fill thickness, $D = 0.15$m, and for a much stronger subgrade, $s_u = 102$kN/m^2. The equivalent loading in this case, $(p/s_u)_n \times 1/f_n = 3.33/0.28 = 11.9$, corresponds to a road thickness at failure after $N = 15{,}000$ load repetitions of $D \tan \beta/R = 0.42$ (Figure 12.25 or Equation 12.36). The theoretical fill thickness for failure for the same range of load-spread angles as above are $D = 0.08, 0.10$ and 0.12m, for $\beta = 45°, 40°$ and $35°$, respectively.

An expected load-spread angle, $\beta = 40°$, would predict failure after 15,000 load repetitions in a reinforced road of thickness, $D = 0.10$m. In fact the road was 50% thicker than this, $D = 0.15$m, and remained distant from failure at the end of trafficking, as the analysis would suggest.

The results for the second reinforced road, case B, could be found on the design charts in Figures 12.17c and 12.16a, for $\beta = 45°$ and $35°$, respectively, and for the equivalent static loading, $(p/s_u)_n \times 1/f_n = 11.9$. The result when $\beta = 40°$, would be deduced by interpolation. The equivalent load in the first trial, $(p/s_u)_n \times 1/f_n = 39.1$, is beyond the range of the general charts presented.

Unreinforced test section
In an unreinforced unpaved road, the influence of the fill is governed by the angle of friction, ϕ', the load-spread angle, β, and by a non-dimensional measure of the fill weight with respect to the subgrade strength, $s_u/\gamma R$. It is always conservative in the analysis for repeated loading to use the chart for the initial value, $s_u/\gamma R$ (Section 12.8.1).

When fatigue is interpreted as reducing the undrained strength of the subgrade, $(s_u)_n = s_u \times f_n$, the fill plays an increasingly important role as the value, $(s_u)_n/\gamma R$, decreases. This can be seen by comparing the required fill thickness for unreinforced roads in the design charts for the same load-spread angle, $\beta = 35°$, but the two values,

$s_u/\gamma R$ = 5 and 20 (Figure 12.18a and c). The higher the value, $s_u/\gamma R$, the greater the required fill thickness in the unreinforced road.

To illustrate this point, the analysis for the unreinforced test section above has been carried out for the two extreme values, $s_u/\gamma R$ = 7 for the initial conditions, and $(s_u)_n/\gamma R$ = 2.9 after the 90 load repetitions (Table 12.4).

In the first case, a load-spread angle in the range, $45° \geq \beta \geq 40°$, and a mobilised angle of friction, $45° \geq \phi' \geq 40°$, closely reproduce the measured failure, as illustrated in Figure 12.32a. Slightly less load-spreading would apply in the second case, $40° \geq \beta \geq 35°$, for the same range of angle of friction in the fill, $45° \geq \phi' \geq 40°$ (Figure 12.32b). The range of values are consistent with the back-analysis of Hammitt's (1970) data on unreinforced unpaved roads (Section 12.9.1).

As discussed earlier (Section 12.8), the approach that reflects most accurately the physical mechanisms governing fatigue in unreinforced unpaved roads will only become clearer after further research. For now, designers need be aware of the two possibilities, and to allow for an appropriate degree of load-spreading.

The merit of the first approach is that it is always conservative. However, it is considered more reasonable to expect that repeated loading will progressively reduce the undrained strength of the subgrade, and that consequently there will be slightly less effective load-spreading in an unreinforced, compared to a reinforced, unpaved road, as the above analysis implies. Thus the second approach is believed to reflect more accurately the physical mechanisms at work, and is the approach that it recommended.

Required reinforcement force

The required reinforcement force for the equilibrium in the reinforced unpaved road case B may be estimated following the procedures described in Section 12.8.2.

The recommended procedure considers the equilibrium at failure, N_f = 12,000, and assumes that the actual load applies, p = 340kN/m², and that the strength of the subgrade has deteriorated due to fatigue, f_n = 0.29, so that $(s_u)_n$ = 30 × 0.29 = 8.7kN/m². The initial loading, $(p/s_u)_n$ = 11.33, rises as a consequence of fatigue to an equivalent value at failure, $(p/s_u)_n \times 1/f_n$ = 39.1. The actual fill thickness in this case is, $(D/R)_n$ = 0.36/0.194 = 1.86.

For the fully reinforced equilibrium, N_c^r = 5.69, and the load-spread angle that fits with the equivalent loading and the fill thickness is β = 41° (Equation 12.36). The above parameters define the equilibrium at failure and may be substituted into Equation (12.23) to determine the corresponding reinforcement force. For an expected strength in the fill, ϕ' = 40°, the maximum required force is P_R = 1.5kN/m. However, as discussed in Section 12.8.2, the conservative choice is to assume that at failure the fill has been remoulded sufficiently to reach the critical state, $\phi' = \phi'_{cv}$. Making this assumption,

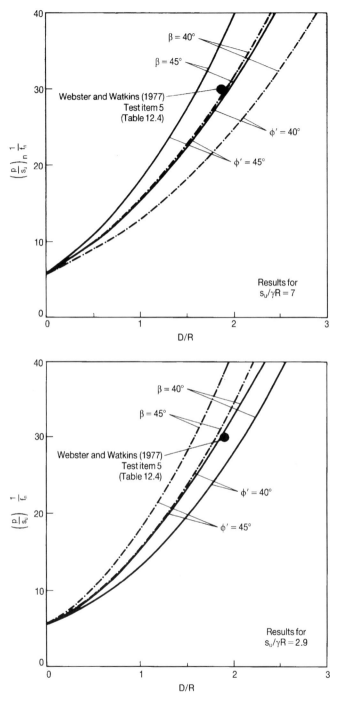

Figure 12.32 *Results for the back-analysis of the unreinforced unpaved road tested by Webster and Watkins (1977)*

and with ϕ'_{cv} = 35°, the maximum required reinforcement force increases to P_R = 4.0kN/m.

Giroud and Noiray (1981) (Section 12.8.2) examine the initial equilibrium in the reinforced case, p/s_u = 11.3, (f_n = 1). For a chosen load-spread angle (β = 41° is used here to allow a direct comparison), the required fill thickness just to maintain the reinforced equilibrium is found, D/R = 0.46, (Equation 12.36). For the assumed angle of friction, ϕ' = 40°, the maximum required reinforcement force is P_R = 3.7kN/m (Equation 12.23).

This latter case is within the range of the charts given earlier, $s_u/\gamma R$ = 7.7, and the maximum required force in a reinforced unpaved road of depth, D/R = 0.46, may be found from Figures 12.16b and 12.17d, for the cases of β = 35° and β = 45°, respectively, and for $s_u/\gamma R$ = 10. The values, $P_R/s_u R$ = 0.6 and 0.7, correspond to a mobilised angle of friction, ϕ' = 40°, and give a force, P_R = 3.5 and 4kN/m, for the two cases respectively. Interpolation between the charts is needed, but at low values, D/R < 1, the maximum required force does not depend greatly on small differences in load-spread angle.

If in design the maximum allowable tensile strain in the reinforcement had been specified as ε_{all} = 3%, the minimum required stiffness for the reinforcement would be $J_{t,T}$ = 4/0.03 = 135kN/m, based on the largest estimated value for the required reinforcement force. The measured stiffness from index tests on the T-16 reinforcement fabric used in the road was J_{index} = 200kN/m.

Reinforcement with insufficient modulus

When the reinforcement in an unpaved road has insufficient modulus to mobilise the maximum required reinforcement force at an acceptable elongation, failure will occur (due to excessive rutting) at an intermediate equilibrium, ($N_c < N_c^r$). In this case the reinforcement is able to support only a portion of the outward shear stress, and the remainder is transmitted to the underlying clay, as described in Section 12.2.6 (Figure 12.11).

Knowing the maximum allowable force in the reinforcement (derived from the reinforcement stiffness and the maximum allowable elongation for a serviceable road) it is possible to determine the limiting road capacity, p_{all}, which will fall between the fully reinforced and unreinforced cases, $N_c^r > (N_c)_{all} > N_c^u$ (Section 12.2.6).

In an unpaved road that is deteriorating due to traffic, the undrained shear strength of the subgrade reduces progressively, $s_u.f_n$, and likewise the equivalent load increases, $(p/s_u)_n.1/f_n$. Where there is insufficient reinforcement, the capacity of the unpaved road is limited by an allowable bearing capacity, $(N_c)_{all}$, rather than by the (fully) reinforced capacity, N_c^r (Figure 12.33).

What is currently lacking is a method to assess how rapidly the deterioration in the road to this end point will occur. All that is certain is that the fatigue coefficient, f_n, is

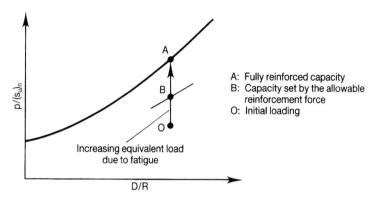

Figure 12.33 *Illustration of the increasing equivalent load due to fatigue and the limiting capacity caused by insufficient reinforcement modulus*

likely to fall within the range established by the unreinforced and the (fully) reinforced cases, $0.30 \geq \exp \geq 0.16$.

The pessimistic assumption would be to select the same rate of degradation in an insufficiently reinforced road as in an unreinforced unpaved road. This would set the lower limit to the expected number of load repetitions to cause failure (and is the approach implicit in Giroud and Noiray (1981) who build Hammitt's (1970) relation for unreinforced roads into their analysis for reinforced roads).

At present there is no basis available on which to judge by how much reinforcement with insufficient modulus can reduce the rate of degradation in an unpaved road, compared to the case with no reinforcement.

12.10 Discussion

A substantial amount of design information has been presented on working platforms and unpaved roads, and some final remarks are warranted to help set it in context.

The static analysis for working platforms is straightforward and falls well within the scope of reinforced soil design that was discussed in earlier chapters. The extension of the static analysis to a three-dimensional loading, and the application of this analysis to design is also well within the conventional knowledge of reinforced soil, except for the loading applied to the geotextile reinforcement (Figure 12.15). The reinforcement is subjected to an outward radial shear which is likely to cause non-uniform tension across the loaded portion of the reinforcement.

It was suggested that for static loading conditions it may well be adequate to compare the stresses in the reinforcement to those in a biaxial test, and to derive the necessary properties for the reinforcement from biaxial testing. For this reason, the average tension across the loaded portion of the geotextile was selected as the value to be reported by the analysis (Section 12.5.4).

In the above cases involving (quasi) static loading, it is possible to apply the same procedures for the selection of design parameters and safety margins, and for checking the fill bearing capacity, as used throughout this book.

Extending the analysis to allow for traffic raises a number of new issues that are not well established for reinforced soil. For example, the testing methods to measure the parameters for geotextile reinforcement subjected to the rapid load-unload cycles in an unpaved road, and over an extended period, are not well established. Such shortcomings must be clearly recognised.

However, it has proved possible to develop an analysis for unreinforced and reinforced unpaved roads in a way that is entirely consistent with the previous methods and data (Hammitt, 1970; Giroud and Noiray, 1981). The key to this development has been the recognition of the fundamental interaction between bearing capacity and outward shear stress. Through this mechanism, the properties of the fill have been introduced into the analysis, and this has shown that the earlier work gives results corresponding to the middle of the likely range for typical fill properties. But the range can be quite large.

Thus the design method which has been presented provides a more versatile tool for the analysis of unreinforced and reinforced unpaved roads. However, some considerable uncertainties remain; e.g. in the rate of degradation that will apply when an unpaved road is reinforced by a geotextile with insufficient modulus, or in the analysis for the fill bearing capacity under repeated traffic loading.

Further developments in the design method will be made as more research is carried out and more data obtained on the behaviour of reinforced unpaved roads under traffic loading and on the behaviour of geotextile materials under repeated, multi-axial loading. The new analysis should provide a useful tool for the interpretation and future application of the data.

12.11 Synopsis of Chapter 12

(1) In an unreinforced working platform or unpaved road, outward shear stress is applied to the subgrade, together with the vertical stress, and this results in a lower bearing capacity than if there was no outward shear.

(2) Reinforcement placed over a soft subgrade can support the outward shear stress thereby increasing the bearing capacity, i.e. improving the load-carrying capacity; without any ruts being formed. This does not depend on deformation (or rutting) taking place.

(3) The analysis for unreinforced and reinforced fills on soft subgrades is derived for plane-strain loading, relevant to tracked vehicles on working platforms, and for axi-symmetric loading, relevant to wheel loading on an unpaved road.

(4) The load-carrying capacity of unreinforced and reinforced unpaved roads may be summarised in design charts, and several examples are given.

(5) The extension of the static analysis to allow for the fatigue caused by traffic loading has been presented. The analysis has been shown to provide a more complete interpretation of the field data of Hammitt (1990).

(6) It has been observed that the rate of degradation due to traffic on a reinforced unpaved road is significantly less than in an equivalent unreinforced road. This important source of improvement from reinforcement has been included in the new analysis, based on the field observations of comparative reinforced and unreinforced test sections.

(7) A complete design method for unreinforced and reinforced unpaved roads has been developed which offers much greater versatility. The method reproduces the results from earlier methods.

(8) The relative lack of knowledge of the behaviour of soils and geotextiles under repeated loading should not be overlooked, and the design of unpaved roads must still rely on a substantial element of empiricism.

Key references

De Groot, M., Janse, E., Maagdenberg, T.A.C. and Van den Berg, C. (1986). Design method and guidelines for geotextile application in road construction. *Proc. 3rd Int. Conf. on Geotextiles*. Vienna, Vol. 3, pp. 741–7.

Giroud, J.P. and Noiray, L. (1981). Geotextile-reinforced unpaved road design, *Proc. ASCE Journal Geotechnical Engineering*. Vol. 107, No. GT9, 1233–54.

Hammitt, G.M. (1970). Thickness requirements for unsurfaced roads and airfields, bare base support. *US Army Waterways Research Station*. Vicksburg, TR2-70-5.

Houlsby, G.T. and Jewell, R.A. (1990) Design of reinforced unpaved roads for small rut depths, *Proc. 4th Int. Conf. on Geotextiles, Geomembranes and Related Products*. The Hague, Balkema.

Milligan, G.W.E., Jewell, R.A., Houlsby, G.T. and Burd, H.J. (1989). A new approach to the design of unpaved roads–Part II. *Ground Engineering,* November, 37–42.

13   From design to specification

This book introduces the concepts and purposes of soil reinforcement, describes the data to be gathered and assessed, and explains the analytical procedures. These are the major elements of the design process but, in the course of a specific project, there is a continuing interaction between these elements, and with the development of the specification and quality assurance plan to ensure that the design assumptions are achieved. An important step in the analysis and checking process is to assess the degree of uncertainty inherent in the methods, material properties or design parameters.

This chapter, therefore, draws attention to matters which require special attention in the design of reinforced soil. Some concern overall planning for the use of reinforced soil, some the uncertainties in current knowledge – where further research is needed – and some are points for specifications or construction detailing. For design and construction to come together successfully, these types of question have to be resolved.

The chapter is introduced by a brief review of some likely future developments in reinforced soil which can already be foreseen. Some final remarks on reinforced soil are given at the end of the chapter.

13.1 Future developments

Dramatic advances have been made over the past 10 to 15 years in reinforced soil techniques and in the geotextile and geogrid materials that may be used for these applications. Reinforced soil and geotextiles are now widely used in earthworks. The progress continues apace, with increased knowledge and confidence stemming from successful applications, and with new developments in polymer materials and their manufacturing processes. The range and cost-effectiveness of polymer reinforcement materials should be expected to increase in the foreseeable future.

Four developments in reinforced soil which are likely to become widely established in coming years are identified below.

Soil may be reinforced by fibres. Individual fibres when intermixed with granular soil can provide a remarkable increase in shear strength and stability, which is not yet fully explained within the conventional principles of soil mechanics. Fibre reinforced soil could be used in all the main application areas of reinforced soil, and wider practical application will follow the development of effective mixing and placing techniques, with increased knowledge of likely damage and the resulting durability of fibres intimately mixed with soil, and in the methods of analysis. Fibre reinforced soil offers the particular advantage of great ductility and tolerance to seismic loading.

The reinforcement of soil *in situ* to form excavations and stabilise slopes is now well established, but with steel reinforcement. The increasing use of *in-situ* soil reinforcement is likely to bring the application of polymer reinforcement materials to this form of construction.

Anchored earth and loop-anchor construction takes advantage of the available bearing resistance between reinforcement and soil, and these techniques are applied in the construction of steep slopes and walls (Figure 10.32). Wider application of this form of reinforced soil construction should be expected.

The combination of functions in one material will increase. For example, there are composites which allow drainage as well as providing reinforcement, and these have allowed silty clay materials to be used for the construction of steep slopes. Another new technique is to use a substantial structural facing in combination with a reduced quantity of reinforcement to form retaining walls, with the face playing a vital structural role.

13.2 Designing reinforced soil structures

13.2.1 Concept

As with any design, the conceptual thinking at the start of the project has to be clear. Reinforced soil structures have widened the options open to engineers and in some cases have provided viable solutions to otherwise costly if not intractable problems. In many instances, reinforced soil is one of various options, often as an alternative to either a reinforced concrete retaining wall or a conventional earth slope. But the choice of one or other construction method depends on a number of interactions: costs, time and space constraints, and available fill material or other resources. Less obvious, perhaps, are questions of the structure's compatibility – with the foundation, with the external finish, with adjacent or internal structures – and how its structural form matches these functional requirements.

All the main applications of soil reinforcement, described in this book, are suitable for relatively short-term usages. Specifically, reinforcement of embankments on soft clay foundations is needed only until the foundation has gained strength by consolidation; hardstandings are construction expedients, and unpaved roads are often site haul roads; many vertical wall structures are built as temporary works during a project. But vertical walls, steep slopes, embankment slip repairs and unpaved roads can all be long-term structures, and reinforced soil techniques are increasingly being used for them. Therefore clarity is needed in considering the appropriate length of the design life and the changes which occur during this period.

13.2.2 Compatibility

Perhaps the primary consideration for a reinforced soil structure is recognising (a) that it has to deform to develop its strength, (b) that it continues to deform, and (c) that, as a consequence, its available 'strength' is not constant, but variable (Chapter 4).

This inherent flexibility is often advantageous: within limits, a reinforced soil structure can accommodate a degree of externally caused movement and is usually less sensitive to such movements than, say, a masonry alternative. Thus combining reinforced soil construction with other techniques of ground improvement, such as vertical drains or stone columns in order to improve a poor fill, can achieve compatibility between a compressible foundation and the superimposed structure.

Other components of a project, however, may be relatively more rigid, such as a bridge abutment and its wingwalls to which a reinforced soil embankment leads. The soil-structure interactions here are complex and depend very much on the construction sequence as well as on the detailing at the junction. Should, for example, the reinforced soil approach be constructed first and the abutment and wingwalls built as stand-alone units? Should there be some transitional foundation treatment beneath the embankment in the approach to the abutment?

Two extreme examples from a very soft clay site illustrate the point. From a pontoon in a shallow estuarial creek, H-piles had been driven to support a light vehicle bridge. The low approach embankment to the bridge was constructed over the soft clay using a strong, woven geotextile. Fill placing was with low-weight plant and carefully controlled but, despite this, mud waves were created ahead and to the side of the filling. The displacement of soft clay ahead of the filling imposed high lateral forces on the steel piles and bent them, and new piles had to be installed later through the constructed embankment (Figure 13.1).

A prefabricated steel culvert had to be constructed through a reinforced soil embankment on soft clay. The culvert is flexible and can accommodate a substantial amount of differential settlement, but at what stage in the construction of the embankment should it have been installed? If placed virtually upon the basal reinforcement prior to embankment filling, subsequent compression of the soft clay foundation could result in the culvert being at too low an elevation. If placed later after excavating a cut through the fill, the embankment stability could be in jeopardy due to a failure in the longitudinal direction (i.e. at right angles to the direction for which the reinforcement was designed); and, at the least, there would be a risk of damaging the reinforcement in the excavation process (Figure 13.2). Later still, provided the culvert did not have to be in-place at an early stage, the foundation would have consolidated sufficiently to allow the cut to be made safely.

These two examples epitomise the need for two types of compatibility: with external structures and with internal structures. The principles apply equally to vertical walls or

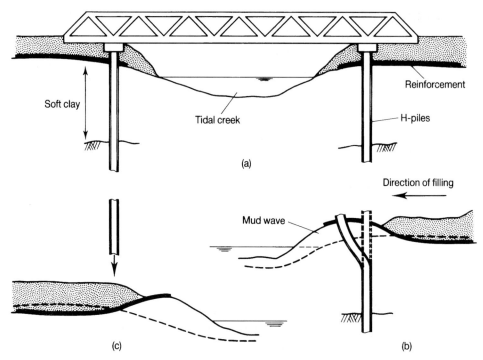

Figure 13.1 *Possible effect of sequence of opertions at a soft-clay site: (a) proposed light bridge founded an H-piles, (b) fill placement deforms pre-installed piles, (c) piles installed after construction of approach embankment*

steep slopes, and demand that attention be paid to structural and construction detailing.

There is much to recommend the approach of constructing the reinforced soil first, allowing it to deform and the foundation to consolidate substantially, before the construction of relatively rigid adjacent structures, such as abutments and wingwalls. This applies also where the final appearance of the wall facing is critical, when the final wall facing can be set after the reinforced soil has deformed (Jones, 1988).

13.2.3 Timing and structural life

The integration of a reinforced soil structure with other components in a project has to be planned carefully, not only in the sequencing but also in the actual timing. Again the points are illustrated by the two soft-clay examples given above; the sequencing for the installation of H-piles in the bridge abutment and, in the case of the culvert, of the importance of time – where there was less risk of foundation instability after the clay had time to consolidate under the embankment self-weight.

Also, where wick drains are to be installed ahead of reinforced embankment construction, either a working platform must be formed with a sacrificial reinforcement

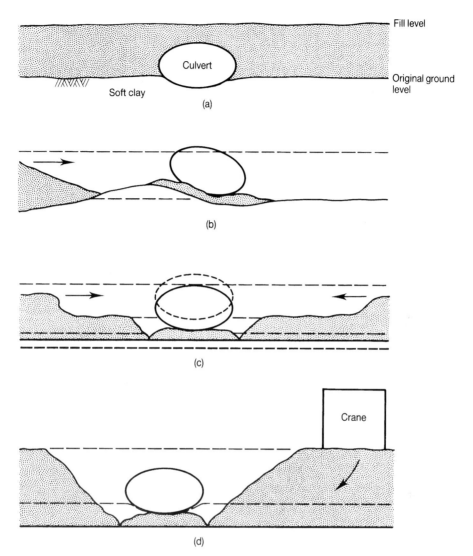

Figure 13.2 *Possible effects of sequence of operations when installing a culvert through a basally reinforced embankment on soft clay*

layer through which the wick drains are punched (the main reinforcement being installed subsequently on the working platform), or an allowance would need to be made for the damage to the reinforcement caused by the installation of the wick drains.

Another example is in slope reconstruction to repair a slip failure using reinforced soil. Care is needed not to precipitate additional instability by the excavation to allow reconstruction. The sequence of excavation must be carefully planned.

A critical question for reinforced soil is assessment of the material characteristics of the reinforcement which are appropriate to the required design life. The soil, the biochemical conditions at the site, the care and diligence of construction, may all influence the material properties. Clarity is needed in selecting the relevant loading periods and conditions for the reinforcement in the field when examining the stability at various stages during and following construction (Chapter 2).

13.2.4 Foundation and fill materials

The site investigation requirements for a reinforced soil structure are no more onerous than those for alternative conventional structures. Arguably, because of its greater tolerance to settlement and ability to accommodate localised weak spots, reinforced soil is a more forgiving form of construction than a more rigid structure, for example a reinforced concrete retaining wall. Nevertheless, it is essential that the foundation is fully investigated to establish the variability of the ground, the groundwater regime and the strength and compressibility of the foundation soils.

Much depends on the material properties of the fill. Often these may not be known for certain at the design stage when imported fill is to be used from a source that is not known until the contract starts. The designer will have to take a conservative view of what quality fill can realistically be assumed for the construction, and then thoroughly specify the minimum performance requirements for the fill, so as to ensure that the assumed properties are met.

13.2.5 Facings and slope protection

An increasingly wide variety of options are available to designers of steep slopes and walls, from simple fabric wrap-arounds to architectural-finish precast units. While the facings do not contribute to the overall stability of a vertical reinforced soil wall, they are an essential part of the fill containment system, preventing ravelling or erosion. In that the facings are connected to the reinforcement, not only does their installation have to be integrated into the fill placement process, but the mechanical nature of the connection (and the amount and direction of relative movement that is permitted) has to be designed carefully.

Sufficient detail must be given in the specification (and implemented on site) to ensure that the reinforcement-to-facing connection is not overloaded. For example, heavy compaction just behind the facing, or poor workmanship with the reinforcement connected at the bottom limit of a vertical sliding joint (designed to allow relative vertical settlement of the reinforced fill) could both lead to stress concentration at the connection between the reinforcement and the face.

In steep slopes reinforced by geotextiles, a steel mesh former is sometimes used at the face. This contains lightweight geotextile materials which not only contain the fill, but are combined with growing agents and mulches to allow vegetation to establish to provide an evenly vegetated slope. There are practical limits to the steepness that can be achieved with even vegetation, of the order, $\beta = 60°$. The open box facings used in loop-anchor walls allow creepers or similar vegetation to be grown on steeper faces (Figure 10.32).

13.3 Construction specification and quality assurance

There is an increasing literature on specifications and standard construction details and practices for reinforced soil. Advantage should be taken of these in the development of specifications; see, for example, Jones (1988); GCO (1989); OECD (1991); and BSI (1991).

13.3.1 Reinforcement materials

The proper reception, storage, handling and quality assurance testing of the reinforcement material is of great importance. Geotextile reinforcement can be damaged by inappropriate handling and sustained exposure to heat and light (Chapter 2). The reception and storage of the materials on site must be planned and controlled, as must be the handling of the material as it is built into the earthworks. Undue direct exposure of geotextiles to sun and heat should be avoided, as can occur if materials are placed and jointed too far in advance of filling.

The delivered materials must be clearly labelled so that there is no possible confusion on site when one or more geotextiles or geogrids are used. Colour coding sprayed directly on the reinforcement is an effective and practical means of identification on site. Sufficient testing is needed to make sure that the correct material has indeed been delivered to site, and that it has the specified properties. Some of this testing may be carried out at the place of manufacture, prior to dispatch to site, by independent certifying organisations.

Quality control testing of material damaged by construction on site is needed to assess whether adequate allowance for this was made in design. Such testing may also be required to determine whether a particular area of reinforcement that has been unduly exposed, or otherwise damaged on site, still meets the specified properties. The biochemical properties of the soil and groundwater should be checked to see that an adequate allowance for these were made in the assumed factors for environmental degradation (Section 2.5.2).

13.3.2 Site preparation and construction control

Attention must be given to the site preparation when reinforcement is to be placed directly on existing ground. Features that would damage the reinforcement, such as sharp objects, should be removed or fully covered. The specification must set out clear criteria for an adequate subgrade, dealing with levelling (high and low spots), acceptable surface vegetation and surface roughness, and types of surface materials that might act to the detriment of the reinforcement or the structure, and which must be removed.

For steep slopes or walls, it is often convenient to precut the reinforcement to length in the factory, so that only the connection to the facing need be made on site. Constant supervision is needed on site to ensure that the correct reinforcement materials are incorporated at the appropriate elevations.

Attention to detail is needed at corners and areas where reinforcement overlaps. This mostly raises issues of practical concern, but unexpected weakness could result, for example, where two geotextile layers at a corner are placed directly in contact with one another to create a geotextile-to-geotextile interface.

The quality control test results on materials and joints should be compiled into a permanent record of construction. Sufficient quantities of the reinforcement materials should be stored for future comparative testing against any samples recovered from the structure.

13.4 Topics of special concern

In several of the chapters of this book, mention is made to gaps in current knowledge and to aspects of design which ought to be improved (i.e. our capability to design with soil reinforcement is to some extent limited). That there are such uncertainties is not surprising in so rapidly developing a subject. These and some other aspects of reinforced soil behaviour merit special attention, and are noted below for review by designers. Particular care is needed in the choice of design parameters and safety margins in these cases. The listing is not exhaustive, but covers the main areas of uncertainty.

13.4.1 Limit state design

The framework of limit state design is essential in reinforced soil because stability and behaviour depend critically on both the soil and the reinforcement properties (Chapter 6). Also, two quite distinct properties of the reinforcement material are significant for design, namely the strength for stability, and the stiffness for serviceability. It is unsatisfactory to try to combine these quite separate concerns into one calculation, by introducing an allowable reinforcement force, based on a limiting elongation, into a stability analysis.

Limit state design must be adopted. Stability is then assessed using potential combinations of the worst expected loadings and the lowest expected resistances that might occur in the reinforced soil structure (Chapter 7). For the reinforcement material, the concerns are potential rupture of the reinforcement, bond failure between the reinforcement and the soil (causing pullout), and gross direct sliding of soil across the surface of a reinforcement layer.

The expected values of the loadings and resistances are examined in a separate analysis of serviceability which is concerned with the magnitude and distribution of force mobilised in the reinforcement under the expected (working) conditions (Chapter 7). The expected displacement in the structure caused by extension in the reinforcement layers may then be assessed. When the displacements are unacceptably large, the reinforcement has insufficient modulus. Either more layers should be included (to reduce the force and elongation in each), or another geotextile selected with a higher modulus.

Limit equilibrium calculations are recommended in this book as the most practical means to assess serviceability. The link between the mobilised soil shearing resistance and the reinforcement force is established from the knowledge of compatibility (Section 4.3). To simplify the analysis, it has proved convenient to define a maximum allowable elongation in the reinforcement for each application which is known to be compatible with a serviceable structure, based on the available data from satisfactory structures (Section 7.3).

Further developments are likely in the analysis of serviceability, and in the identification of the appropriate soil and reinforcement properties. There will be a greater sophistication in the definition of allowable elongation. The practical implementation of finite element analysis for design will become increasingly common, and is ideally suited to the analysis of serviceability.

13.4.2 Geotechnical properties

The material behaviour of soil is increasingly well understood. The knowledge of the relation between the mean applied stresses, the relative density and the critical state angle of friction for granular soil provides a sound basis for selecting strength properties for reinforced soil design (Section 5.2.2). Similar principles apply for clay soils, where the degree of overconsolidation, rather than relative density, plays a key role in determining the peak shearing resistance that can be mobilised (Section 5.2.4). The requirements for selecting the appropriate strength properties of soil for the limit state analysis of reinforced soil are substantially similar to those for the limit state analysis of other geotechnical structures.

Particle size effects can also be important for reinforced soil, both in the increased bearing capacity that results when the particle size becomes significant (and a continuum can no longer be assumed), and in the more practical question of particle penetration (or interlock) in the apertures of geogrid reinforcement (Section 4.6).

There is still relatively little experience in the use of compacted clay fills in steep reinforced slopes, and caution is required in the design of such applications. The assumption of a critical state strength in the clay fill, and a realistic estimate of the long-term porewater pressures in the slope, should probably be made in the stability analysis.

Another uncertainty is in the analysis of stability involving soft clay beneath an embankment, both for conditions during and after consolidation. Special care is recommended in the application of both total and effective stress analysis to this case (Section 11.3).

The progressive reduction in the shearing resistance in a clay subgrade beneath an unpaved road subject to traffic loading is an aspect of soil behaviour for which there is a lack of data. Empirical relations for the effects of traffic loading are currently used (Section 12.10).

13.4.3 Geotextile properties

The main aspects of behaviour of the polymer materials used in geotextiles are well known, and suitable methods have been developed to allow for the time-dependent nature of these properties in reinforced soil design. The long-term testing of polymers remains problematical due to the uncertainties inherent in methods of accelerated testing (Section 2.2.3).

While the general aspects of the long-term behaviour of these polymer materials are known, it is likely that this knowledge will develop greatly in the coming years. Designers must pay attention to such development to make sure that the new information is taken into account. Testing for the aged life of geotextiles (i.e. the resistance to complete chemical breakdown in the very long term) is not yet widely established, but it should form part of the data used to justify the long-term properties and survivability assumed in design (Section 2.3.4).

Another aspect is the joints and connections needed in reinforced soil. Any potential reduction in the short or long-term strength (with respect to the intact reinforcement material) at joints with the facing, or at sewn joints between adjacent geotextile sheets for construction over soft ground, should be carefully assessed and allowed for in design.

An area of concern for unpaved road design is the lack of knowledge on the behaviour of geotextiles under multi-axial repeated loading. It has been suggested that biaxial tests may provide a basis upon which to select relevant geotextile properties for the design of reinforced unpaved roads (Section 12.5.4). A great deal more testing and development work is needed before the design of unpaved roads can rely less on empiricism.

A related topic is the effect of confinement in the soil on the properties of non-woven geotextiles. Although generally considered to be relatively weak and extensible, non-woven geotextiles may offer the order of strength and stiffness required in some unpaved road applications once the influence of (a) confinement in the soil, (b) multi-axial loading, and (c) the high rate of strain that applies under traffic load, are considered together. Again, lack of data prevents such an assessment being made at present.

13.4.4 Environmental considerations

The long-term effects of exposure to chemical and biological agents are difficult to define precisely, not least because of the practical challenge in obtaining reliable data on long-term phenomena in a relatively short period of testing. Designers must be prudent in their choice of long-term properties (Section 2.5). Provision can be made to extract reinforcement material during the life of the structure to check on degradation.

13.4.5 Interaction properties

The bond and direct sliding coefficients set the limiting stresses that apply in these two modes of interaction between soil and reinforcement (Section 4.4). The two interaction coefficients have the same value for conventional non-woven and woven geotextiles, which may be measured in a modified direct shear test.

The interaction between soil and geogrid reinforcement is more complex, and because of the different mechanisms that apply (shear on plane surfaces, bearing stress and shear of soil over soil through the apertures of the grid) the bond and direct sliding coefficients normally have different values. Care is needed, therefore, to select the appropriate values of the interaction coefficients for the design analysis with geogrid reinforcement; i.e. is the grid pulling out from the soil, for which the bond coefficient applies? or is soil sliding across the surface of the grid layer, and the underlying soil, when the direct sliding coefficient applies? While the direct sliding resistance for a geogrid is easily measured in a modified direct shear test, there is no simple test to measure bond coefficient.

Pull-out testing is at best difficult to accomplish and interpret, particularly where the extensibility of the geogrid causes non-uniform shear along the length of grid being tested (Section 4.6). A theoretical analysis for the bond coefficient of geogrid reinforcement has been presented in terms of the grid geometry and the soil properties. Where effects due to the extensibility of the geogrid are of concern, it is suggested that a lower bond coefficient may be found by using a large strain (critical state) angle of friction for the soil in the analysis.

13.4.6 Combined applications

The five main applications of reinforced soil are described in the design chapters of this book. The main concern for steep slopes and walls, and in the strengthening of clay embankment slopes, is the stability of the fill. Checks are made on overall and foundation stability in these reinforced structures, but in most cases examined the foundation conditions are sufficient not to affect stability greatly. In contrast, it is the foundation stability that is of main concern in the design of applications on soft soil, such as embankments, working platforms and unpaved roads.

In the majority of cases, the reinforced soil application will fall into one or the other of the above categories. However, there are occasions where a combined application is desired, such as a reinforced slope or retaining wall over a relatively poor foundation. In such cases, the potential action of a basal reinforcement layer (extending a significant distance back from the face and into the fill) to reduce the magnitude of outward shear stress acting on the foundation surface may be considered, using the analyses described (Sections 5.4 and 5.5). But, if the required vertical bearing pressure beneath the reinforced soil exceeds the foundation bearing capacity for vertical loading only (i.e. with basal reinforcement already supporting the outward shear stress) then special foundation improvement techniques will have to be used.

Combined applications with reinforcement layers maintaining stability in the fill and a basal layer of reinforcement boosting stability in the foundation should be designed with great attention to detail. In particular, the potential influence of the foundation on the stability of the reinforced fill, and *vice versa*, must be considered explicitly in the design analysis. The movements caused by foundation deformation are likely to be a major concern in design.

13.4.7 Unpaved roads

While developments in the analysis for unreinforced and reinforced unpaved roads have been presented in Chapter 12, it is necessary to emphasise the substantial empiricism that still remains in the design of such structures. The lack of knowledge of the behaviour and properties for both the soil and the reinforcement under repeated traffic loading is one reason for the empiricism. So too is the paucity of data with which to correlate the analysis of the required reinforcement force through the life of the road.

However, the risk of a poorer than expected performance is usually manifested simply by increased rutting which can be repaired. This may be only of limited concern in the case of site haul roads and hardstandings.

13.5 Concluding remarks

Reinforced soil is a powerful construction technique that has demonstrated its value in a wide range of practical applications, the five most important of which are described in this book. The versatility of reinforced soil and of geotextile materials is far from exhausted, and new methods and materials should be expected in the coming years. Improved polymer materials can only make reinforced soil more economically attractive.

The experience from the wide usage of reinforced soil will improve the knowledge and confidence in the techniques, and provide more data on the behaviour of reinforced soil structures. Additional measurements of long-term properties for polymer reinforcement materials relevant to field conditions, as well as in the laboratory, will increase our knowledge of the material behaviour. Resulting from these developments will be refinements in the limit state analysis of reinforced soil, particularly under serviceability conditions.

The process of codification and standardisation in reinforced soil is underway, but a balance must be struck between preserving sufficient freedom for continued development of the technology, while capturing present best practice in widely accepted standards which will encourage further the widespread application of reinforced soil throughout the construction industry. The latter has been one of the main objectives of this book.

13.6 Synopsis of Chapter 13

(1) In order to integrate the design and specification of a reinforced soil structure with its construction methods careful planning is need for:
- the timing of placing the reinforced soil in relation to other structures
- the different toleration deformation of reinforced soil
- the design detailing, construction sequence and workmanship for incorporating facings and their connections.

(2) Equally important for construction is the quality plan. It is critical to check and document that the reinforcement materials built into the structure have the specified properties, and were placed and connected precisely in the desginated locations.

(3) It is natural in a rapidly developing subject that there are areas in which the knowledge is still limited. These areas should be given special attention in design. They are reviewed in Section 13.4, which may be used by designers as a checklist of potentially important items.

(4) Reinforced soil is a powerful, and versatile, construction technique, well established and increasingly used, but which will develop even more as new materials and methods give engineers the opportunity to extend its capabilities.

Key references

British Standards Institution (1991). *Code of Practice for Strengthened/Reinforced Soils and Other Fills*. Draft Code BS 8006, issued for public comment. British Standards Institution, London.

Geotechnical Control Office (GCO) (1989). *Model Specification for Reinforced Fill Structures*. Geotechnical Control Office, Hong Kong.

Jones, C.J.F.P. (1988). *Earth Reinforcement and Soil Structures,* 2nd edition. Butterworths, London.

Organisation for Economic Co-operation and Development (OECD) (1991). *Ground Engineering Applications of Geotextiles in Road Construction and Maintenance*. Report of Expert Group I88. Transport and Road Research Laboratory, Crowthorne, UK.

References

Ahlvin, R.G. (1959). Developing a set of CBR design curves. *US Army Waterways Research Station*, Instruction Report 4. Vicksburg.

Anderson, M.G. and Kneale, P.E. (1980a). Pore water pressure and stability conditions on a motorway embankment, *Earth Surface Processes,* Vol. 5, pp. 37–46.

Anderson, M.G. and Kneale, P.E. (1980b). Pore water pressure changes in a road embankment, *Journal of the Institution of Highway Engineers,* May, pp. 11–77.

Arthur, J.R.F. and Menzies, B.K. (1972). Inherent anisotropy in sand, *Geotechnique,* Vol. 22, No. 1, pp. 115–129.

Atkinson, J.H. and Bransby, P.L. (1978). *The Mechanics of Soils,* McGraw-Hill, London.

Atkinson, J.H. and Farrar, D.M. (1985). Stress path tests to measure soil strength parameters for shallow landslips, *Proc. 12th Int. Conf. on Soil Mechanics and Foundation Engineering.* San Francisco, Vol. 4, pp. 983–986.

Atkinson, J.H. and Crabb, G.I. (1991). Determination of soil strength parameters for the analysis of highway slope failures, *Int. Conf. on Slope Stability Engineering.* Thomas Telford, London.

Bassett, R.H. (1988). Original design of the Stanstead Abbotts trial embankment, *Prediction Symposium on a Reinforced Embankment on Soft Ground* (1986), Kings College, London.

Bassett, R.H. and Yeo, K.C. (eds) (1988). *Prediction Symposium on a Reinforced Embankment on Soft Ground,* (Proceedings of the Symposium held in September 1986), Department of Civil Engineering, Kings College, London.

Beckham, W.K. and Mills, W.H. (1935). Cotton-fabric reinforced roads, *Engineering News-Record,* Vol. 115, No. 14, (October), pp. 453–455.

Been, K. and Jefferies, M.G. (1986). Discussion: a state parameter for sand, *Géotechnique,* Vol. 36, No. 1, pp. 127–132.

Billing, J.W., Greenwood, J.H. and Small, G.D. (1990). Chemical and mechanical durability of geotextiles, *Proc. 4th Int. Conf. on Geotextiles, Geomembranes and Related Products.* The Hague, Balkema, Rotterdam.

Bishop, A.W. and Henkel, D.J. (1957). *The Measurement of Soil Properties in the Triaxial Test,* William Arnold, London.

Bishop, A.W. and Morgenstern, N.R. (1960). Stability coefficients for earth slopes, *Géotechnique,* Vol. 10, pp. 129–150.

Bishop, A.W., Webb, D.L. and Lewin, P.I. (1965). Undisturbed samples of London Clay from the Ashford Common Shaft: strength-effective stress relationships, *Géotechnique*, Vol. 15, No. 1, pp. 1–31.

Bjerrum, L. (1972). Embankments on soft ground, *Proc. Spec. Conf. of Earth and Earth-Supported Structures*. Purdue, ASCE, New York, Vol. 2, pp. 1–54.

Bjerrum, L. (1973). Problems of soil mechanics and construction of soft clays and structurally unstable soils, *Proc. 8th Int. Conf. on Soil Mechanics and Foundation Engineering*, Moscow, Vol. 3, pp. 111–159.

Bolton, M.D. (1979). *A Guide to Soil Mechanics*. Macmillan, London.

Bolton, M.D. (1981). Limit state design in geotechnical engineering, *Ground Engineering*, September, pp. 39–46.

Bolton, M.D. (1986). The strength and dilatancy of sands, *Géotechnique*, Vol. 36, No. 1, 65–78.

Bolton, M.D. (1987). Discussion on the strength and dilatancy of sands, *Géotechnique*, Vol. 37, No. 2, pp. 225–226.

Bolton, M.D. (1990). *Geotechnical Stress Analysis for Bridge Abutment Design*. Transport Research Laboratory Report, Crowthorne, United Kingdom.

Bonaparte, R. and Christopher, B.R. (1987). Design and construction of reinforced embankments over weak foundations. *Transportation Research Record*, 1153, pp. 26–39.

British Standards Institution (1981). BS 2846. *Guide to Statistical Interpretation of Data*, Part 2, Estimation of the mean: confidence interval. British Standards Institution, London.

British Standards Institution (1987). BS 6906. *British Standard Methods of Test for Geotextiles*, Part 1, Determination of the tensile properties using a wide-width strip. British Standard Institution, London.

British Standards Institution (1991a). Draft Code BS 8006, *Code of Practice for Strengthened/Reinforced Soils and Other Fills,* issued for public comment. British Standards Institution, London.

British Standards Institution (1991b). BS 6906, *British Standard Methods of Test for Geotextiles*, Part 8, Determination of sand-geotextile frictional behaviour by direct shear. British Standards Institution, London.

Broms, B.B. (1971). Lateral pressures due to compaction of cohesionless soils, *Proc. 4th Conf. on Soil Mechanics*, Budapest, pp. 373–384.

Burd, H.J. and Brocklehurst, C.J. (1990). Finite element studies of the mechanics of reinforced unpaved roads, *Proc. 4th Int. Conf. on Geotextiles, Geomembranes and Related Products*, Balkema, Rotterdam, Vol. 1, pp. 217–221.

Burland, J.B. and Burbridge, M.C. (1985). Settlement of foundations on sand and gravel. *Proc. Inst. Civ. Engrs.*, Pt. 1, Vol. 78, pp. 1325–1371.

Busbridge, J.R., Chan, P., Milligan, V., La Rochelle, P. and Lefebrve, L.D. (1985). *The Effect of Geogrid Reinforcement on the Stability of Embankments on a Soft Sensitive Champlain Sea Clay Deposit.* Report for Transportation Development Centre, Montreal.

Bush, D.I. (1988). Evaluation of the effects of construction activities on the physical properties of polymeric reinforcing elements. *Theory and Practice of Earth Reinforcement*, Kyushu, pp. 63–68.

Caquot, A., Kerisel, J. and Absi, E. (1973). *Tables de butée et de poussée*, 2nd edn., Gauthier-Villars, Paris.

CEI (1990). *Guide for the determination of thermal endurance properties of electrical insulating materials,* CEI 216–1, 4th edn., International Electrotechnical Commission, Geneva.

Chandler, R.J. (1988). The in-situ measurement of the undrained shear strength of clays using the field vane. In A.F. Richards (ed.) ASTM Special Publication 1014. ASTM, Philadelphia, pp. 13–44.

Colin, G., Mitton, M.T., Carlsson, D.J. and Wiles, D.M. (1986). The effect of soil burial exposure on some geotechnical fabrics, *Geotextiles and Geomembranes*, Vol. 4, pp. 1–8.

Comité Européen du Beton (1975). *Common Unified Rules for Different Types of Construction Material*, CEB Bulletin 111.

Comité Européen de Normalisation (CEN) (1990). *Geotextiles and Geotextile-related Products: Terms and Definitions.* Draft European Standard, CEN/TC 189/WG 2 N 16.

Commission of the European Communities (1989). *Draft Eurocode No. 7: Geotechnics.* Incomplete draft November 1989.

Coulomb, C.A. (1773). Essai sur une application des règles *de maximis and minimis* à quelques problèmes de statique, relatifs à l'architecture. *Memoires de Mathematique and de Physique*, l'Academie Royale des Sciences par divers Savans, Paris, Vol. 7, pp. 343–382.

Crabb, G.I., West, G. and O'Reilly, M.P. (1987). Groundwater conditions in three highway embankment slopes, *Proc. 9th European Conf. on Soil Mechanics and Foundation Engineering*, Dublin, Vol. 1, pp. 401–406.

Crabb, G.I. and Atkinson, J.H. (1991). Determination of soil strength parameters for the analysis of highway slope failures, *Slope Stability Engineering*. Thomas Telford, London.

Davis, E.H. and Booker, J.R. (1973). The effect of increasing strength with depth on the bearing capacity of clays, *Geotechnique*, Vol. 23, No. 4, pp. 551–563.

De Groot, M., Janse, E., Maagdenberg, T.A.C. and Van den Berg, C. (1986). Design method and guidelines for geotextile application in road construction. *Proc. 3rd Int. Conf. on Geotextiles.* Vienna, Vol. 3, pp. 741–747.

Delmas, P., Matichard, Y., Gourc, J.P. and Riondy, G. (1986). Unsurfaced roads reinforced by geotextiles – a seven-year experiment. *Proc. 3rd Int. Conf. on Geotextiles,* Vienna, Vol. 3, pp. 1015–1021.

Den Hoedt, G. Creep and relaxation of geotextile fabrics. *Geotextiles and Geomembranes,* Vol. 4, pp. 83–92.

Department of Transport (DTp) (1978). *Reinforced Earth Retaining Walls and Bridge Abutments for Embankments,* Technical memorandum BE 3/78. DTp, London.

Duncan, J.M. and Seed, R.B. (1986). Compaction-induced earth pressures under K_0 conditions, *J. Geotech. Eng.,* ASCE, 112, No. 3, pp. 317–333.

Duncan, J.M., Schaefer, V.R., Franks, L.W. and Collins, S.A. (1987). Design and performance of a reinforced embankment for the Mohicanville Dike No. 2 in Ohio, *Transportation Research Record 1153,* ASCE, pp. 15–25.

Dyer, M.R. (1985). *Observation of the Stress Distribution in Crushed Glass with Applications to Soil Reinforcement,* D.Phil. Thesis, University of Oxford.

Edgar, S. (1984). The use of high tensile polymer grid mattress on the Musselburgh and Portello bypass. In *Polymer Grid Reinforcement in Civil Engineering.* Thomas Telford, London, pp. 103–111.

Fannin, R.J. (1987). *Geogrid reinforcement of granular layers on soft clay – a study at model and full scale.* D.Phil. thesis, University of Oxford.

Garbulewski, K. (1990). Direct shear and pull-out frictional resistance at the geotextile-mud interface. *Proc. 4th Int. Conf. on Geotextiles, Geomembranes and Related Products.* The Hague, Balkema, Rotterdam.

Geotechnical Control Office (GCO) (1989). *Model Specification for Reinforced Fill Structures.* Geotechnical Control Office, Hong Kong.

Giroud, J.P. (1986). From geotextiles to geosynthetics: a revolution in geotechnical engineering. *Proc. 3rd Int. Conf. on Geotextiles,* Vienna, Vol. 1, pp. 1–18.

Giroud, J.P., Ah-Line, C., and Bonaparte, R. (1985a). Design of unpaved roads and trafficked areas with geogrids, *Polymer Grid Reinforcement* (Proceedings of a conference held in London 1984), Thomas Telford, London, pp. 116–127.

Giroud, J.P., Arman, A. and Bell, J.R., with cooperation of Koerner, R.M. and Milligan, V. (1985b). Geotextiles in geotechnical engineering, practice and research, *Geotextiles and Geomembranes,* Vol. 2, No. 3, pp. 179–242.

Giroud, J.P. and Noiray, L. (1981). Geotextile-reinforced unpaved road design, *Proc. ASCE Journal Geotechnical Engineering.* Vol. 107, No. GT9, pp. 1233–1254.

Greenwood, J.H. (1990). The creep of geotextiles. *Proc. 4th Int. Conf. on Geotextiles, Geomembranes and Related Products,* The Hague, Balkema, Vol. 2, pp. 646–650.

Greenwood, J.R., Holt, D.A. and Herrick, G.W. (1985). Shallow slips in highway embankments constructed of overconsolidated clay. In *Failures in Earthworks*. Thomas Telford, London, pp. 79–92.

Gudehus, G. (1981). *Bodenmechanik*, Ferdinand Enke Verlag, Stuttgart.

Hammitt, G.M. (1970). Thickness requirements for unsurfaced roads and airfields, bare base support, *US Army Waterways Research Station*. Vicksburg, TR2-70-5.

Henderson, J., Harwood, N. and Rooney, D. (1987). Creep characterisation of a type 315 austenitic steel, *High Temperature Technology*, Vol. 5, No. 4, pp. 181–192.

Henkel, D.J. (1956). Discussion: Earth movement affecting LTE railway in deep cutting east of Uxbridge, *Proc. Inst. Civ. Engnrs.*, Part II, Vol. 5, No. 2, pp. 320–323.

Hird, C.C. and Kwok, C.M. (1990) Parametric studies of the behaviour of a reinforced embankment, *Proc. 4th Int. Conf. on Geotextiles, Geomembranes and Related Products*, The Hague, Balkema, Vol. 1, pp. 137–142.

Houlsby, G.T. and Jewell, R.A. (1988). Analysis of unreinforced and reinforced embankments on soft clays by plasticity analysis, *Proc. 6th Int. Conf. on Numerical Methods in Geomechanics,* Innsbruck, Vol. 2, pp. 1443–1448.

Houlsby, G.T. and Jewell, R.A. (1990). Design of reinforced unpaved roads for small rut depths, *Proc. 4th Int. Conf. on Geotextiles, Geomembranes and Related Products*, The Hague, Balkema, Rotterdam.

Houlsby, G.T., Milligan, G.W.E., Jewell, R.A. and Burd, H.J. (1989). A new approach to the design of unpaved roads–Part 1. *Ground Engineering*, April, pp. 25–29.

Humphrey, D.N. and Holtz, R.D. (1986). Reinforced embankments – a review of case histories, *Geotextiles and Geomembranes*, Vol. 4, pp. 129–144.

Ingold, T.S. (1979). The effects of compaction on retaining walls, *Géotechnique*, Vol. 29, No. 3, pp. 265–283.

Ingold, T.S. and Miller, K. (1988). *Geotextiles Manual*. Thomas Telford, London.

International Standards Organisation (ISO) (1973). *General Principles for the Verification of the Safety of Structures*. ISO 2394.

Jamiolkowski, M., Ladd, C.C., Germaine, J.T. and Lancellotta, R. (1985). New developments in field and laboratory testing of soils, *Proc. Int. Conf. Soil Mechanics and Foundation Engineering*, San Francisco, Balkema, Vol. 1, pp. 57–153.

Jarrett, P.M. and McGown, A. (eds.) (1988). *The Application of Polymeric Reinforcement in Soil Retaining Structures* (Proceedings NATO Advanced Research Workshop, Kingston). Kluwer, The Netherlands.

Jewell, R.A. (1985). Material properties for the design of geotextile reinforced slopes. *Geotextiles and Geomembranes*, Vol. 2, pp. 83–109.

Jewell, R.A. (1988). The mechanics of reinforced embankments on soft soils, *Geotextiles and Geomembranes*, Vol. 7, No. 4, pp. 237–273.

Jewell, R.A. (1989). Revised design charts for steep reinforced slopes. *Proc. Symp. Reinforced Embankments: Theory and Practice in the British Isles.* Thomas Telford, Cambridge.

Jewell, R.A. (1990). Reinforcement bond capacity, *Géotechnique,* Vol. 40, No. 3, pp. 513–518.

Jewell, R.A. and Greenwood, J.H. (1988). Long term safety in steep soil slopes reinforced by polymer materials, *Geotextiles and Geomembranes*, Special issue on Durability, Vol. 7, Nos. 1 and 2, pp. 81–118.

Jewell, R.A., Milligan, G.W.E., Sarsby, R.W. and DuBois, D.D. (1984). Interactions between soils and grids. In *Polymer Grid Reinforcement in Civil Engineering.* Thomas Telford, London, pp. 18–20.

Jewell, R.A. and Milligan, G.W.E. (1989). Deformation calculations for reinforced soil walls. *Proc. 12th Int. Conf. Soil Mechanics and Foundation Engineering.* Rio de Janeiro, Vol. 2, pp. 1257–1262.

Jewell, R.A. and Wroth, C.P. (1987). Direct shear tests on reinforced sand, *Géotechnique*, Vol. 37, No. 1, pp. 53–68.

Jones, C.J.F.P. (1988). *Earth reinforcement and soil structures*, 2nd edn. Butterworths, London.

Jones, C.J.F.P., Cripwell, J.B. and Bush, D.I. (1990). Reinforced earth trial structure for Dewsbury road, *Proc. ICE,* Part 1, Vol. 88, pp. 321–345.

Jones, C.J.F.P. and Edwards, L.W. (1980). Reinforced earth structures on soft foundations, *Geotechnique*, Vol. 30, No. 2, pp. 207–211.

Jones, C.J.F.P., McGown, A. and Varney, D.J. (1988). Construction methods, economics and specifications. In P.M. Jarrett and A. McGown (eds) *The Application of Polymeric Reinforcement in Soil Retaining Structures*, Kluwer Series E, Vol. 147. Kluwer, pp. 573–611.

Kerisel, J.(1972). The language of models in soil mechanics. *5th European Conf. Soil Mech. and Foundation Engineering,* Madrid, Vol. 2, pp. 9–30.

Kishida, H. and Uesugi, M. (1987). Tests on the interface between sand and steel in the simple shear apparatus. *Géotechnique*, Vol. 37, No. 1, pp. 45–52.

Koerner, R.M. (ed.) (1987). *Soft Soil Stabilisation Using Geosynthetics*, Elsevier Applied Science, London, p. 252. (Reprinted from *Geotextiles and Geomembranes Journal,* Vol. 6.)

Koerner, R. M. (1990). *Designing with Geosynthetics.* 2nd edn., Prentice-Hall, New Jersey.

Ladd, C.C., Foott, R., Ishihara, K., Schlosser, F. and Poulos, H.G. (1977). Stress-deformation and strength characteristics. *Proc. 9th Int. Conf. on Soil Mechanics and Foundation Engineering,* Tokyo, Vol. 2, pp. 421–494.

Ladd, C.C. (1981). Discussion on laboratory shear devices. In R.N. Yong and F.L. Townsend (eds), *Laboratory Shear Strength of Soil*, ASTM Special Publication STP740. ASTM, Philadelphia.

Ladd, C.C. (1991). Stability evaluation during staged construction, *ASCE Geotechnical Journal*, Vol. 117, No. 4, April.

Lambe, T.W. and Whitman, R.V. (1969). *Soil Mechanics,* John Wiley, New York.

Larsson, R. (1980). Undrained shear strength in stability calculation of embankments and foundations on soft soil, *Canadian Geotechnical Journal*, Vol. 17, No. 4, pp. 591–602.

Leflaive, E. (1988). Durability of geotextiles: the French experience. *Geotextiles and Geomembranes* 7, Nos. 1 & 2, pp. 23–32.

Leroueil, S., Magnan, J.P. and Tavenas, F. (1985). *Remblais sur Argiles Molles. Technique et Documentation*, Lavoisier, Paris.

Leschinsky, D. (1987). Short term stability of reinforced embankment over clayey foundation, *Soils and Foundations*, JSSMFE, Vol. 27, No. 3, pp. 43–57.

Leshchinsky, D. and Boedecker, R.H. (1989). Geosynthetic reinforced soil structures, *ASCE Journal of Geotechnical Engineering*, Vol. 115, No. 10, October, pp. 1459–1478.

Love, J.P., Burd, H.J., Milligan, G.W.E. and Houlsby, G.T. (1987). Analytical and model studies of reinforcement of a layer of granular fill on a soft clay subgrade, *Canadian Geotechnical Journal*, Vol. 24, pp. 611–622.

Low, B.K. and Duncan, J.M. (1985). *Analysis of the behaviour of reinforced embankments on weak foundations*. Report VPI&SU/CE-GT-85-09. Virginia Polytechnic.

Lupini, J.F., Skinner, A.E. and Vaughan, P.R. (1981). The drained residual strength of cohesive soils, *Géotechnique*, Vol. 31, No. 2, pp. 181–213.

Mandel, J. and Salençon, J. (1969). The bearing capacity of soils on a rigid foundation. *7th Int. Conf. on Soil Mechanics and Foundation Engineering,* Mexico, Vol. 2, pp. 157–164.

Mandel, J. and Salençon, J. (1972). Force portante d'un sol sur une assise rigide (Étude theorique), *Géotechnique*, 22, No. 1, pp. 79–93.

McGown, A. Andrawes, K.Z. and Al-hasani, M.M. (1978). Effects of inclusion properties on the behaviour of sand. *Géotechnique*, Vol. 28, No. 3, pp. 327–346.

McGown, A., Andrawes, K.Z., Yeo, K.C. and DuBois, D. (1984). The load-strain-time behaviour of Tensar geogrids. In *Polymer Grid Reinforcement in Civil Engineering*. Thomas Telford, London, pp. 11–30.

McGown, A., Paine, N. and DuBois, D.D. (1984). Use of geogrid properties in limit equilibrium analysis. In *Polymer Grid Reinforcement in Civil Engineering*. Thomas Telford, London, pp. 31–39.

References

Mercer (1987). Lecture to Royal Society, London.

Mesri, G. (1975). Discussion: New design procedure for stability of soft clays, *Proc. ASCE Journal of the Geotechnical Engineering Division,* Vol. 101, No. GT4, pp. 409–412.

Meyerhof, G.G. (1953). The bearing capacity of foundations under eccentric and inclined loads. *Proc. 3rd Int. Conf. Soil Mechanics and Foundation Engineering,* Switzerland, Vol. 1, pp. 440–445.

Milligan, G.W.E., Jewell, R.A., Houlsby, G.T. and Burd, H.J. (1990). A new approach to the design of unpaved roads – Part 11. *Ground Engineering,* November, pp. 37–42.

Milligan, V. and La Rochelle, P. (1985). Design methods for embankments over weak soils. In *Polymer Grid Reinforcement in Civil Engineering.* Thomas Telford, London, pp. 95–102.

Mitchell, J.K. and Villet, C.B. (1987). Reinforcement of earth slopes and embankments. *National Cooperative Highway Research Program Report 290.* Transportation Research Board, Washington, 323pp.

Montalvo, J.R. (1989). Evaluation of the degradation of geotextiles. *Proc. Geosynthetics '89 Conference,* San Diego, USA, IFAI Publishers, Vol. 2, pp. 501–512.

Murray, R. T. (1985). Reinforcement techniques in repairing slope failures. In *Polymer Reinforcement in Civil Engineering.* Thomas Telford, London, pp. 47–53.

Murray, R.T. and Farrar, D.M. (1988). Temperature distributions in reinforced soil retaining walls, *Geotextiles and Geomembranes,* Vol. 7, Nos. 1–2.

Netlon Limited (1990). *The Long-term Performance of Tensar Geogrids.* Technical report, Netlon Limited, Kelly Street, Blackburn, UK.

O'Rourke, T.D. and Jones, C.J.F.P. (1990). Overview of earth retention systems: 1970–1990. In Lambe, T.W. and Hansen, B. (eds). *Design and Performance of Earth Retaining Structures,* ASCE Geotechnical Special Publication No. 25. ASCE, New York, pp. 22–51.

Organisation for Economic Co-operation and Development (OECD) (1991). *Ground Engineering Applications of Geotextiles in Road Construction and Maintenance.* Report of Expert Group I8. Transport and Road Research Laboratory, Crowthorne, UK.

Palmeira, E.M. and Milligan, G.W.E. (1989). Scale and other factors affecting the results of pullout tests of grids buried in sand, *Géotechnique,* Vol. 39, No. 3, pp. 511–524.

Parry, R.H.G. (1960). Triaxial compression and extension tests on remoulded saturated clay, *Géotechnique,* Vol. 8, pp. 183–186.

Parry, R.H.G. (1972). Stability analysis of low embankments on soft clays. *Stress Strain Behaviour of Soils* (Proceedings Roscoe Memorial Symposium, Foulis, Henley-on-Thames) pp. 643–668.

Parsons, A.W. and Perry, J. (1985). Slope stability problems in ageing highway earthworks. *Failures in Earthworks*. Thomas Telford, London, pp. 63–78.

Paul, J. (1988). Reinforced soil systems in embankments – construction practices, *Theory and Practice of Earth Reinforcement*, Kyushu, pp. 461–466.

Paulson, J.N. (1990). Summary and evaluation of construction related damage to geotextiles in reinforcing applications. *Proc. 4th Int. Conf. on Geotextiles, Geomembranes and Related Products*.

Pedley, M.J. (1990). *Experimental study of soil reinforcement interaction*. D.Phil Thesis, University of Oxford.

Perry, J. (1989). A survey of slope condition on motorway earthworks in England and Wales. *Research Report 199*. Transport and Road Research Laboratory, Crowthorne, UK.

Potts, D.M., Dounias, G.T. and Vaughan, P.R. (1987). Finite element analysis of the direct shear test, *Géotechnique*, Vol. 37, No. 1, pp. 11–24.

Potyondy, J.G. (1961). Skin friction between cohesive granular soils and construction materials. *Géotechnique*, Vol. 11, No. 4, pp. 339–353.

Rankilor, P.R. (1988). D.S.F. fabrics, the third generation of geotextiles. *Geotechnical Fabrics Report*, IFAI, Vol. 6, No. 1, pp. 18–20.

Rankine, W.J.M. (1857). On the stability of loose earth, *Phil. Trans. Royal Society*, 147, p. 9.

RILEM (1988). *Durability of Geotextiles*. Chapman and Hall, London.

Risseeuw, P. and Schmidt, H.M. (1990). Hydrolysis of HT polyester yarns in water at moderate temperatures. *Proc. 4th Int. Conf. on Geotextiles, Geomembranes and Related Products*, Vol. 2, pp. 691–696.

Rowe, R.K. (1982). The analysis of an embankment constructed on a geotextile. *Proc. 2nd Int. Conf. on Geotextiles*, Las Vegas, Vol. 2, pp. 677–682.

Rowe, R.K. and Mylleville, B.L.J. (1988). The analysis of steel-reinforced embankments on soft clay foundations. *Numerical Methods in Geotechnical Engineering*, Innsbruck, pp. 1273–1278.

Rowe, R.K. and Mylleville, B.L.J. (1989). Consideration of strain in the design of reinforced embankments, *Proc. Geosynthetics '89 Conf.*, San Diego. IFAI Publishers, Vol. 1, pp. 124–135.

Rowe, R.K. and Mylleville, B.L.J. (1990). Implications of adopting an allowable geosynthetic strain in estimating stability, *Proc. 4th Int. Conf. on Geotextiles, Geomembranes and Related Products*, Vol. 1, pp. 131–136.

Russell, D. (1992). Finite Element Analysis of Embankments on Soft Ground Incorporating Reinforcement and Drains. PhD Thesis, University of Sheffield.

Scarpelli, G. (1991). Resistenza e dilatanza dei Terreni naturali, *National Convention of Geotechnical Engineering*. Ravello, Italy, 27–28 February, p. 27.

Schofield, A.N. and Wroth, C.P. (1968). *Critical State Soil Mechanics*. McGraw-Hill, London.

SETRA, (1979). *Les ouvrages en terre armée, recommendations et règles de l'art*. Services d'Etudes Techniques de Routes et Autoroutes, Paris.

Simpson, B., Pappin, J.W. and Croft, D.D. (1981). An approach to limit state calculations in geotechnics. *Ground Engineering*, Vol. 4, No. 6, September, pp. 21–28.

Skempton,A.W. (1970). First time slides in over-consolidated clays, *Géotechnique*, Vol. 20, pp. 320–324.

Sotton, M. (1986). Durabilité des textiles: cas particulier des geotextiles. *Bulletin Scientific ITF,* Vol. 15, pp. 49–63.

Symes, M.F. (1984). Discussion: embankments. In *Polymer Grid Reinforcement in Civil Engineering*. Thomas Telford, London, pp. 113–114.

Tatsuoka, F. (1987). Discussion on strength and dilatancy of sand, *Géotechnique,* Vol. 37, No. 2, pp. 219–225.

Tatsuoka, F. (1992). Roles of facing rigidity in soil reinforcing. *Earth Reinforcement Practice* (Proceedings of International Symposium on Earth Reinforcement, Kyushu), Balkema.

Terzaghi, K. (1943). *Theoretical Soil Mechanics*. John Wiley, New York.

Troost, G.H. and Ploeg, N.A. (1990). Influence of weaving structure and coating on the degree of mechanical damage during installation, *Proc. 4th Int. Conf. on Geotextiles, Geomembranes and Related Products*. The Hague, Balkema, Rotterdam.

Van Harten, K. (1986). The relaxation between specifications of geotextiles and their essential properties, *Geotextiles and Geomembranes*, Vol. 3, pp. 53–76.

Van Zanten, R.V. (ed.) (1986). *Geotextiles and Geomembranes in Civil Engineering*. Balkema, Rotterdam.

Vaughan, P.R., Hight, D.W., Sodha, V.G. and Walbanke, H.J. (1978). Factors controlling the stability of clay fills in Britain, *Proc. Conf. on Clay Fills*. Institution of Civil Engineers, London.

Verdu, J. (1988). Problémes liés à la prediction du comportment à long terms des materiaux polymeres. In *Durability of Geotextiles*. Chapman and Hall, London.

Vesic, A.S. (1975). Bearing capacity of shallow foundations. In H.F. Winterkorn and H.Y. Fang (eds) *Foundation Engineering Handbook*. Van Nostrand Reinhold, ch. 3.

Viezee, D.J., Voskamp, W., den Hoedt, G., Troost, G.H. and Schmidt, H.M. (1990). Designing soil reinforcement with woven geotextiles: the effect of mechanical damage and chemical ageing. *Proc. 4th Int. Conf. on Geotextiles, Geomembranes and Related Products*.

Ward, I.M. (1984). The orientation of polymers to produce high performance materials. In *Polymer Grid Reinforcement in Civil Engineering*. Thomas Telford, London, pp. 4–10.

Watts, G.R.A. and Brady, K.C. (1990). Site damage trials on geotextiles. *Proc. 4th Int. Conf. on Geotextiles, Geomembranes and Related Products*. The Hague, Balkema, Rotterdam.

Webster, S.L. and Alford, S.J. (1978). Investigation of construction concepts for pavements across soft ground. *US Army Waterways Research Station*. Vicksburg, TR-S-78-6.

Webster, S.L. and Watkins, J.E. (1977). Investigation of construction techniques for tactical bridge approach roads across soft ground, *Technical Report S-77-1*. US Army Waterways Experiment Station, Vicksburg.

Wernick, E. (1977). Comparison and discussion of angles of shearing resistance measured in conventional shear tests and in pullout tests on piles, *Proc. 5th Danube Conf. Soil Mechanical Foundation Engineering*. Bratislava.

Wilding, M.A. and Ward, I.M. (1981). Routes to improved creep behaviour in drawn linear polyethylene, *Plastics and Rubber Processing and Applications*, Vol. 1.

Williams, N.D. and Houlihan, M.F. (1987). Evaluation of interface friction properties between geosynthetics and soils. *Geosynthetics '87 Conference*, New Orleans, pp. 616–627.

Winterkorn, H.F. and Fang, H.Y. (1975). *Foundation Engineering*, Van Nostrand Rheinhold. New York.

Wisse, J.D.M. (1988). The role of thermo-oxidative ageing in the long-term behaviour of geotextiles. In *Durability of Geotextiles*. Chapman and Hall, London.

Wisse, J.D.M., Broos, C.J.M. and Boels, W.H. (1990). Evaluation of life expectancy of polypropylene geotextiles: a case study. *Proc. 4th Int. Conf. on Geotextiles, Geomembranes and Related Products*.

Wood, D.M. (1990). *Soil Behaviour and Critical State Soil Mechanics*. Cambridge, Cambridge University Press.

Wrigley, N.E. (1987). Durability and long-term performance of Tensar polymer grids for soil reinforcement, *Materials Science and Technology*, Vol. 3, pp. 161–170.

Wroth, C.P. (1972). General theories of earth pressures and deformations. General Report. *Proc. 5th Int. Conf. on Soil Mechanics and Foundation Engineering*. Madrid, Vol. 2, pp. 33–52.

Wroth, C.P. (1984). The interpretation of in situ soil tests, *Géotechnique*, Vol. 34, No. 4, pp. 449–489.

Wroth, C.P. and Houlsby, G.T. (1985). Soil mechanics – property characterisation and analysis procedures, *Proc. 11th Int. Conf. on Soil Mechanics and Foundation Engineering*. San Francisco, Vol. 1, pp. 1–55.

SOIL REINFORCEMENT WITH GEOTEXTILES

worst expected live loading 89
woven geotextiles 2, 6, 33-4, 39, 51, 141
    allowing steepening of side slopes 230
    direct sliding coefficient 50
    index strength 229

    interaction coefficients 54-5
    properties of 40-1, 226, 227, *227*

yield point 19-20, 19

zones, in steep reinforced fill 105-6, *106*